GCSE Chemistry for CCEA

second edition

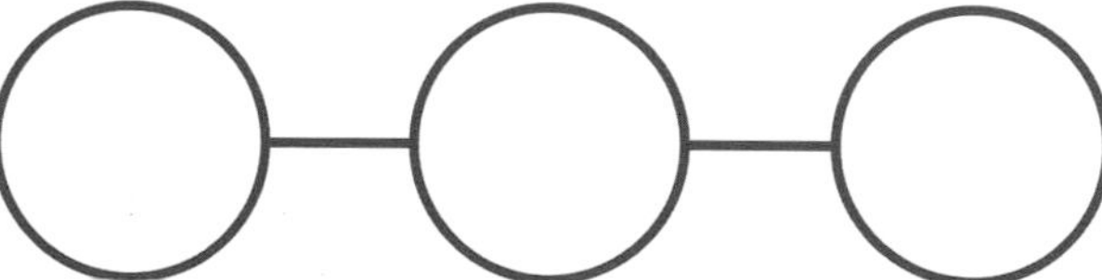

Theo Laverty
Teresa Quigg

HODDER EDUCATION

Endorsed by CCEA on 17th July 2011. If in any doubt about the continuing currency of CCEA endorsement, please contact Heather Clarke at CCEA, 29 Clarendon Road, Belfast, BT1 3BG.

Orders: please contact Bookpoint Ltd, 130 Milton Park, Abingdon, Oxon OX14 4SB. Telephone: (44) 01235 827720. Fax: (44) 01235 400454. Lines are open 9.00–17.00, Monday to Saturday, with a
24-hour message answering service. Visit our website at www.hoddereducation.co.uk

First published in 2011 by
Hodder Education
Carmelite House
50 Victoria Embankment
London EC4Y 0DZ

Impression number	6
Year	2016

Illustrations by Barking Dog Art
Typeset in 12/14pt Bembo by Tech-Set Ltd., Gateshead.
Printed in Dubai.

A catalogue record for this title is available from the British Library

ISBN 978 0340 985038

Contents

During the writing of this book my very good friend and colleague Dr. Theo Laverty sadly passed away after a short illness. Theo was a creative, generous, spirited individual whose genuine humility belied his many accomplishments in the political, sporting and chemistry arenas. He was an inspirational teacher who encouraged both pupils and colleagues to strive to achieve their full potential. Hopefully, this publication will serve as a fitting testimonial to the major contribution Theo made to the teaching of chemistry.

Teresa Quigg

Preface

The GCSE Science for CCEA series comprises three books: GCSE Biology for CCEA, GCSE Chemistry for CCEA and GCSE Physics for CCEA, which together cover all aspects of the material needed for students following the CCEA GCSE specifications in:

* Science: Double Award
* Science: Biology
* Science: Chemistry
* Science: Physics

GCSE Chemistry for CCEA covers all the material relating to the chemistry component of the CCEA Science Double Award, together with the additional material required for the CCEA Science: Chemistry specification.

Theo Laverty and Teresa Quigg are both chemistry teachers and examiners.

Identifying Specification and Tier

The material required for each specification and tier is clearly identified using the following colour code:

All material not on a tinted background is required for foundation tier students following either the GCSE Double Award Science or the GCSE Chemistry specifications. All foundation tier material can also be assessed at higher tier.

Material required for the higher tier students following either the GCSE Double Award Science or the GCSE Chemistry specification is identified with a green tinted background.

Material required for foundation tier students following the GCSE Chemistry specification is identified with a blue tinted background.

Material required for higher tier students following the GCSE Chemistry specification is identified with a red tinted background.

Controlled Assessment of Practical Skills

During your course you will be required to carry out a number of controlled assessment tasks.

Double Award Science students complete **two** controlled assessment tasks from a choice of six supplied by CCEA at the start of the GCSE course. The two tasks must come from different subject areas within the specification. So, for example, they cannot both come from the chemistry section of the Double Award Science specification.

For GCSE Chemistry students, CCEA sets two comparable tasks at the start of the GCSE course. Candidates must take at least **one** of these controlled assessment tasks in the course of the two years.

Acknowledgements

The Publishers would like to thank the following for permission to reproduce copyright material.

Photo credits

p.1 *t* © World History Archive/Alamy, *b* © Mary Evans Picture Library/Alamy; **p.2** © The Print Collector/Alamy; **p.8** © Tony Cordoza/Alamy; **p.21** © Tim Hester/Alamy; **p.22** © Photolibrary Group; **p.24** © Gèrard Lemaire – Fotolia; **p.25** *tl* DMM Photography Art – Fotolia, *tm* philipus – Fotolia, *tr* Fatbob – Fotolia, *m* © Kevin Allen/Alamy, *b* © National Geographic Image Collection/Alamy; **p.31** *from tl to br* © Leslie Garland Picture Library/Alamy, © Medical-on-Line/Alamy, © Glenn Young – Fotolia, © Andrew Lambert Photography/Science Photo Library, © Leslie Garland Picture Library/Alamy, © martin33 – Fotolia, © marcel – Fotolia, © ImageState/Alamy, © sciencephotos/Alamy, © Nic Cleave Photography/Alamy; **p.34** *t* © Dorling Kindersley/Getty Images, *b* © Lawrence Migdale/Science Photo Library; **p.36** *l* © Tim Hill/Alamy, *m* © Big City Lights – Fotolia, *r* © Katie Little – Fotolia; **p.40** *l* © Mary Evans Picture Library/Alamy, *r* © Leslie Garland Picture Library/Alamy; **p.42** *t* © Erik Viktor/Science Photo Library, *b* Heinz Kluetmeier/Sports Illustrated/Getty Images; **p.48** *l* © Science Photo Library, *r* © Peter Arnold, Inc./Alamy; **p.53** © Arctic Images/Alamy; **p.66** *tl* © ImageState/Alamy, *tm* © sciencephotos/Alamy, *tr* © sciencephotos/Alamy, *bl* © Wildlife GmbH/Alamy, *br* © Leslie Garland Picture Library/Alamy; **p.70** *t* © sciencephotos/Alamy, *mt* © Phil Degginger/Alamy, *mb* © sciencephotos/Alamy, *b* © Andrew Lambert Photography/Science Photo Library; **p.80** *from tl to br* © Judith Collins/Alamy, Poles – Fotolia, © matka_Wariatka – Fotolia, © Greg – Fotolia, © Charles Bach/Science Photo Library, © Art Directors & TRIP/Alamy, © D. Hurst/Alamy, © foodfolio/Alamy; **p.81** *from t to b* © Art Directors & TRIP/Alamy, © Andrew Lambert Photography/Science Photo Library, © Leslie Garland Picture Library/Alamy, © Gustoimages/Science Photo Library; **p.82** *l* © Martyn F. Chillmaid/Science Photo Library, *r* © studiomode/Alamy; **p.86** *t* © jeremy sutton-hibbert/Alamy, *b* © Day, Alice/the food passionates/Corbis; **p.90** *t* © Martyn F. Chillmaid, *m* © sciencephotos/Alamy, *b* © Charles D. Winters/Science Photo Library; **p.91** © Martyn F. Chillmaid; **p.97** *t* © Sandra Brunsch – Fotolia, *bl* © NatUlrich – Fotolia, *bm* © evgenyb – Fotolia, *br* © Moodboard/photolibrary.com; **p.98** *tl* © evgenyb – Fotolia, *tm* © NatUlrich – Fotolia, *tr* © Moodboard/photolibrary.com, *m* © sciencephotos/Alamy, *b* © Andrew Lambert Photography/Science Photo Library; **p.114** *l* Rob Bouwman – Fotolia, *r* Science Photo Library; **p.119** Science Photo Library; **p.120** Martyn F. Chillmaid; **p.124** *t* LockStockBob – Fotolia, *m* khlorine1983 – Fotolia, *b* iStock Exclusive/Getty Images; **p.129** *t* NASA Photo/Tony Landis, *m* Lawrence Livermore National Laboratory/Science Photo Library, *b* Jerry Mason/Science Photo Library; **p.136** Etrayne04 – Fotolia; **p.137** *t* Simone Brandt/Imagebroker RF/photolibrary.com, *b* Dr P. Marazzi/Science Photo Library; **p.140** *from l to r* © The Granger Collection, NYC/TopFoto, © Ashmolean Museum, University of Oxford, UK/The Bridgeman Art Library, © Christine Strover/Alamy, © TTL Images/Alamy, © imagebroker/Alamy, © David Lee/Rex Features; **p.142** © Martyn F. Chillmaid/Science Photo Library; **p.144** *all* © Science Photo Library; **p.147** *from t to b* ksena32@ukrpost.ua – Fotolia, rgbdigital.co.uk – Fotolia, © Andrew Wilson/Alamy, © Stock Connection Blue/Alamy, © Hartmut Neidiger – Fotolia; **p.148** *t* © Dinodia Photos/Alamy, *b* © Francesco Ridolfi/Alamy; **p.149** *from t to b* © soleilc1 – Fotolia, © Springfield Gallery – Fotolia, © Joe Gough – Fotolia, © Michael Neelon(misc)/Alamy; **p.152** © Charles D. Winters/Science Photo Library; **p.153** *tr* © Wayne Hutchinson/Alamy, *tl* Filipebvarela – Fotolia, *m* Martyn F. Chillmaid/Science Photo Library, *bl* Djordje Korovljevic – Fotolia, *bm* © Christopher Nash/Alamy, *br* Sheila Terry/Science Photo Library; **p.154** *from t to b* © Jason Stitt – Fotolia, © Ingram Publishing, © Kayros Studio – Fotolia, © Elena Kharichkina – Fotolia; **p.157** © JoeFoxMarbleArch/Alamy; **p.158** *tl* © David J. Green/Alamy, *r* © Science Photo Library, *bl* © raphotography – Fotolia; **p.160** *tl* © Martyn F. Chillmaid, *tm* © Coprid – Fotolia, *tr* © studiomode/Alamy, *b* © photolibrary.com; **p.164** *from t to b* © Vanessa Miles/Alamy, © Stock Connection Blue/Alamy, © tlorna – Fotolia, iStock Exclusive/Getty Images; **p.181** *t* © Faber-Castell Aktiengesellschaft, *b* © tlorna – Fotolia; **p.184** © The Art Archive/Musée National de la voiture et du tourisme Compiègne/Gianni Dagli Orti; **p.186** *t* © Beboy – Fotolia, *m* © Ashley Cooper/Barcroftmedia/Getty Images, *b* © KPA/Zuma/Rex Features; **p.191** *t* © Cameron Spencer/Getty Images, *b* © Sipa Press/Rex Features; **p.192** © Danny Hooks – Fotolia; **p.193** *t* © Bon Appetit/Alamy, *b all* © Andrew Lambert Photography/Science Photo Library; **p.194** *l* © Science Photo Library, *r* © Andrew Lambert Photography/Science Photo Library; **p.195** © Martyn F. Chillmaid; **p.196** *l* Imagebroker RF/photolibrary.com, *r* Science Photo Library; **p.198** Emilio Segre Visual Archives/American Institute of Physics/Science Photo Library; **p.199** *l from t to b* © Andrew Lambert Photography/Science Photo Library, © Martyn F. Chillmaid, © Martyn F. Chillmaid, © Martyn F. Chillmaid, © Martyn F. Chillmaid, *tr* © Jerry Mason/Science Photo Library, *br* © Martyn F. Chillmaid; **p.201** © Charles D. Winters/Science Photo Library; **p.202** *tl* © sciencephotos/Alamy, *m from l to r* © sciencephotos/Alamy, © Charles D. Winters/Science Photo Library, © Lawrence Migdale/Science Photo Library, © sciencephotos/Alamy, *bl* © Science Photo Library, *br* © Leslie Garland Picture Library/Alamy; **p.204** *t* © vom – Fotolia, *m* © Photolibrary Group, *b* © Vanessa Miles/Alamy; **p.206** *t* © David Taylor/Science Photo Library, *b* © sciencephotos/Alamy; **p.211** *from t to b* © Science Photo Library/Alamy, © diego cervo – Fotolia, © Frog 974 – Fotolia, © Jiri Hera – Fotolia; **p.213** KeystoneUSA-ZUMA/Rex Features; **p.219** *tl* sue120502 – Fotolia, *tr* Ivonne Wierink – Fotolia, *bl* Driving South – Fotolia, *br* © studiomode/Alamy; **p.221** *tl* Jack Rom – Fotolia, *tr* © Realimage/Alamy, *ml* Jan Quist – Fotolia, *mr* Driving South – Fotolia, *bl* nito – Fotolia, *br* Marek – Fotolia; **p.222** *tl* © Jim Holden/Alamy, *tr* © Srebrina Yaneva/iStockphoto.com, *bl* © Chris Howes/Wild Places Photography/Alamy; **p.224** © Auto Express/Rex Features; **p.225** *t* © Jack Sullivan/Alamy, *b* © Smalik – Fotolia; **p.226** © Photodisc/Getty Images; **p.234** *both* © Andrew Lambert Photography/Science Photo Library; **p.236** *l* © Martyn F. Chillmaid, *m* © sciencephotos/Alamy, *r* © Charles D. Winters/Science Photo Library; **p.237** *t* © Martyn F. Chillmaid, *b* © Andrew Lambert Photography/Science Photo Library; **p.241** *tl* © khlorinc1983 – Fotolia, *ml* © geogphotos film/Alamy, *bl* © sciencephotos/Alamy, *br* © iStock Exclusive/Getty Images; **p.242** *t* © Dirk Wiersma/Science Photo Library, *m* © John Morrison/Alamy, *b* © Quarry Products Association NI/www.qpani.org, www.virtualquarry.co.uk.

t = top, *b* = bottom, *l* = left, *r* = right, *m* = middle

Every effort has been made to trace all copyright holders, but if any have been inadvertantly overlooked, the Publisher will be pleased to make the necessary arrangements at the first opportunity.

1 Atomic Structure

► Development of atomic structure theory

The idea that matter is composed of small indivisible particles called **atoms** was first put forward around two thousand years ago by the Greek philosophers Democritus and Leucippus. Unfortunately, the ideas of another Greek philosopher, Aristotle, were considered more acceptable. Aristotle believed that matter was composed of the four 'elements', air, earth, fire and water, and used these ideas to explain matter and its behaviour.

It was not until 1808 when John Dalton published his Atomic Theory that the idea of matter being made up of small particles was taken seriously by scientists. Dalton stated **'that all elements are made up of small indivisible particles called atoms'**. The ideas of Dalton remained until 1897 when the **electron** was discovered by J. J. Thomson and a new model of atomic structure was proposed. Thomson made his discovery when he was investigating the way gases conduct electricity. In his experiments he passed a high voltage across the terminals of a tube containing air and found out that the rays produced travelled in straight lines from the negative terminal (Figure 2) and that these rays were deflected when they passed through charged plates. The particles were approximately 2000 times lighter than a hydrogen atom and he called them electrons.

Figure 1 John Dalton and J. J. Thomson

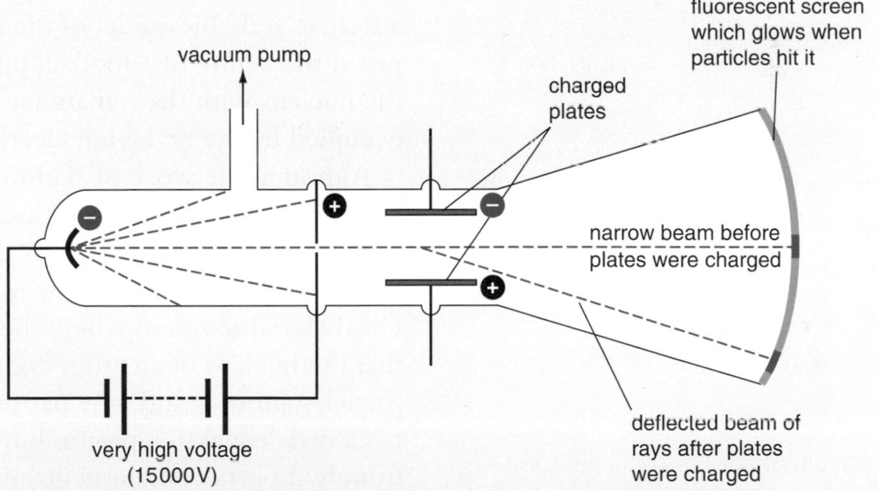

Figure 2 Electrons being deflected when they pass through charged plates

Using the **Plum Pudding Model** of the atom, Thomson put forward the idea that in the atom there are rings of negative electrons embedded in a sphere of positive charge, just like currants embedded in a Christmas pudding. Thomson further put forward the idea that the atom was neutral as it contained equal numbers of positive and negative charges.

The work of Ernest Rutherford

In 1913, Ernest Rutherford and his researchers used alpha particles to probe inside atoms and this led to the discovery of the **atomic nucleus**. Rutherford's research showed that:

* the atom consisted of electrons revolving around a positively charged nucleus
* the positive particles in the nucleus are called **protons** and they are about 2000 times heavier than electrons
* atoms have equal numbers of protons (+) and electrons (−) and so overall atoms are neutral as the charges cancel out
* virtually all of an atom's mass is contained in the nucleus and electrons are contained in a much larger region of space around the nucleus.

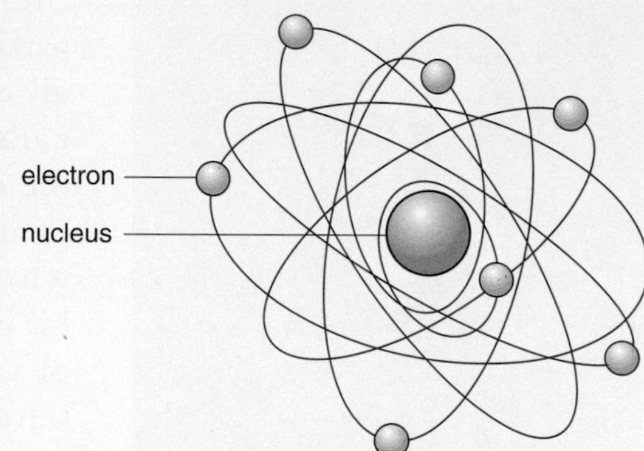

Figure 3 Ernest Rutherford and his model of the atom

Rutherford compared his model of electrons revolving around the positive nucleus to that of the planets revolving around the sun. On a relative scale his model of the atom could be compared to a small pea at the centre of a football pitch, where the small pea represents the nucleus with the remainder of the pitch representing the space occupied by the revolving electrons.

Although the work of Thomson and Rutherford explained most aspects of atomic structure, there was still one big problem to resolve. The mass of atoms was greater than expected; for example, an atom of helium was twice as heavy as expected. In 1932, James Chadwick discovered where the extra mass came from. He showed that the nucleus of an atom contained two different types of particles, protons and new particles, called **neutrons**. The neutron has a mass equal to a proton but it has no charge. All atoms, apart from hydrogen, contain neutrons.

Present day ideas of the atom

Present day understanding of atomic structure shows that the atom is made up of a very small, dense, positively charged nucleus composed of protons and neutrons with negatively charged electrons in shells orbiting the nucleus. The radius of an atom is very small and only measures about 10^{-8} cm. Table 1 summarises the relative masses and charges of a proton, neutron and electron and their positions in an atom.

Particle	Relative mass/atomic mass units	Relative charge	Position
Neutron	1	0	nucleus
Proton	1	+1	nucleus
Electron	$\frac{1}{1840}$	−1	shell

Table 1 Mass, charge and position of protons, electrons and neutrons

Questions

1 Name the scientist who discovered the:
a) electron **b)** neutron **c)** proton.

2 Copy and complete the table below about particles which make up atoms.

Particle	Relative mass	Charge	Position in the atom
		−1	
	1		nucleus
proton		+1	

3 In Thomson's experiment (Figure 2), how did he show that electrons had a negative charge?

4 Suggest a reason why neutrons were discovered much later than protons and electrons.

5 IT: Use PowerPoint to produce a presentation showing the historical development of the structure of the atom. You should include:
* the work of Thomson, Rutherford and Chadwick
* the relative charge, relative mass and position of the particles which make up the atom
* the present day model of the atom.

▶ Atomic number and mass number

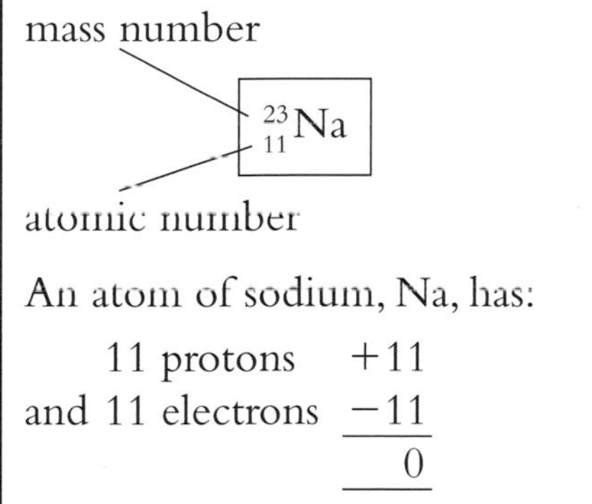

The terms **atomic number** and **mass number** provide scientists with important information about the number of protons, neutrons and electrons contained in atoms. The atomic number of an element is the number of protons in an atom of that element.

Atoms of different elements have different numbers of protons; for example, hydrogen has one proton, sodium has 11 and calcium has 20. Elements are arranged in the Periodic Table according to their atomic number. Fluorine has nine protons, so it is the ninth element in the Periodic Table. When we want to find the atomic number of an element we use the Periodic Table. The atomic number is the subscript number at the left side of the symbol, e.g. $_{11}Na$. This tells us that an atom of sodium has 11 protons.

Since all atoms are neutral there are always the same number of electrons as protons in each atom, e.g. $_{11}Na$ has 11 protons (11+) so there are 11 electrons (11−). Here we see the 11+ charges cancel out with the 11− charges leaving the sodium atom neutral. It is important to remember that **atoms are always neutral**. The mass number of an element is the total number of protons and neutrons in the nucleus of an atom of that element.

Like the atomic number, the mass number can be obtained from the Periodic Table. For the element in question, it is the superscript number at the left side of the symbol, e.g. for sodium, ^{23}Na. Thus the mass number is 23 and this means that the total number of protons and neutrons is 23. Since we know there are 11 protons from the atomic number, we can now work out the number of neutrons, 23 − 11 = 12 neutrons. So to obtain the number of neutrons we subtract the atomic number from the mass number.

Calculating the number of protons, neutrons and electrons for some elements

$^{12}_{6}C$ atomic number = 6, so 6 **protons**

in the neutral atom, therefore C has 6 **electrons**

Number of neutrons = mass number − atomic number
= 12 − 6
= 6 neutrons.

$^{19}_{9}F$ atomic number = 9, so 9 **protons**

in the neutral atom, therefore F has 9 **electrons**

Number of neutrons = mass number − atomic number
= 19 − 9
= 10 neutrons.

It is important to realise that the number of protons may equal the number of neutrons in an element but this is only true for some elements.

Questions

6 Explain the meanings of the terms atomic number and mass number.

7 Explain why atoms are always neutral.

8 Use your Periodic Table to work out the mass number and atomic number for:

a) K **b)** O **c)** P

9 Use your Periodic Table to identify the elements that have the following atomic numbers:

a) 17 **b)** 35 **c)** 7

10 Calculate the number of electrons, protons and neutrons in the following elements:

a) $^{39}_{19}K$ **b)** $^{56}_{26}Fe$ **c)** $^{40}_{18}Ar$ **d)** $^{16}_{8}O$

11 Copy and complete the table below:

Element	Atomic number	Number of neutrons
Copper	29	
	25	
Phosphorus		16

▶ How electrons are arranged in atoms

It is now understood that the atom is composed of a very small, dense, positively charged nucleus composed of protons and neutrons, with negatively charged electrons in shells, orbiting the nucleus.

Figure 4 shows how the electrons are arranged in the first shell of the atoms of the two lightest elements, hydrogen and helium:

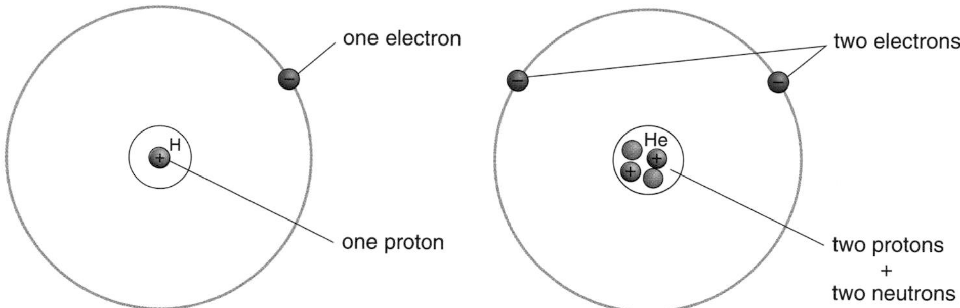

Figure 4 Electronic structures of hydrogen and helium

For GCSE, the following guidelines will apply when filling electrons into shells:

* Electrons are filled into shells starting from the first shell which is the one closest to the nucleus.
* Moving out from the first shell, electrons are then filled into the second shell, third shell and so forth.
* The first shell can hold a maximum of two electrons while other shells, 2nd, 3rd etc., can hold a maximum of eight electrons.
* Before filling electrons into a new shell it is important to fill the existing shell. Thus we must put two electrons into the first shell before adding an electron into the second shell. Likewise the second shell must be filled before adding an electron into the third shell.

Filling electrons into shells for nitrogen and sodium

Remember: the phrases electronic structure and electronic configuration refer to the same thing – the arrangement of electrons in the shells of an atom.

$^{14}_{7}$Nitrogen has seven electrons and this means that two electrons are placed in the first shell with the remaining five electrons placed in the second shell. For $^{23}_{11}$Na which has 11 electrons, two are used to fill the first shell while the next eight electrons fill the second shell and the remaining electron goes into the third shell. These electronic configurations may be written as: nitrogen 2,5 and sodium 2,8,1 as shown in Figure 6.

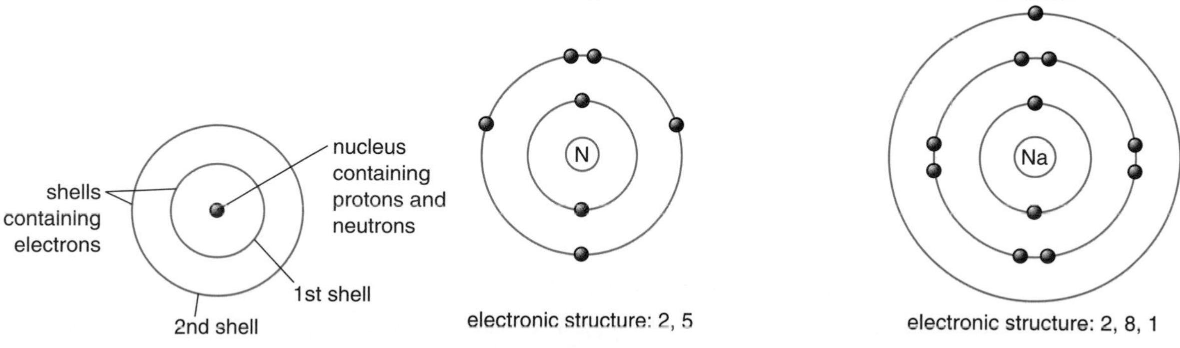

Figure 5

Figure 6 Electronic structures of nitrogen and sodium

Structure of the first twenty elements in the Periodic Table

In Table 2, the atomic number and mass number of the first 20 elements in the Periodic Table have been used to work out the number of electrons, protons and neutrons which each element contains. The last column provides a description of each element's structure in terms of electrons in shells.

Element	Symbol	Atomic number	Mass number	Number of protons	Number of electrons	Number of neutrons	Electronic structure (electrons in shells)
Hydrogen	$^{1}_{1}H$	1	1	1	1	0	1
Helium	$^{4}_{2}He$	2	4	2	2	2	2
							First shell is full
Lithium	$^{7}_{3}Li$	3	7	3	3	4	2,1
Beryllium	$^{9}_{4}Be$	4	9	4	4	5	2,2
Boron	$^{11}_{5}B$	5	11	5	5	6	2,3
Carbon	$^{12}_{6}C$	6	12	6	6	6	2,4
Nitrogen	$^{14}_{7}N$	7	14	7	7	7	2,5
Oxygen	$^{16}_{8}O$	8	16	8	8	8	2,6
Fluorine	$^{19}_{9}F$	9	19	9	9	10	2,7
Neon	$^{20}_{10}Ne$	10	20	10	10	10	2,8
							Second shell is full
Sodium	$^{23}_{11}Na$	11	23	11	11	12	2,8,1
Magnesium	$^{24}_{12}Mg$	12	24	12	12	12	2,8,2
Aluminium	$^{27}_{13}Al$	13	27	13	13	14	2,8,3
Silicon	$^{28}_{14}Si$	14	28	14	14	14	2,8,4
Phosphorus	$^{31}_{15}P$	15	31	15	15	16	2,8,5
Sulfur	$^{32}_{16}S$	16	32	16	16	16	2,8,6
Chlorine	$^{35.5}_{17}Cl$	17	35 or 37*	17	17	18 or 20	2,8,7
Argon	$^{40}_{18}Ar$	18	40	18	18	22	2,8,8
							Third shell is full
Potassium	$^{39}_{19}K$	19	39	19	19	20	2,8,8,1
Calcium	$^{40}_{20}Ca$	20	40	20	20	20	2,8,8,2

(*chlorine has two isotopes as shown in Table 3, on page 7)

Table 2 Electronic structures of the first 20 elements

Questions

12 Draw the electronic structures of the following atoms:

a) $^{35}_{17}Cl$ **b)** $^{20}_{10}Ne$ **c)** $^{40}_{20}Ca$ **d)** $^{11}_{5}B$

13 From the following table, select an element which has:

a) 5 electrons in its outer shell

b) a filled outer shell

c) 1 electron in its outer shell

Element	Mass number	Number of neutrons
A	40	22
B	7	4
C	28	14
D	31	16
E	14	6

14 Copy and complete the table below about atomic structure:

Element	Mass number	Atomic number	Electronic configuration
?	27	?	2,8,3
?	24	12	?
Fluorine	?	9	?
?	16	?	2,6

▶ Isotopes

Isotopes are atoms of the same element that have the same atomic number but different mass numbers.

This means that isotopes are atoms of the same element that have the same number of protons in their nuclei but different numbers of neutrons.

Atoms of a particular element always have the same atomic number which means that they have the same number of protons and electrons; however, for many elements their atoms can have different mass numbers. When this occurs elements are said to have **isotopes**. Isotopes are atoms of the same element which have the same atomic number but different mass numbers and so different numbers of neutrons.

From the definition it is seen that isotopes have the same atomic number but different mass numbers. Table 3 shows the common isotopes of two elements, chlorine and hydrogen.

Isotope	Number of protons	Number of electrons	Number of neutrons
$^{35}_{17}Cl$	17	17	18
$^{37}_{17}Cl$	17	17	20
$^{1}_{1}H$	1	1	0
$^{2}_{1}H$	1	1	1
$^{3}_{1}H$	1	1	2

Table 3 Protons, electrons and neutrons for the isotopes of chlorine and hydrogen

Looking at the two isotopes of chlorine, Cl-35 and Cl-37, it is seen that they both have 17 protons but Cl-35 contains 18 neutrons while Cl-37 contains 20. Thus the only way the isotopes differ is in the number of neutrons.

As both isotopes of chlorine contain the same number of electrons, arranged in the same way, it means that their chemical reactivity is identical. The only difference between the isotopes is that Cl-35 is a lighter atom with two fewer neutrons. Consequently the isotopes have different physical properties; for example Cl-37 has a greater density and a different melting and boiling point than Cl-35.

It has been shown that naturally occurring chlorine is made up of 75% Cl-35 and 25% Cl-37. Using these mass numbers it is possible to calculate the **relative atomic mass** for a chlorine atom. This is explained in more detail on page 108.

Relative atomic mass = [(35 × 75) + (37 × 25)]/100 = 35.5

The word 'relative' is used as the masses of all atoms are measured relative to the mass of an atom of carbon-12. See page 107.

Questions

15 Calculate the relative atomic mass of boron given that it contains 20% B-10 and 80% B-11.

16 Complete the table.

Atom	Number of protons	Number of electrons	Number of neutrons	Atomic number	Mass number
Magnesium	12		12	12	
Potassium		19		19	39
Boron	5		6		11

17 Complete the table below to show the atomic structure of the two isotopes of chlorine.

Isotope	Number of electrons	Number of neutrons	Number of protons
^{37}Cl		20	17
^{35}Cl	17		

18 Copy and complete the table to show the number of protons, electrons and neutrons in the three isotopes of carbon.

	Electrons	Protons	Neutrons
$^{12}_{6}C$	6		
$^{13}_{6}C$	6		
$^{14}_{6}C$			8

► Exam questions

1 a) All PlayStations and games consoles contain a microchip made from the **element** silicon which has the symbol Si and **atomic number** 14.

i) What is meant by the term element? *(2 marks)*

ii) What is meant by the term atomic number? *(1 mark)*

b) An atom of silicon contains protons, electrons and neutrons. Complete the table below to show the relative mass and relative charge of each particle.

Particle	Relative mass	Relative charge
proton		
electron		
neutron		

(3 marks)

2 An atom is made up of three particles: electrons, protons and neutrons.

a) Complete the table below to show the selected properties of the different particles.

Particle	Relative charge	Position in the atom
electron		
proton		
neutron		

(3 marks)

b) The table below gives the dates when the different particles within the atom were discovered.

Particle	Date discovered
electron	1897
proton	1913
neutron	1932

From your knowledge of atomic structure give a reason why the neutron was discovered at a much later date than the electron or proton.

(1 mark)

3 Complete the table below to show the relative masses and charges of the three main particles which are found in most atoms. Two have been done for you.

Particle	Charge	Relative mass
electron		1/1840
neutron		
proton	+1	

(4 marks)

4 The table below gives information about the structure of some atoms. Complete the table (you may find your Data Leaflet helpful).

Symbol	Mass number	Number of protons	Number of neutrons	Electronic structure
Li	7	3		2,1
F	19		10	
Al		13	14	
			20	2,8,8,1

(8 marks)

5 a) Atoms of chlorine can have two different mass numbers and can be represented as shown below.

^{35}Cl	^{37}Cl

i) What is the name given to atoms of the same element with different mass numbers?

(1 mark)

ii) Complete the table to give information about each chlorine atom.

Atom	Atomic number	Mass number	Number of protons	Number of neutrons	Number of electrons
^{35}Cl	17	35			
^{37}Cl	17	37			

(2 marks)

b) Chlorine reacts with metals. It reacts with the element calcium, Ca, to form the compound calcium chloride. Write the electronic structure of

i) an atom of calcium

ii) an atom of chlorine.

(2 marks)

6 Lead exists as a mixture of isotopes: $^{206}_{82}Pb$, $^{207}_{82}Pb$, $^{208}_{82}Pb$. Complete the table below to show the similarities and differences between these isotopes.

Isotope	Mass number	Number of protons	Number of neutrons	Number of electrons
$^{206}_{82}Pb$		82		
$^{207}_{82}Pb$			125	
$^{208}_{82}Pb$				82

(4 marks)

2 Bonding and Structures

The elements neon and argon are found as individual atoms in very small quantities in the atmosphere. The elements aluminium and iron are found in great quantities in the Earth's crust; however, they are always found combined with atoms of another element, usually oxygen. Why do some elements exist as single atoms and show no interest in joining up with each other or with other elements, while others are only stable when they are paired up or joined to atoms of other elements? The answer lies with the electronic configuration (electronic structure, arrangement of electrons) of the atom.

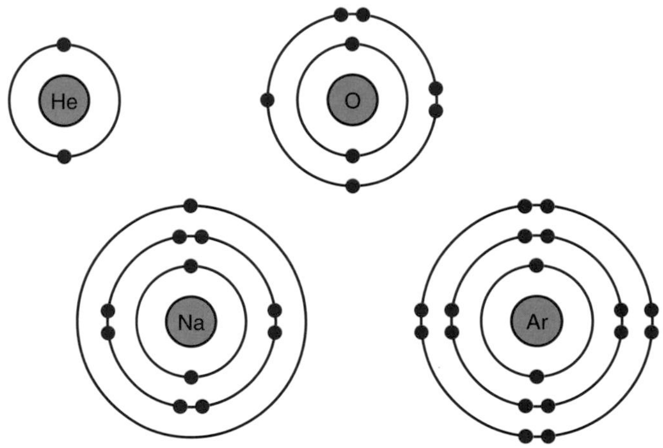

Argon and helium are unreactive gases. They exist as single atoms with lots of space between each atom at room temperature. These atoms have full outer shells. Two electrons fill the outer shell in the atom of helium. Eight electrons fill the outer shell in the atom of argon. Sodium and oxygen are very reactive elements. They will react to try to obtain a full outer shell of electrons. The study of chemical bonding and structure is the study of how atoms move, transfer or share electrons on their outer shells to try to obtain a full outer shell. The study of chemical bonding and structure leads to an understanding of the properties and uses of materials and eventually to the creation of new materials for a specific purpose.

Figure 1

There are three types of bonding studied at GCSE level.

1. Ionic bonding

2. Covalent bonding
   a) simple molecular
   b) giant covalent

3. Metallic bonding

In each type of bonding, atoms use different techniques to try to obtain a full outer shell of electrons, resulting in different types of compounds with different properties.

▶ Ionic bonding

* Ionic bonds form when a metal **transfers** electrons to a non-metal, producing positive and negative ions. An ion is a particle formed when an atom loses or gains one or more electrons. The ionic bonds that form are the strong attractions between oppositely charged ions.
* When atoms lose or gain electrons they obtain a more stable electron arrangement, a full outer shell.
* To obtain the charge on the ions consider the number of protons and electrons on each atom before and after electron transfer.
* Ionic bonds are strong bonds and require a lot of energy to break them.

Example 1: Sodium chloride, NaCl

When a sodium atom, electronic configuration 2,8,1, reacts with a chlorine atom, electronic configuration 2,8,7, the electron in the outer shell of the sodium atom transfers to the outer shell of the chlorine atom (Figure 2). After the transfer process the sodium and chlorine atoms become charged and form ions. Sodium forms a positive ion (cation) Na^+ with an electronic configuration 2,8, while chlorine forms a chloride anion (negative ion) Cl^-, with configuration 2,8,8.

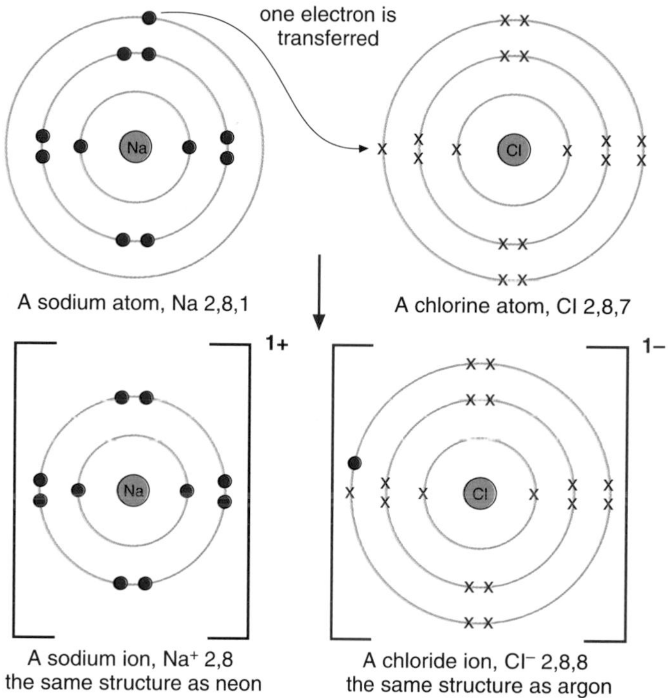

Figure 2 Formation of the ionic compound, sodium chloride, NaCl

> An **ion** is a particle formed when an atom loses or gains one or more electrons.
>
> A **cation** is a positive ion formed when an atom **loses** one or more electrons.
>
> An **anion** is a negative ion formed when an atom gains one or more electrons.

The sodium ion has a charge of '1+' as after electron transfer it has 11 protons (+) and 10 electrons (−) which overall gives a charge of '1+'. The chloride ion has a charge of '1−' as after electron transfer it has 17 protons (+) and 18 electrons (−) which gives an overall charge of '1−'. The ionic bond for sodium chloride is the strong attraction between the positive sodium ions and the negative chloride ions. The ions are held together by strong electrostatic forces.

Note that the negative chloride ion Cl^- has its ending changed from chlor**ine** to chlor**ide** but there is no change for the metal ion.

Example 2: Calcium chloride, $CaCl_2$

A calcium atom has an electronic configuration of 2,8,8,2 while that of chlorine is 2,8,7. Two chlorine atoms are therefore required to accept the two electrons from the outer shell of calcium; see Figure 6. The calcium ion, Ca^{2+}, has a charge of 2+ as after losing two electrons it has 18 electrons (−) and 20 protons (+) while the chloride ion Cl^- has a charge of 1− as after gaining one electron it has 17 protons (+) and 18 electrons (−).

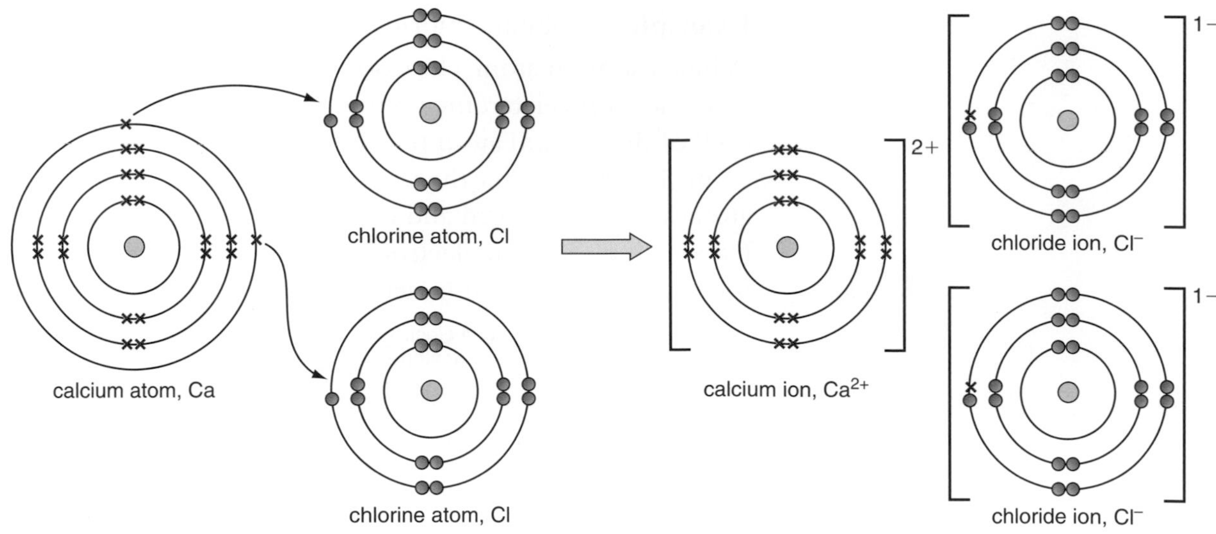

Figure 3 Ionic bonding in calcium chloride

The ionic compound calcium chloride contains the ions Ca^{2+} and $2Cl^-$ and the formula is written $CaCl_2$.

Example 3: Magnesium oxide, MgO
A magnesium atom has an electronic configuration 2,8,2 while that of oxygen is 2,6. This means that to have filled outer shells of electrons, magnesium needs to lose two electrons while oxygen needs to gain two electrons; see Figure 4.

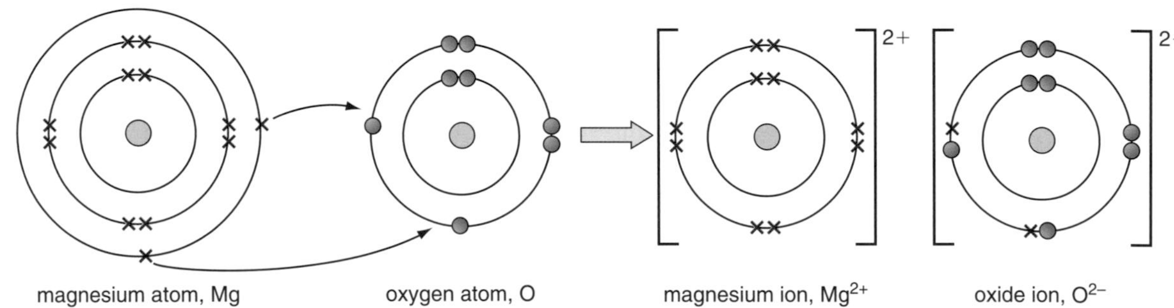

Figure 4 Ionic bonding in magnesium oxide

	Mg atom	Mg^{2+} ion
proton (+)	12+	12+
electron (−)	12−	10−
overall charge	0	2+

Table 1 Calculating the charge on a magnesium ion

The charge on the magnesium ion, Mg^{2+}, is 2+ as after transferring its two outermost electrons there are 12 protons (+) and 10 electrons (−). For the oxide ion, O^{2-}, the charge is 2− as after gaining two electrons it contains 8 protons (+) and 10 electrons (−). The two ions Mg^{2+} and O^{2-} give the ionic compound magnesium oxide, MgO.

Questions

1 Give the electronic configuration for the following ions:
   a) Na^+ **b)** Mg^{2+} **c)** Al^{3+}
   d) F^- **e)** S^{2-}
   f) For parts **a)** to **e)** calculate the number of protons, electrons and neutrons in each of the ions.

2 The following table contains information about the structure of some particles which are either atoms or ions.

Particle	Number of protons	Number of neutrons	Number of electrons
A	6	6	6
E	11	12	10
F	20	20	18
G	6	7	6
H	12	12	10

a) Name the particle with a 1+ charge.
b) Give the letters of the two particles which are isotopes.
c) Name the two particles which have a charge of 2+.
d) Give the symbol for the particle with a mass number of 23.

3 The table below gives details of the electronic arrangement of four ions formed from elements represented by the letters A, B, C and D. The letters do not represent the symbols for elements.

Element	Ion formed	Electronic arrangement
A	A^-	2,8
B	B^{2+}	2,8
C	C^{2-}	2,8
D	D^{3+}	2,8

a) Using your knowledge of the Periodic Table, identify the elements represented by the letters A, B, C and D.
b) What is the formula of the compound formed from the two ions B^{2+} and A^-?

4 Copy and complete the following passage for the reaction between calcium and oxygen.

Calcium and oxygen react to form calcium ________. When this happens a calcium atom transfers two ________ to an oxygen atom. After the reaction calcium ions with a charge of ________ form while oxide ions with a charge of ________ form. The ions are held together by strong ________ attractions. The chemical bond which results from these attractions is called an ________ bond.

5 a) Draw electron diagrams (dot-and-cross diagrams) to show the arrangement of electrons in a lithium atom and a fluorine atom.
b) How does the arrangement of electrons in lithium and fluorine change when lithium fluoride forms?
c) Show how the charges on the lithium and fluoride ions can be worked out.
d) Which noble gases have the same electron structures as a lithium ion and a fluoride ion?

6 Write out the electronic structures of the following atoms and use them to predict the charges that these atoms will have when they form ions:
a) magnesium **b)** potassium **c)** chlorine **d)** aluminium
e) oxygen **f)** calcium **g)** fluorine

7 Use a dot-and-cross diagram to explain why lithium oxide has the chemical formula Li_2O.

Ionic lattices

In the ionic compound sodium chloride there are strong attractions between the oppositely charged Na^+ and Cl^- ions. These strong **electrostatic attractions** between the ions are known as **ionic bonds**. In a crystal of sodium chloride there are millions of oppositely charged ions bonded together in a giant three-dimensional ionic structure as shown in Figure 5.

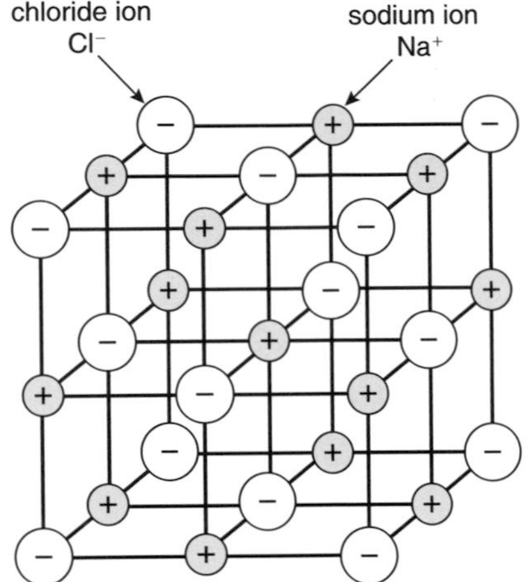

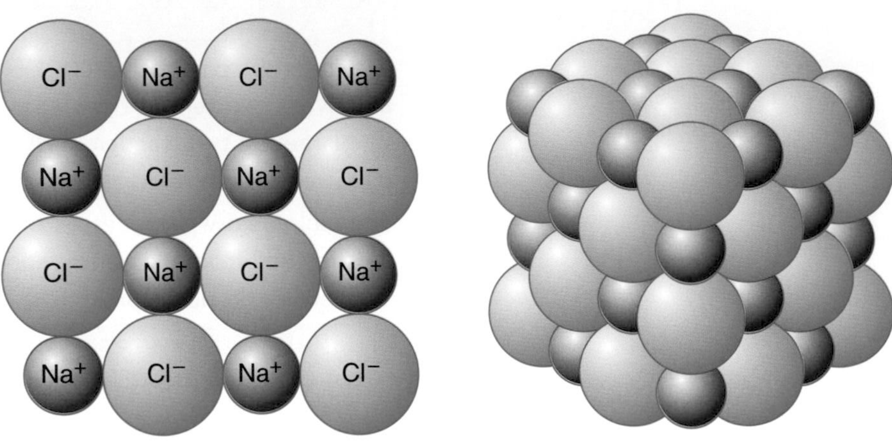

Figure 5 Sodium chloride crystal

This **ionic structure** has the formula NaCl and from the diagram it is seen that each Na^+ ion is surrounded by six Cl^- ions and each Cl^- is surrounded by six Na^+ ions. Ionic bonds are strong and it is these strong bonds that give the ionic compounds their typical physical properties.

Physical properties of ionic compounds

High melting point and boiling point

Strong ionic bonds hold the ions firmly together in ionic compounds. This means that ionic compounds are solids and have high melting points and boiling points. Large amounts of energy are required to break down the strong ionic attractions (ionic bonds) between the oppositely charged ions. **Bond breaking is an endothermic process** and energy must be provided to break the ionic bonds. Figure 6 shows what happens when an ionic compound like sodium chloride is melted.

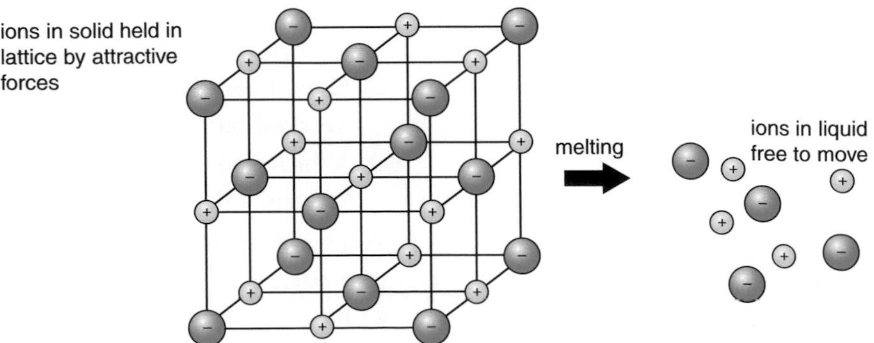

Figure 6 Melting an ionic compound allows the ions to move freely

Some ionic compounds have very high melting points and this makes them very useful for many high temperature processes. For example,

magnesium oxide with a melting point of 2800 °C is used for making refractory bricks in the blast furnace. See page 146.

Electrical conductivity

Ionic compounds conduct electricity when molten or dissolved in water but do not conduct in the solid state. When an ionic compound is melted or dissolved in water the strong electrostatic attractions are overcome and ions are free to move and carry the charge (Figure 7). This is explained in more detail in Chapter 10, page 131.

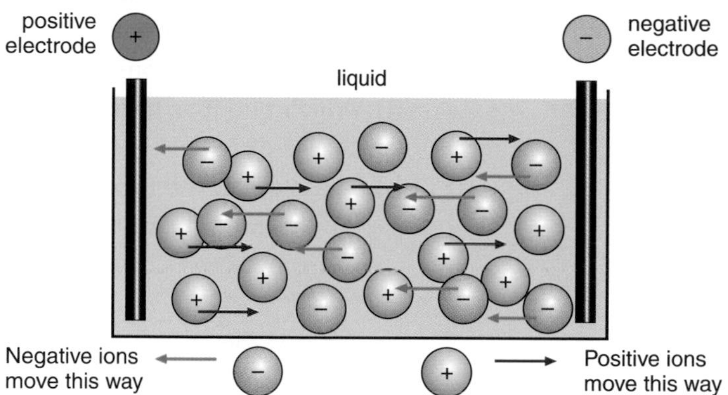

Figure 7 Ionic compounds conduct electricity when molten or dissolved

Ionic compounds cannot conduct electricity in the solid state as the ions are in fixed positions and are not free to move.

Solubility in water

Ionic compounds usually dissolve in water. When an ionic compound dissolves in water, the ionic lattice breaks down and the ions become free to move about in solution. Both the positive and negative ions get surrounded by water molecules. The ions are now said to be hydrated (surrounded by water molecules) and this is shown in Figure 8.

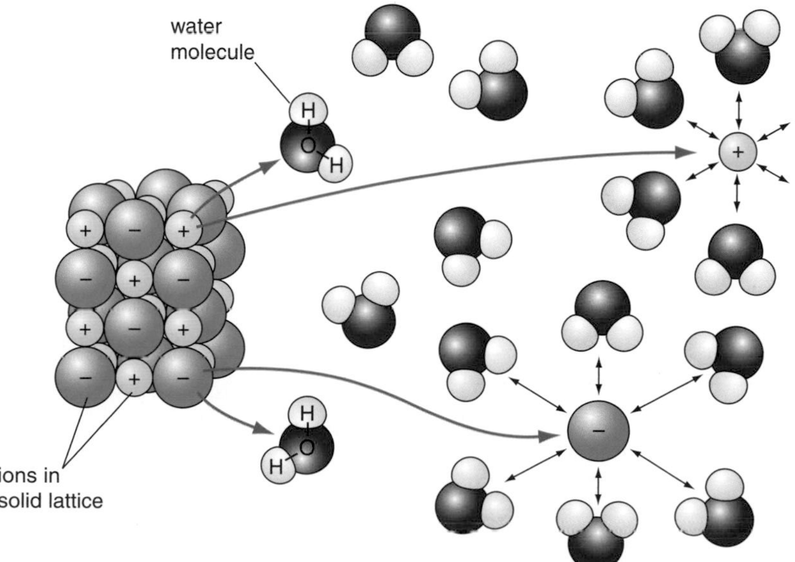

Figure 8 A model for dissolving an ionic substance. In a solution of an ionic compound the positive and negative ions are free to move about separately, held apart by the water molecules which surround the ions.

Questions

8 a) Draw diagrams to show the arrangement of the electrons in a calcium atom and in a fluorine atom.

b) Use dot-and-cross diagrams to show how the arrangement of electrons in a calcium atom and in a fluorine atom change when calcium fluoride is formed.

c) Why is calcium fluoride classified as a compound?

d) Give the formula of calcium fluoride and state the type of bonding present in this compound.

9 The table gives information about five different ions.

Ion	Number of protons	Number of neutrons	Number of electrons
A	12	12	10
B	19	20	18
C	8	8	10
D	11	12	10
E	9	10	10

a) Which two ions have a charge of 1+?

b) Select the correct formula for the compound that forms between C and B.

CB C_2B B_2C C_2B_2

c) What is the charge on ion E?

d) Use your Periodic Table to identify ion D.

► Covalent bonding

The study of ionic compounds shows how a chemical bond can be formed by transferring the outermost electrons from a metal to a non-metal in order that both types of atom can obtain a more stable electronic structure. It is also possible for **two non-metals** to form a chemical bond by **sharing** electrons and this leads to another type of bonding known as covalent bonding.

A **covalent bond** is formed when two non-metal atoms **share an electron pair** to obtain a stable electron structure. A hydrogen molecule, H_2, contains a covalent bond, **a shared pair** of electrons between the two hydrogen atoms as shown in Figure 9.

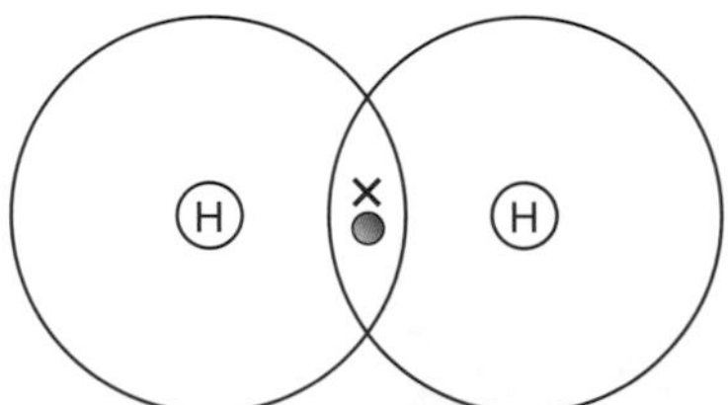

Figure 9 A covalent bond in hydrogen, H_2

A molecule is a substance that contains a covalent bond.

When two electrons are shared in this way the bond is called a **single covalent bond**. By sharing electrons each hydrogen atom has now attained a full outer shell. H_2 is now called a **molecule**. A molecule is a substance that contains a covalent bond. A covalent bond in hydrogen can be represented as 'H—H' where the long dash represents the shared pair of electrons. Two atoms bonded together in this way are called a **diatomic molecule**, i.e. a small particle containing two atoms covalently bonded together. **Covalent bonds are strong bonds** and require a lot of energy to break them.

Like hydrogen, chlorine forms a covalent diatomic molecule, Cl_2, where each chlorine atom (2,8,7) shares an electron to obtain a full outer shell (Figure 10).

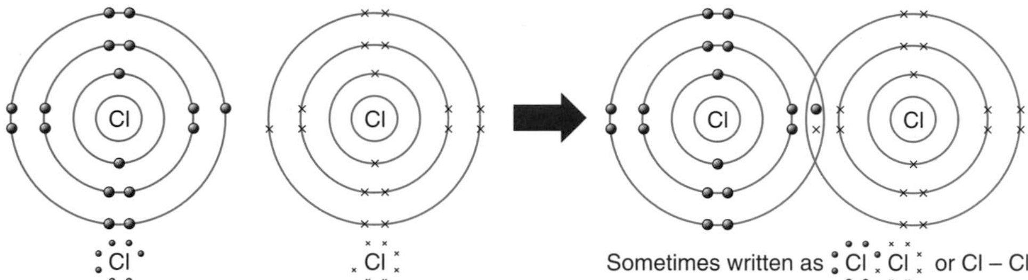

Figure 10 Formation of a chlorine molecule, Cl_2

Bonding diagrams like Figure 10, where the electronic configuration of one atom is shown as a series of dots (•) and the electron configuration of the other atom is shown as a series of crosses (×), are know as 'dot-and-cross' diagrams.

Covalent bonding in compounds

Water, H_2O

Figure 11 shows hydrogen and oxygen combining to form the covalent compound water, H_2O. In this compound, hydrogen and oxygen atoms share electrons to achieve stable electron structures. Since oxygen has the electronic configuration 2,6 it will share two electrons (one from each hydrogen atom) to obtain an electronic configuration of 2,8. At the same time each hydrogen atom obtains a full outer shell. In Figure 11 it is seen that in the outer shell of oxygen there are two bonded pairs of electrons between the oxygen atom and hydrogen atoms and also **two lone pairs of electrons**.

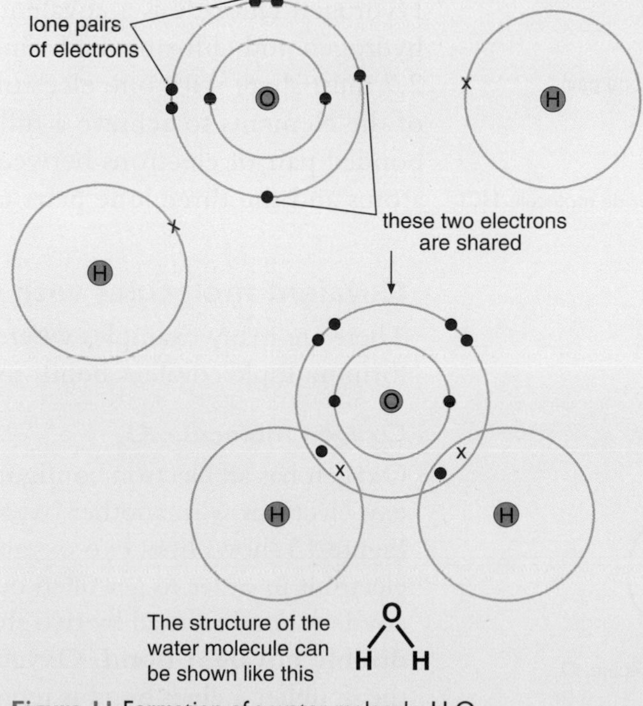

Figure 11 Formation of a water molecule, H_2O

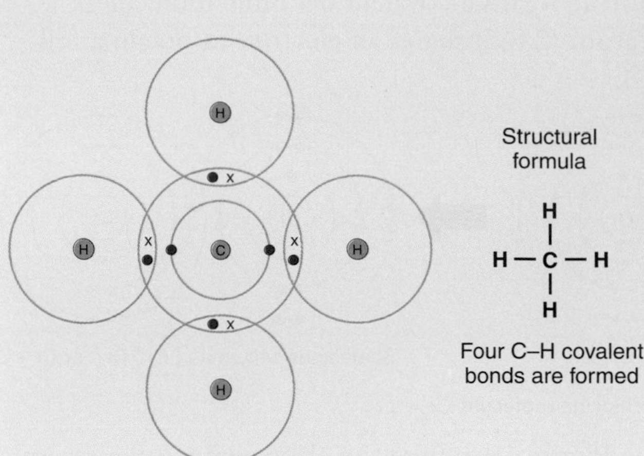

Figure 12 Covalent bonding in methane, CH_4

Methane molecule, CH_4

Methane is a covalent gas made up of the two non-metals, carbon and hydrogen. Carbon with an electronic configuration 2,4 must share with four electrons from four hydrogen atoms for each of the elements to achieve a full outer shell. Figure 12 shows the four shared or bonded pairs of electrons in this molecule. Methane is a molecule with four single covalent bonds.

Ammonia molecule, NH_3

Ammonia is a covalent gas made up of the two non-metals, nitrogen and hydrogen. Nitrogen with an electronic configuration 2,5 must share with three electrons from three hydrogen atoms for each of the elements to achieve a full outer shell. Figure 13 shows the **three bonded pairs and one lone pair of electrons** on the outer shell of the nitrogen in the ammonia molecule. Ammonia is a molecule with three single covalent bonds.

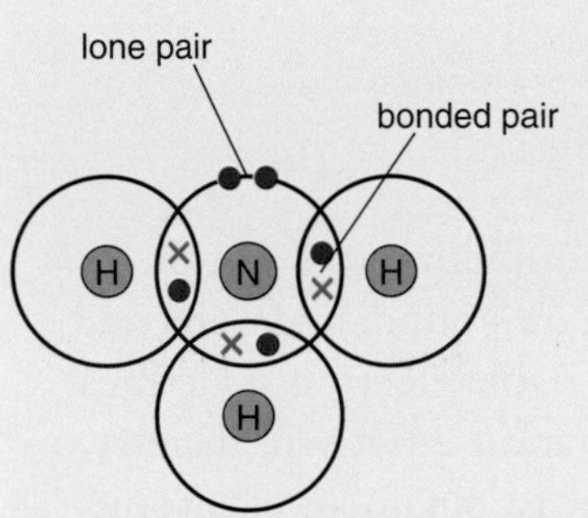

Figure 13 Ammonia molecule, NH_3, showing only outher electrons

Hydrogen chloride molecule, HCl

Hydrogen chloride is a covalent gas made up of two non-metals, hydrogen and chlorine. Chlorine with an electronic configuration 2,7 must share with one electron from a hydrogen atom for each of the elements to achieve a full outer shell. Figure 14 shows the bonded pair of electrons between the chlorine and hydrogen atoms and the three lone pairs of electrons around the chlorine.

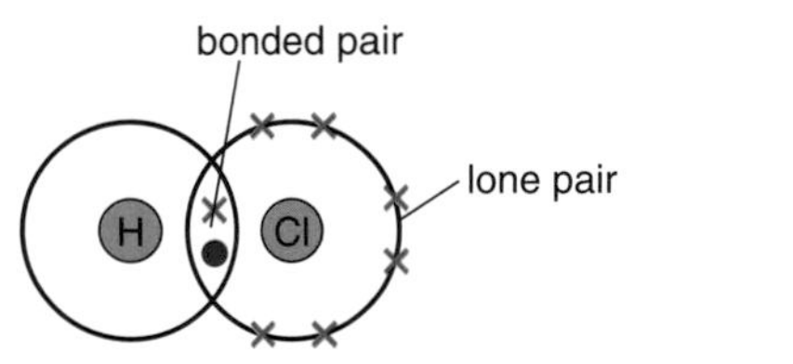

Figure 14 Hydrogen chloride molecule, HCl

Covalent molecules with multiple covalent bonds

There are many examples where some non-metal elements must form multiple covalent bonds to achieve a full outer shell.

Oxygen molecule, O_2

Oxygen has an electron configuration of 2,6 and needs to share two electrons with another oxygen atom to get a full outer shell. Figure 15 shows how two oxygen atoms form two shared pairs of electrons in order to get filled outer shells of electrons. The multiple covalent bond formed by two shared pairs of electrons is called a **double covalent bond**. Oxygen is often written O=O where the double covalent bond is represented by a double dash.

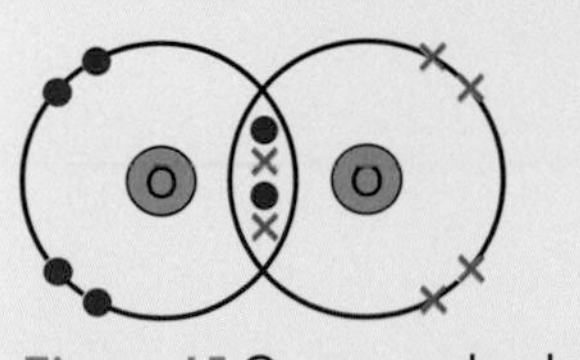

Figure 15 Oxygen molecule, O_2

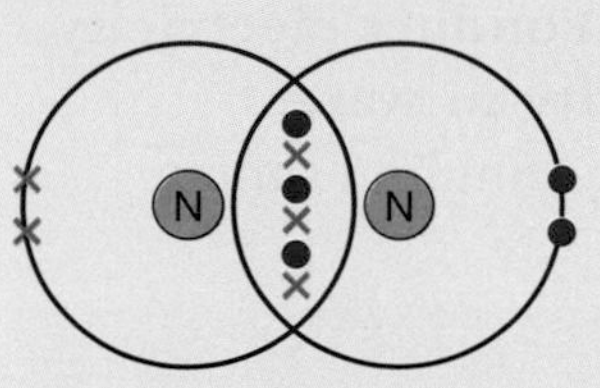

Figure 16 Formation of a triple covalent bond in nitrogen

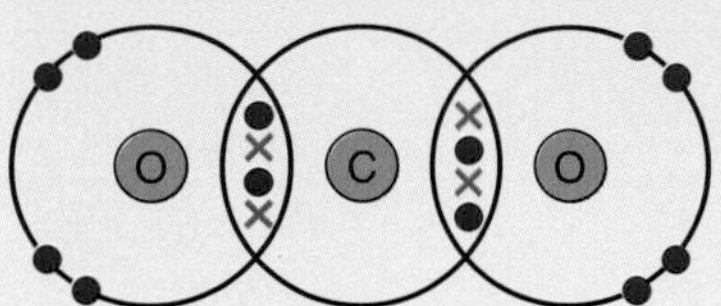

Figure 17 Carbon dioxide molecule

Figures 14–17 show only the electrons on the outer shell of each atom.

Nitrogen molecule, N_2

Nitrogen has an electron configuration of 2,5 and needs to share three electrons with another nitrogen atom to get a full outer shell. Figure 16 shows how the two nitrogen atoms each share three electrons to obtain a filled outer shell. The multiple covalent bond formed by three shared pairs of electrons is called a **triple covalent bond**.

N_2 is often written N≡N, where the triple dash represents the triple covalent bond.

Carbon dioxide molecule, CO_2

Figure 17 shows how the electrons are arranged in a carbon dioxide molecule. As carbon has an electron configuration of 2,4 and oxygen has an electron configuration of 2,6 a carbon atom will therefore need to share with four electrons to obtain a full outer shell while each oxygen atom needs to share with two electrons to obtain a filled outer shell of electrons. This means that a carbon atom needs to share its outer shell electrons with two oxygen atoms. The two oxygen atoms form double bonds with the carbon atom and carbon dioxide is sometimes written as O=C=O.

Properties of simple covalent molecules

The covalent molecules studied so far can all be classified as simple covalent substances. In these simple covalent molecules the atoms are held together in each molecule by **strong covalent bonds** as shown in Figure 18. Although these covalent bonds within the molecules are **strong** there are only **weak forces** of attraction between the separate molecules. These weak attractive forces between covalent molecules are called **van der Waals' forces** (Figure 19). Figure 18 shows the strong covalent bonds within a methane molecule while Figure 19 shows the weak van der Waals' forces between the methane molecules.

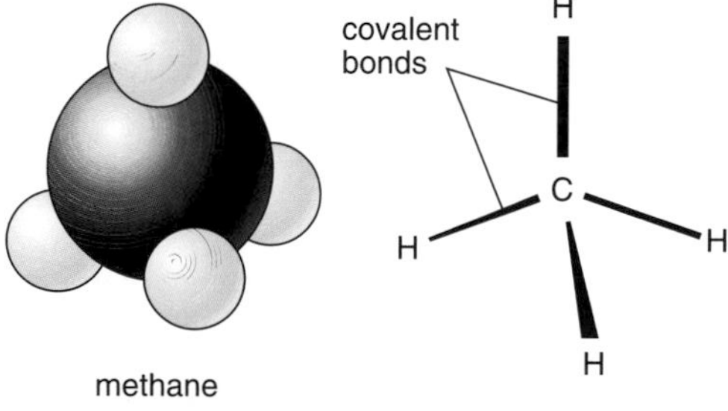

Figure 18 Strong covalent bonds in methane

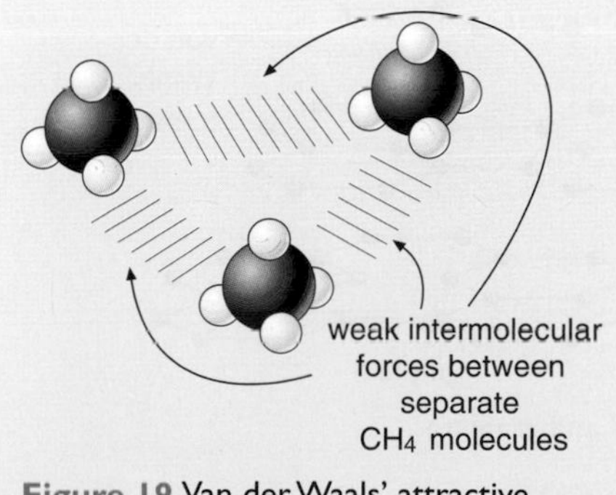

Figure 19 Van der Waals' attractive forces in methane

Simple covalent substances can be elements or compounds and they exist as solids, liquids or gases at room temperature. Although there are strong covalent bonds within the molecules there are **only weak attractive forces between the molecules** and this results in simple molecular substances having **low melting points and boiling points**. Little energy is needed to separate the molecules as it does not involve breaking the strong covalent bond. Covalent bonds require a great amount of energy to break them.

As simple molecular substances are composed of small molecules with no charges or free electrons they **do not conduct electricity**. Simple covalent molecules have **a low solubility in water**.

Table 2 gives the physical properties of some common simple covalent substances.

Substance	Formula	State at room temperature	Melting point /°C	Boiling point /°C	Conducts electricity	Solubility in water
Hydrogen	H_2	Gas	−259	−252	No	Insoluble
Carbon dioxide	CO_2	Gas	−55.6	−78.5	No	It reacts to give carbonic acid
Iodine	I_2	Solid	113.5	184	No	Slightly soluble in water
Bromine	Br_2	Liquid	−7.2	59	No	Slightly soluble in water

Table 2 Physical properties of some simple molecular substances

Questions

10 a) Explain what is meant by the term covalent bond.

b) Use dot-and-cross diagrams to show how the electrons are arranged in the following covalent molecules:

i) H_2 **ii)** Cl_2 **iii)** O_2 **iv)** NH_3 **v)** H_2O **vi)** CH_4

11 a) Show how the electrons are arranged in a CCl_4 molecule.

b) Explain why the formula of ammonia is NH_3 and not NH_2.

c) Explain why methane, CH_4, is a gas with a low boiling point of −182 °C.

12 Use your knowledge of intermolecular forces to explain why bromine is a liquid and iodine is a solid.

Giant covalent structures

Covalent bonding is the bonding between the atoms in a simple covalent molecule; however, covalent bonding is also the bonding that holds **giant covalent molecular crystals** together. The examples of giant covalent structures that will be studied are the allotropes of carbon, **diamond** and **graphite**; see Figure 20.

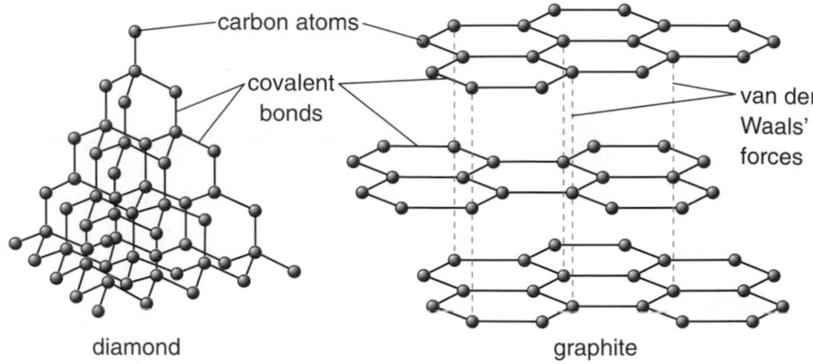

Figure 20 Giant covalent structures of diamond and graphite

Allotropes are alternative forms of the same element in the same physical state.

Diamond

Structure

Figure 20 shows that each carbon atom in diamond is covalently bonded to four other carbon atoms in a giant covalent structure. The symmetrical, tetrahedral arrangement of the carbon atoms along with the strong covalent bonds in all directions make the structure difficult to break apart.

Properties of diamond

1. **Non-conductor of electricity**
   Diamond is a non-conductor of electricity as it contains no ions or free electrons to carry the charge. All the electrons in the outer shell of each carbon atom are held firmly in covalent bonds throughout the structure.

2. **High melting point and boiling point**
   The carbon atoms in this giant covalent structure are held together by very strong covalent bonds. It takes a lot of energy to break these strong covalent bonds. A temperature of over 3500 °C is required before the carbon atoms can vibrate fast enough to break away and form a liquid. Likewise it takes a temperature of over 4800 °C before the carbon atoms can break free and form a gas.

3. **Hard**
   Diamond is very hard as it has a giant covalent structure and it is difficult to break the strong covalent bonds between the carbon atoms.

4. **Insoluble in water**
   Water molecules are unable to break down the strong covalent bonds in diamond and this makes it insoluble.

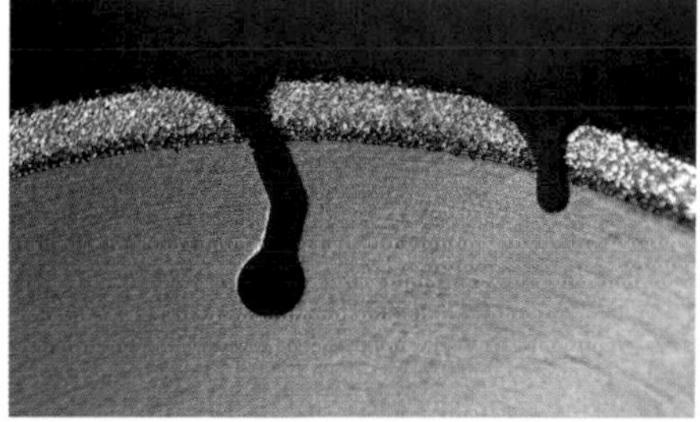

Figure 21 A diamond-tipped cutting tool

Use of diamond in cutting tools

Due to the great hardness of diamond, it is used in cutting tools, for example, glass cutters, diamond-studded cutters and in drill bits.

Graphite

Structure

Figure 20 shows that in graphite the carbon atoms are held by strong covalent bonds within the layers. The layers are made up of hexagonal rings where each carbon atom is bonded to three others. This means that each carbon atom has a free electron which forms a cloud of delocalised electrons between the layers. It is the delocalised or free moving electrons which allow graphite to conduct electricity.

While there are strong covalent bonds within the layers, there are only weak attractive forces or **van der Waals'** attractions between the layers.

Properties of graphite

1. **Conducts electricity**
   Graphite is a good conductor of electricty as the delocalised electrons are free to move and carry the charge.

2. **Soft and slippery**
   The van der Waals' forces of attraction between the layers are weak and this allows the layers of atoms to slip over each other. As the layers can slide over each other graphite feels soft and slippery.

3. **High melting and boiling point**
   While the layers of graphite can slip over each other readily, it is extremely difficult to break the strong covalent bonds between the carbon atoms within the hexagonal layers. Due to this graphite has a high melting point and boiling point. It melts at approximately 3700 °C.

4. **Insoluble in water**
   Water molecules are unable to break down the strong covalent bonds in graphite and so graphite is insoluble in water.

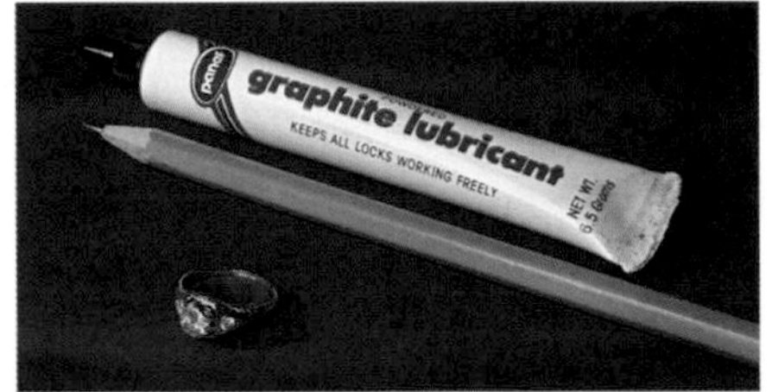

Figure 22 A tube of lubricant oil containing graphite. The layers of graphite can slide over each other which allows it to act as a lubricant

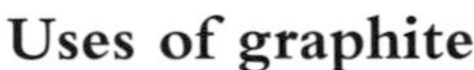

Uses of graphite

Graphite is used as a lubricant and in pencil leads. It is a good lubricant as the layers of atoms can slide over one another. Once applied to moving parts it allows them to move freely. When used as a pencil lead, a little pressure causes the layers of atoms to slide over one another and rub off onto the paper leaving a mark.

Figure 22 shows a tube of graphite lubricant oil.

Allotropes of carbon

Diamond and graphite are allotropes of carbon. **Allotropes are different forms of the same element in the same physical state.**

Diamond and graphite are both made from carbon atoms but it is the way in which the atoms are bonded together that makes them different. Sulfur is another element that has different allotropes. It exists in three forms, rhombic sulfur, monoclinic sulfur and plastic sulfur (page 202).

Questions

13 Make a table to show three similarities and three differences between diamond and graphite.

14 This question is about covalent substances.
- **a)** Explain why diamond has a high melting point and boiling point while chlorine gas has a low melting point and boiling point.
- **b)** Use your understanding of giant covalent structures to explain why graphite conducts electricity.
- **c)** Explain why diamond is very hard and is used in diamond cutting drills.

15 **a)** Explain fully what you understand by the term allotropes.
- **b)** Draw diagrams of the two allotropes of carbon.
- **c)** Do a search to find elements, other than carbon, which have allotropes.

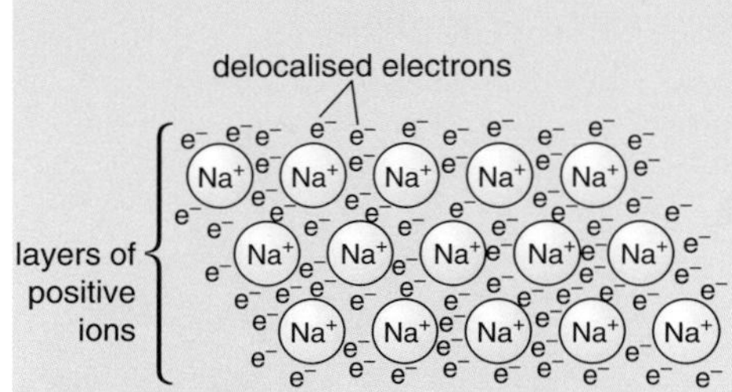

Figure 23 Metallic bonding: a regular arrangement of layers of positive ions held together by a sea of delocalised electrons

Metallic bonding

This occurs when metals use their outermost electrons to form a sea of electrons, which move in all directions throughout the metallic structure as shown in Figure 23.

These **free moving or delocalised electrons** act like 'electron glue' holding the metal ions together in a giant metallic structure. The attraction between the delocalised electrons and the positive metal ions is known as the **metallic bond**.

Metallic bonds are strong and can be used to explain the following properties of metals:

1. Electrical conductors

Metals are good conductors of electricity as the delocalised electrons are free to move and carry the charge. When a metal is connected in an electrical circuit the free moving electrons move towards the positive terminal as shown in Figure 24.

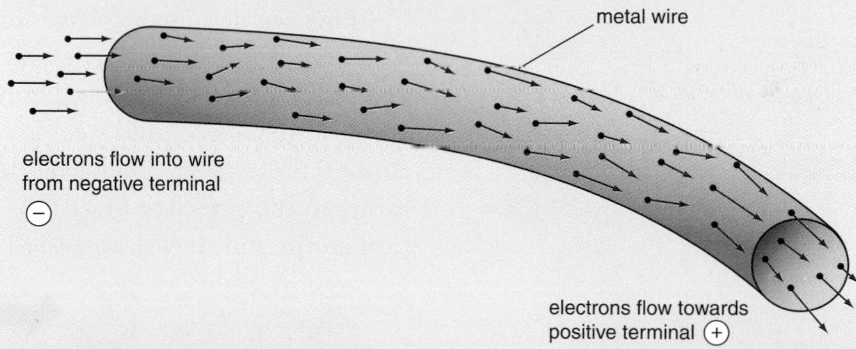

Figure 24 Electrical conductivity of metals

2. Melting point

The melting point of a metal depends on the strength of the metallic bond, the attraction between the layers of positive ions and the delocalised electrons. Metals usually have high melting points. Iron has a melting point of 1540 °C and copper has a melting point of 1080 °C. These metals have high melting points indicating a strong metallic bond. However, some metals have comparatively low melting points; for example, potassium melts at 64 °C and sodium turns from a solid to a liquid at 98 °C.

3. Malleable and ductile

Malleable means that a metal can be bent and hammered into shape while ductile means that a metal can be drawn into a wire. Metals are malleable and ductile because the layers of metal ions can slide over each other when a force is applied. Throughout the process the metallic bonding is maintained as the bonds between the metal atoms are not fixed and rigid. After slipping the atoms settle into their new positions and the structure is restored. Figure 25 shows what happens to the layers of atoms in a metal when a force is applied.

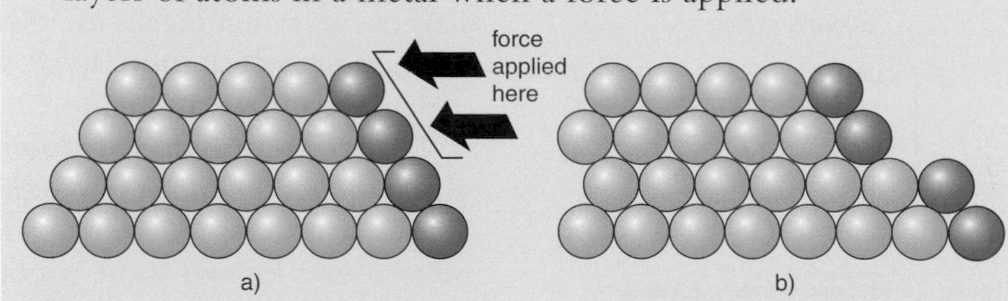

Figure 25 The position of layers in a metal before and after a force is applied

Alloys

Before discussing the uses of metals it is important to understand what an alloy is.

An alloy is a mixture of two or more elements, at least one of which is a metal, and the resulting mixture has metallic properties.

Alloys are designed to have improved properties for a specific use. They can improve properties such as hardness, electrical conductivity and resistance to corrosion. There are many common examples of alloys, for example mild steel is an alloy containing mainly iron with about 0.2% carbon. Steel is harder and less malleable than iron and this is due to the presence of carbon atoms. Carbon atoms are smaller than iron atoms and they distort the layers of iron atoms; see Figure 26.

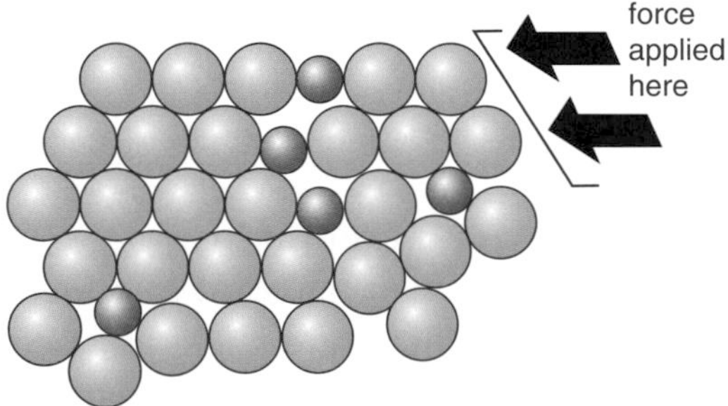

Figure 26 Carbon atoms distorting the layers of iron atoms in steel

The smaller carbon atoms make it more difficult for the layers of iron atoms to slide over each other. This results in an alloy which is much harder and less malleable than iron.

Uses of metals and alloys

Scientists choose a metal or alloy for a particular use because the properties are suited to that use. Some examples are:

1. Aluminium is used to make overhead electrical cables/wires as it is a good conductor of electricity and has a low density. Its low density also makes it suitable for making lightweight alloys.

Figure 27 Overhead electrical cables

2. Copper is used in electrical wiring as it is a good conductor of electricity and is also ductile. It is used in plumbing as it is malleable and it does not react with water. Copper is also used to make a number of important alloys. Brass is an alloy of zinc and copper and is used to make ornaments due to its strength and lack of reactivity. Alloys of copper are used to make coins and this use is again based on their strength and lack of reactivity.

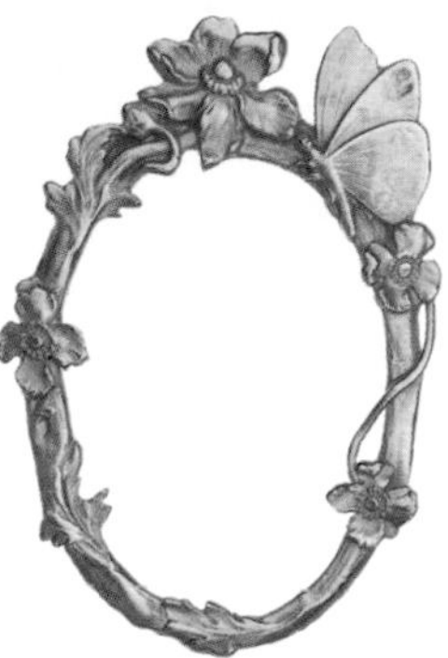

Figure 28 A brass ornament, coin and electrical wires

3. Iron is a very abundant metal. It is a very strong and cheap metal and it is used to build bridges and in the construction of buildings.

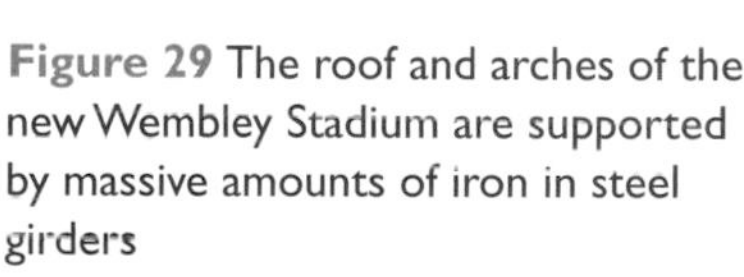

Figure 29 The roof and arches of the new Wembley Stadium are supported by massive amounts of iron in steel girders

4. Magnesium is combined with other metals to make high strength and low density alloys; for example, duralumin is used for making aircraft. It is also used in flares as it burns with a brilliant white flame.

Figure 30 An emergency flare

▶ Using data to classify structures

To use data to distinguish between metals and non-metals it is important to know their properties. The properties that are generally used to do this are electrical conductivity, malleability, melting points and boiling points.

Consider the table below which contains information about the properties of four elements A, B, C and D.

Element	Melting point/°C	Electrical conductivity in solid state	Electrical conductivity in molten state
A	1535	good	good
B	44	poor	poor
C	1083	good	good
D	3550	poor	poor

Elements A and C are metals as they have high melting points and they both conduct electricity in the solid and molten states while elements B and D are non-metals as they are poor conductors of electricity in the solid and molten states. Additionally, we can tell that element D has a giant covalent structure as it has a very high melting point while element B has a simple molecular structure as it has a low melting point.

The following data can be used to distinguish between metallic, giant ionic, simple molecular and giant covalent structures.

Substance	Melting point/°C	Electrical conductivity (solid)	Electrical conductivity (liquid)
W	1540	good	good
X	−7	poor	poor
Y	808	poor	good
Z	1410	poor	poor

Substance W is a metal as it conducts electricity in the solid state and the molten state. Substance X is a simple molecular substance as it has a low melting point and is a poor conductor both in the solid and molten states while Z is a giant covalent substance as it has a high melting point and is a poor conductor in the solid and molten states. Substance Y is a giant ionic structure as it has a high melting point and does not conduct electricity in the solid state but does in the molten state when the ions are free to move and carry the charge.

Questions

16 Explain the meaning of the term 'malleable'.

17 Draw a labelled diagram to show metallic bonding in copper. The labels should include metal ions, ordered arrangement of ions and delocalised electrons.

18 The properties of five metals are shown in the table below.

Metal	Density/ g/cm^3	Relative strength compared with iron	Melting point/°C	Relative electrical conductivity compared with iron	Rate of corrosion	Cost per tonne/£
Aluminium	2.7	0.33	660	3.7	very slow	950
Copper	8.9	0.62	1083	5.8	very slow	1100
Iron	7.9	1.00	1535	1.0	quick	130
Silver	10.5	0.39	962	6.1	very slight	250 000
Zinc	7.1	0.51	420	1.6	very slow	730

Use the information in the table to explain the following uses of the metals.

a) Iron is used to build bridges.

b) Aluminium is used for overhead electrical cables.

c) Copper is used in electrical wiring rather than silver.

d) Iron gates are coated or galvanised with zinc.

e) Copper is used in the base of many steel saucepans.

19 Steel for making car bodies is a low carbon alloy of iron containing 0.2% carbon and 99.8% iron.

a) Explain the meaning of the term 'alloy'.

b) Use your knowledge of alloys to explain how atoms of carbon improve the hardness and malleability of the steel.

20 The properties of five substances are given in the table below.

Substance	Melting point/°C	Boiling point/°C	Electrical conductivity (solid)	Electrical conductivity (liquid)
A	−101	−34	poor	poor
B	1083	2582	good	good
C	3550	4827	poor	poor
D	44	280	poor	poor
E	808	1465	poor	good

a) Which substance, A, B, C, D or E, could be diamond? Explain your answer.

b) Which substance, A, B, C, D or E, is composed of oppositely charged ions?

c) Which substances contain covalent bonds between atoms?

d) Which substances have covalent bonds between atoms and van der Waals' forces between molecules?

Exam questions

1 a) The element chlorine reacts with both metals and non-metals. It reacts with the element calcium to form the compound calcium chloride, and with the element hydrogen to form the compound hydrogen chloride.

i) Using electronic structures, explain how atoms of calcium and chlorine become bonded in the formation of the compound calcium chloride. *(6 marks)*

ii) By means of a diagram, show the bonding in hydrogen chloride. Use outer shells of electrons only. *(3 marks)*

b) The element chlorine contains atoms with two different mass numbers. The table below shows data about these atoms of chlorine.

Atom of chlorine	Mass number	% abundance
^{35}Cl	35	75
^{37}Cl	37	25

Use the data in the table to calculate the relative atomic mass of chlorine. *(3 marks)*

2 Many substances can be classified by structure as giant ionic lattice, covalent molecular, giant covalent and metallic.

a) The table below gives some information about four substances H–K. The letters do not represent symbols of the substances. Use the information to answer the questions which follow the table. Each letter H–K can be used once, more than once or not at all.

Substance	Melting point/ °C	Boiling point/ °C	Electrical conductivity	
			when solid	when molten
H	808	1465	does not conduct	conducts
I	660	2350	conducts	conducts
J	1610	2230	does not conduct	does not conduct
K	−182	−161	does not conduct	does not conduct

i) Which substance is a gas at room temperature? *(1 mark)*

ii) Which substance is a giant ionic lattice? *(1 mark)*

iii) Which substance has a covalent molecular structure? *(1 mark)*

b) Copper is a metal with a metallic structure containing metallic bonding. What is a metallic bond? *(3 marks)*

c) Carbon has two allotropes: graphite and diamond. Graphite, unlike diamond, is soft and conducts electricity.

i) What is meant by the term allotrope? *(2 marks)*

ii) Explain why graphite conducts electricity. *(2 marks)*

3 a) When hydrogen burns in oxygen, water molecules are formed.

i) Draw a dot-and-cross diagram to show the arrangement of all the electrons in a water molecule. *(2 marks)*

ii) Give the formula of one other molecule which you would expect to have the same type of bonding as water. *(1 mark)*

iii) The melting point of water is 0 °C whereas the melting point of calcium fluoride is 1360 °C. Why do you think that water has a much lower melting point than calcium fluoride? *(3 marks)*

b) Iron is ductile and has a high density.

i) Draw a labelled diagram to show the bonding in a metal such as iron. *(3 marks)*

ii) Use your understanding of metallic bonding to explain:

1 Why iron has a high density. *(2 marks)*

2 Why iron is ductile. *(2 marks)*

3 Why iron can conduct electricity. *(2 marks)*

4 Calcium reacts with fluorine to form the compound calcium fluoride.

a) Copy and complete the diagrams below to show the arrangement of all the electrons in a calcium atom and a fluorine atom. (You may find your Data Leaflet helpful.)

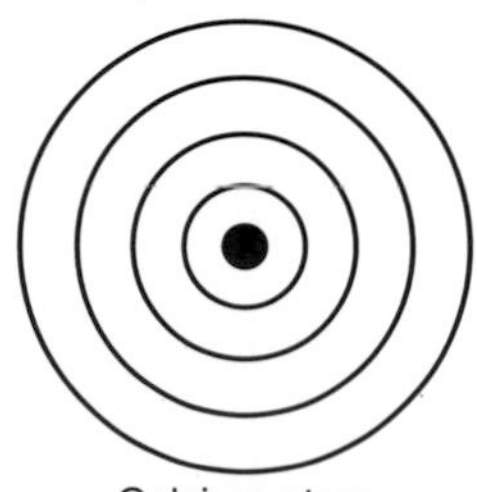

Calcium atom

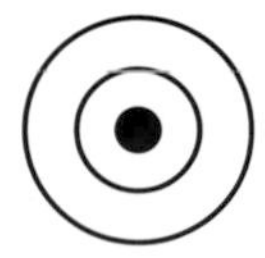

Fluorine atom *(2 marks)*

b) Explain, in terms of the atoms involved, how the electron arrangements change when calcium fluoride is formed from calcium and fluorine. *(3 marks)*

c) Give the formula of calcium fluoride. *(1 mark)*

d) What type of bonding is present in calcium fluoride? *(1 mark)*

5 a) Explain, using electronic structures, how magnesium and oxygen bond to form the compound magnesium oxide.
In this question you will be assessed on using your written communication skills including the use of specialist science terms. *(6 marks)*

b) Explain why magnesium oxide has a high melting point. *(3 marks)*

6 Copper metal is used in electric cables because it is ductile and a good conductor of electricity. Draw a labelled diagram to show the structure of a metal such as copper. *(4 marks)*

7 A single covalent bond is formed when two atoms share a pair of electrons. One electron comes from each atom. The diagram below shows the outer electrons in the single covalent bond in a molecule of chlorine.

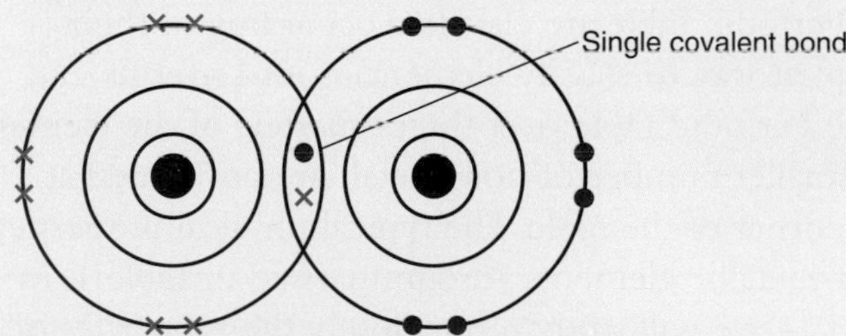

a) Draw a diagram of a molecule of oxygen, showing the outer electrons only. *(2 marks)*

b) A molecule of ammonia contains three single covalent bonds. Draw a diagram of a molecule of ammonia, showing the outer electrons only. *(2 marks)*

8 Some properties of four substances are given in the table below.

Substance	Melting point/°C	Electrical conductivity (solid)	Electrical conductivity (liquid)
A	420	good	good
B	808	poor	good
C	1610	poor	poor
D	44	poor	poor

a) Which substance, **A**, **B**, **C** or **D**, could be zinc? *(1 mark)*

b) Which substance, **A**, **B**, **C** or **D**, has a simple molecular structure? *(1 mark)*

c) What type of bonding is present in **C**? *(1 mark)*

d) Which substance, **A**, **B**, **C** or **D**, is likely to be sodium chloride? *(1 mark)*

9 Diamond and graphite are allotropes of the element carbon.

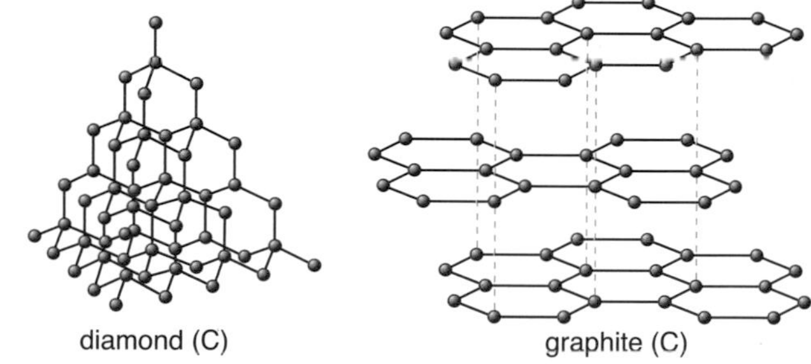

a) What is meant by the term allotrope? *(2 marks)*

b) Graphite is the only non-metal element which can conduct electricity.
Referring to the structure of graphite, explain why graphite can conduct electricity. *(2 marks)*

c) Diamond is used as a cutting tool.
Referring to the structure of diamond, explain why diamond is used in cutting tools. *(1 mark)*

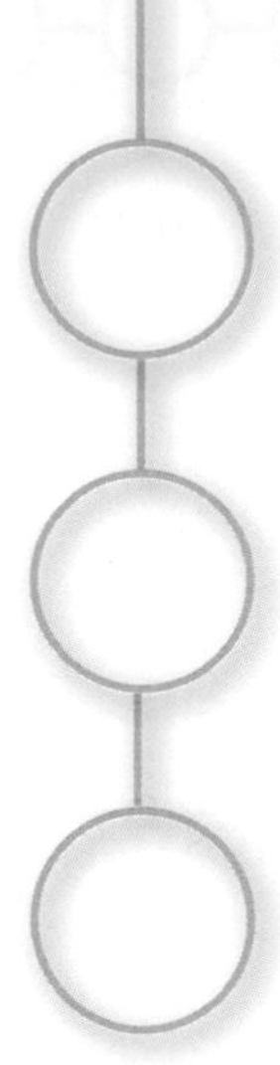

3 Elements, Compounds and Mixtures

In our everyday life we are surrounded by millions of different substances, both naturally occurring and man made. Fortunately for us, scientists have classified this vast range of substances into three groups: **elements, compounds and mixtures**. The basic building blocks for all of these substances are elements and although there is an almost endless number of substances, they are all made from just over 90 naturally occurring elements.

Elements

Copper and limestone are examples of two common substances; limestone is not an element but copper is. We know that limestone is not an element because on heating it can be turned into simpler substances; however, it is not possible to do this for copper. When limestone is heated it decomposes into calcium oxide and carbon dioxide, but no matter how copper is treated it cannot be broken down further.

calcium carbonate → calcium oxide + carbon dioxide

Copper is an element and elements are defined on the left.

An element is a substance that consists of only one type of atom and cannot be broken down into simpler substances by chemical means.

Elements in the Periodic Table are classified according to their properties. The simplest way to classify elements is into **metals** and **non-metals**. In the Periodic Table over three-quarters of the elements are metals and the smaller number of non-metals are positioned at the top right hand corner of the table. The typical physical properties of metallic and non-metallic elements are summarised in Table 1. In Chapters 10, 11 and 14 we will study more closely the properties of metals and non-metals.

Metallic elements	Non-metallic elements
Good conductors of electricity	Poor conductors of electricity (graphite is an exception)
Good conductors of heat	Poor conductors of heat
All solids at room temperature except mercury	Can be gas, liquid or solid at room temperature
Usually have a high density	Usually have a low density

Table 1 Typical physical properties of metals and non-metals

Figure 1 Some metallic and non-metallic elements

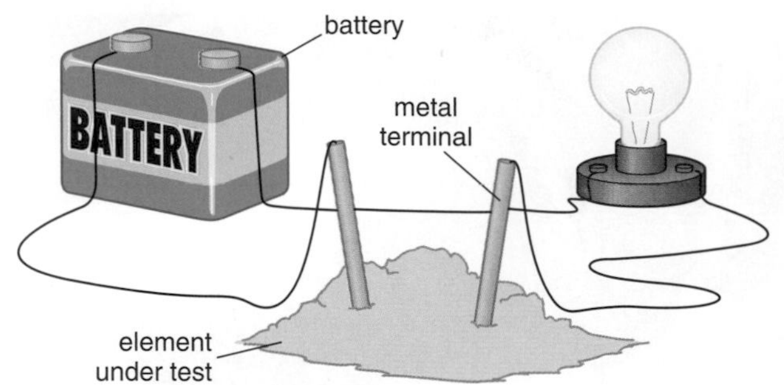

Figure 2 Testing for metals and non-metals

Probably the easiest way to show that an element is a metal or a non-metal is to check the electrical conductivity as shown in Figure 2. Metals will cause the bulb to light up because they are good conductors of electricity.

Table 2 provides information on the physical properties of elements and this allows us to make comparisons between the physical properties of metals and non-metals.

Element	Formula	Structure	Bonding	Melting point/ °C	Boiling point/ °C	Electrical conductivity	State at room temperature
Iron	Fe	Giant metallic	Metallic	1540	2887	Good	Solid
Copper	Cu	Giant metallic	Metallic	1083	2582	Good	Solid
Oxygen	O_2	Simple molecular	Covalent	−219	−183	Poor	Gas
Bromine	Br_2	Simple molecular	Covalent	−7	58	Poor	Liquid
Sulfur	S_8	Simple molecular	Covalent	114	445	Poor	Solid
Carbon (diamond)	C	Giant covalent	Covalent	3550	4827	Poor	Solid

Table 2 How the physical properties of elements relate to their structure and bonding

From the table it is seen that:

* Metallic bonding in metals leads to solids with good electrical conductivity, high melting points and high boiling points;
* Non-metals with a simple molecular structure can be solid, liquid or gas and have poor electrical conductivity and low melting points and boiling points;
* Diamond, a non-metal with a giant covalent structure, is a poor conductor of electricity, with a high melting point and boiling point.

Writing chemical formulae for elements

Chemical formulae are a short-hand way of representing elements and compounds. When writing the formula of an element it is necessary to consider its structure. The following guidelines are helpful in writing an element's formula.

Elements with a giant metallic or giant covalent structure

These elements have a formula which is just the same as their symbol, for example:

Element	Symbol	Formula
Carbon	C	C
Silicon	Si	Si
Copper	Cu	Cu
Calcium	Ca	Ca
Iron	Fe	Fe

Gaseous and liquid elements with a simple covalent molecular structure

These elements form **diatomic molecules** where two atoms are joined by a covalent bond, for example, a hydrogen molecule, H_2, contains two hydrogen atoms covalently joined together.

Element	Symbol	Formula of molecule
Hydrogen	H	H_2
Oxygen	O	O_2
Nitrogen	N	N_2
Fluorine	F	F_2
Chlorine	Cl	Cl_2
Bromine	Br	Br_2

Note: The noble gases are monatomic and do not form diatomic molecules as they have stable electron configurations. Their symbol and formula are the same, for example, helium has the symbol He and the formula He.

Solid elements with a simple covalent molecular structure

For GCSE the only two that you are likely to use are:

Element	Symbol	Formula of molecule
Iodine	I	I_2
Sulfur	S	S_8

Questions

1 Choose suitable elements to match the following three states at room temperature:
   a) a gas **b)** a liquid **c)** a solid.

2 Write symbols for the following elements:
   a) sodium **b)** carbon **c)** bromine
   d) copper **e)** nitrogen.

3 Write the chemical formula for:
   a) copper **b)** chlorine gas **c)** silicon **d)** neon gas.

4 Which of the following substances is not an element?
   a) hydrogen **b)** water **c)** iron
   d) helium **e)** bromine.

Compounds and mixtures

A compound is a substance that consists of two or more elements that are chemically joined together – in other words, a substance that consists of two or more different types of atoms that are chemically combined.

Water, which makes up more than half the mass of the human body and covers around four-fifths of the world's surface, is composed of oxygen and hydrogen chemically joined together. Water is described as a **compound** of hydrogen and oxygen. In the same way carbon dioxide is a compound and is composed of carbon and oxygen chemically joined together. A compound is defined as follows:

A compound is a substance that consists of two or more different elements chemically joined together.

Table 3 shows a number of familiar compounds and the elements that combine to form them.

Common name	Chemical name	Formula	Elements present
Common salt	Sodium chloride	$NaCl$	Sodium and chlorine
Chalk	Calcium carbonate	$CaCO_3$	Calcium, carbon and oxygen
Sugar	Sucrose	$C_{12}H_{22}O_{11}$	Carbon, hydrogen and oxygen
Petrol	Octane	C_8H_{18}	Carbon and hydrogen
Vinegar	Ethanoic acid	CH_3COOH	Carbon, hydrogen and oxygen
Alcohol	Ethanol	C_2H_5OH	Carbon, hydrogen and oxygen

Table 3 Compounds and their elements

Looking at the differences between compounds and elements

To help us understand the differences between compounds and elements we can study the reaction between iron and sulfur that produces the compound **iron sulfide**.

iron + sulfur → iron sulfide

Figure 3 A magnet used to separate a mixture of iron filings and sulfur

When grey iron filings and yellow sulfur powder are added and mixed:

* The resulting mixture is intermediate in colour between that of the iron and sulfur.
* Using a magnifying glass it is possible to distinguish between the sulfur and iron particles.
* The iron and sulfur mixture can be made in any proportion.
* No heat change takes place when the elements are mixed.
* The mixture can be separated into its elements using a magnet; this attracts the iron filings from the mixture but does not attract the sulfur.
* When dilute sulfuric acid is added to the mixture it will react with the iron to produce hydrogen gas but the acid will not react with the sulfur and it remains undissolved in the acid solution.

We can say that the mixture shows the properties of the individual elements, iron and sulfur.

If the mixture is now heated:

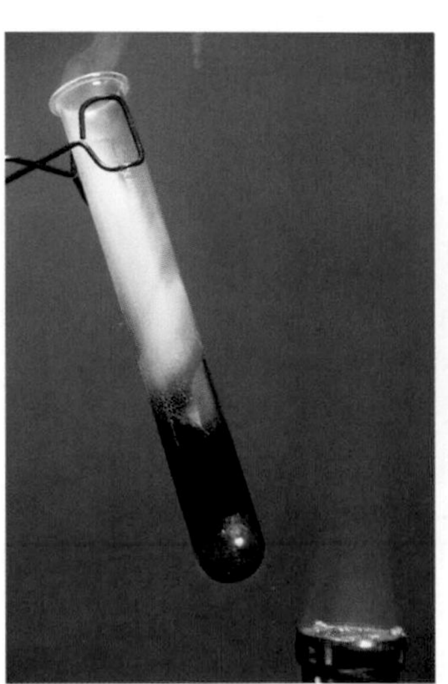

Figure 4 The reaction between iron and sulfur, after heating, to form iron sulfide

* There is a chemical reaction and much heat is given out causing a bright red glow to pass through the mixture as the compound, iron sulfide, FeS, is formed.
* The new compound is greyish-black in colour and it is impossible to distinguish between the particles of iron and sulfur.
* If the solid iron sulfide is ground into a powder it is now impossible to separate the iron from the sulfur using a magnet.
* The compound, iron sulfide, has completely different properties from those of iron or sulfur; for example, when dilute sulfuric acid is added the solid disappears and the poisonous gas hydrogen sulfide is given off. In the case of the mixture it is hydrogen gas that is given off when sulfuric acid is added.
* The compound iron sulfide always contains a fixed ratio of iron to sulfur: one atom of iron always combines with one atom of sulfur.

Questions

5 Using examples, explain the meaning of the following terms:
  a) element **b)** compound **c)** mixture.

6 Separate the following substances into elements, compounds and mixtures:
  copper, marble chips, milk, baking soda, oxygen, sugar, sparkling water, air, sulfur, salt, alumina, diet coke, carbon dioxide and seawater.

7 Complete the following word equations to show how elements combine to form compounds:
  hydrogen + chlorine →
  iron + sulfur →
  magnesium + oxygen →
  sulfur + oxygen →
  calcium + bromine →

8 a) The following five substances are all found in schools.
  sulfur, chlorine, sodium chloride, magnesium sulfate, calcium
  From the above list name the substance that is:
  i) a diatomic gas
  ii) a metal
  iii) a compound made up of two elements only
  iv) a solid non-metal element.

b) Sodium carbonate has the formula Na_2CO_3.
  i) How many different elements are present in sodium carbonate?
  ii) What is the total number of atoms in sodium carbonate?

Differences between mixtures and compounds

From the experiment on page 34 it is also possible to identify several differences between mixtures and compounds. Table 4 summarises the major differences:

Compound	Mixture
Is a pure substance	Contains two or more substances
When a compound is formed, there is an energy change	When a mixture is made, no chemical change occurs
The composition of a compound is always the same	The composition of a mixture can vary
The properties of a compound are different from those of the elements making up the compound	The properties of a mixture are the same as those of the individual substances making up the mixture
Compounds are difficult to separate and are only broken down by chemical means; for example, electrolysis is required to obtain sodium and chlorine from molten sodium chloride	Mixtures are easy to separate using physical means; for example, sodium chloride crystals can be obtained from sodium chloride solution by evaporation

Table 4 Differences between compounds and mixtures

A mixture now can be defined as consisting of two or more substances that are easy to separate.

Mixtures may contain only different elements, elements and compounds or only different compounds. The individual substances are easily separated from the mixture.

Some everyday examples of mixtures are given in Table 5.

Mixture	Type of mixture	Components
Rock salt	Solid/solid	Salt and sand
Sugar solution	Solid/liquid	Sugar and water
Whisky solution	Liquid/liquid (miscible liquids)	Alcohol and water
Soda water	Gas/liquid	Carbon dioxide and water
Air	Gas/gas	Mainly nitrogen and oxygen
Water/oil	Liquid/liquid (immiscible liquids)	Water and oil

Table 5 Some everyday examples of mixtures

Figure 5 Some common everyday mixtures

Methods of separating mixtures

The following methods of separation will be considered: filtration, simple distillation and **fractional distillation**. Before learning about the different separation techniques it is important to understand the meaning of the following terms:

Soluble and **insoluble**; a solid that dissolves in water is described as being **soluble** while solids that do not dissolve in water are described as being **insoluble**. A solid that dissolves is called a **solute** and the liquid it dissolves in is called the **solvent** (water is a common solvent). When a solid dissolves in a solvent, the mixture is known as a **solution**, for example salt dissolved in water is called a **salt solution**.

Miscible and immiscible liquids; liquids that mix are described as **miscible**, for example, water and ethanol. Liquids which do not mix are described as being **immiscible**, for example oil and water.

Filtration

Filtration is used to separate an insoluble solid from a liquid (suspension), for example, separating sand and water as shown in Figure 6.

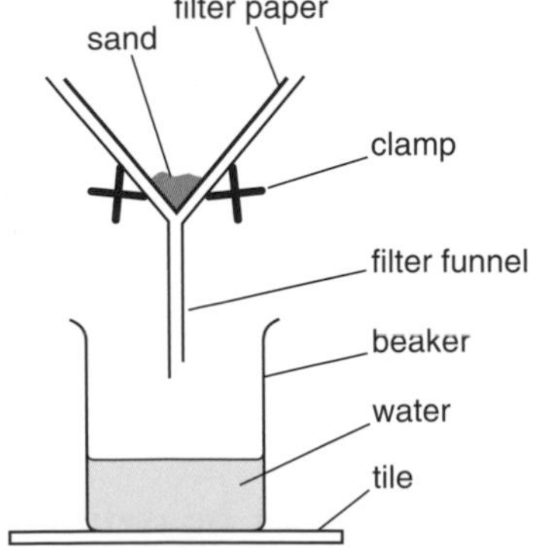

Figure 6 Separation of an insoluble solid from a liquid

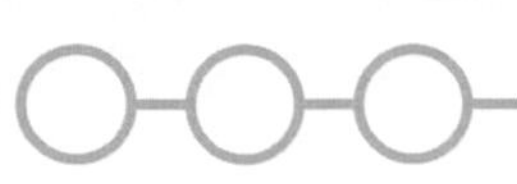

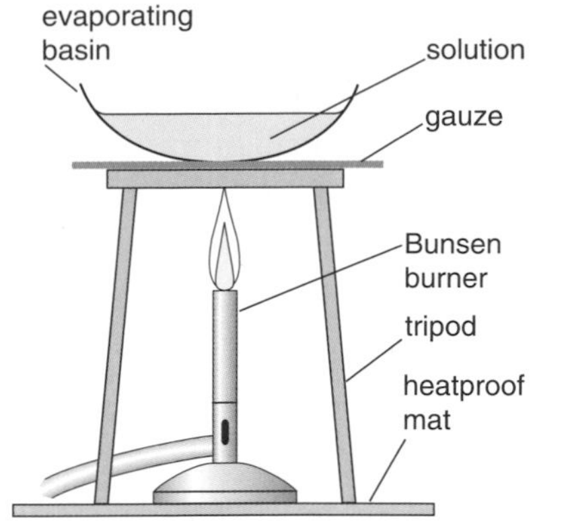

Figure 7 Obtaining salt from a salt solution

The filtered liquid water is called the **filtrate** while the sand remaining on the filter paper is called the **residue**.

Filtration can be used to separate a mixture of salt and sand. Water is added to the mixture, stirred and heated gently. The salt dissolves in the water and the salt solution can now be separated from the sand by filtration. The insoluble sand remains as the residue on the filter paper while the salt solution passes through the filter paper and is collected in an evaporating basin. Salt can then be obtained from the salt solution by evaporating as shown in Figure 7.

To obtain salt crystals from the salt solution it is important to heat the solution gently in an evaporating dish until it is reduced to approximately half of its original value. The concentrated solution is then set aside to cool and crystallise. The solution is not heated to dryness as some salts contain water of crystallisation and heating to dryness would remove this water of crystallisation. Further filtration is used to obtain crystals of pure salt from the concentrated solution. The crystals are then dried between two sheets of filter paper.

Simple distillation

Simple distillation is used to separate a solvent from a solution, for example, water from a salt solution of sodium chloride in water, as shown in Figure 8. It can also be used to separate two miscible liquids with a large difference in boiling point.

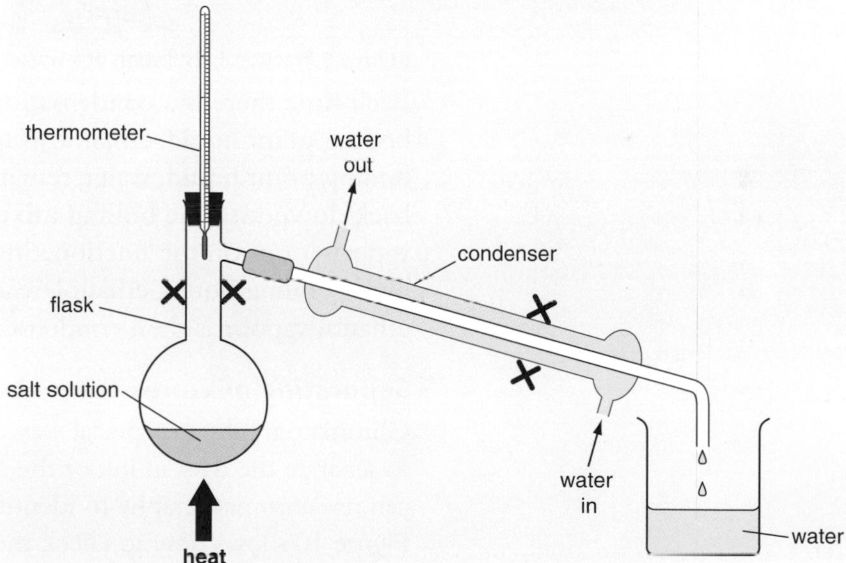

Figure 8 Separating water from a salt solution using simple distillation

When the salt solution is heated it starts to boil and only water molecules are turned into vapour. The sodium ions and chloride ions remain in the boiling solution. The water vapour which boils off passes through the condenser where it is cooled and condensed back into a liquid and collects in the beaker. The water in the beaker is now pure water and contains no salt. The pure water is called the **distillate**. The distillate is the liquid that has been condensed from the vapour during distillation.

Fractional distillation

Simple distillation cannot separate two miscible liquids if their boiling points are close together. Instead fractional distillation must be used. An example of two miscible liquids that can be separated by this method is water (boiling point 100 °C) and ethanol (boiling point 78 °C). The apparatus which is used is the same as that for simple distillation with a fractionating column added (see Figure 9). During fractional distillation the water vapour and ethanol vapour condense and vaporise several times in the fractionating column.

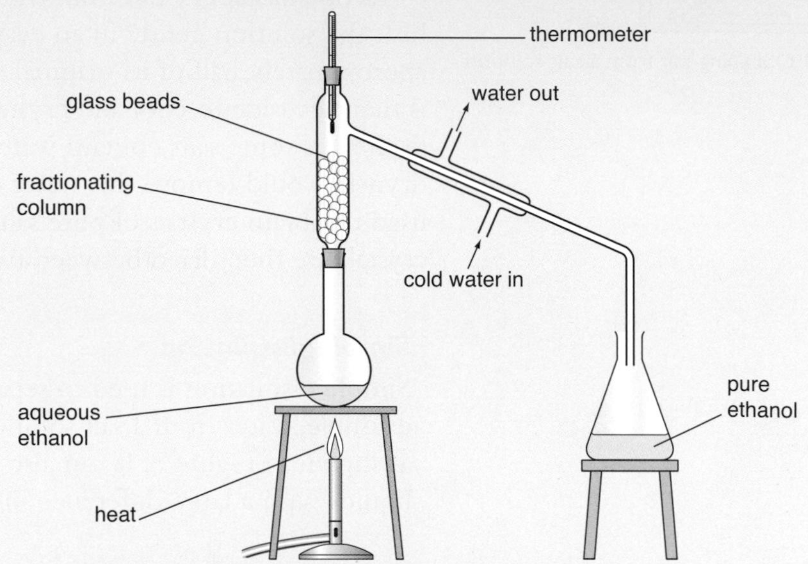

Figure 9 Fractional distillation of a water/ethanol mixture

Each time there is a condensation/vaporisation more of the lower boiling point liquid, ethanol, evaporates and more of the higher boiling point liquid, water, remains on the column and runs back down into the boiling mixture. After many condensations/vaporisations on the fractionating column only the vapours of the lower boiling liquid, ethanol, reach the top of the column. The ethanol vapour is then condensed and collected.

Separating mixtures using chromatography

Chromatography is a special way of separating mixtures. It is often used to separate the dyes in ink or the dyes in food colourings. Scientists can use chromatography to identify the colourings added to foods. Figure 10 shows how to check the orange colouring in an orange drink. A spot of the drink and spots of some permitted food colourings are spotted on to chromatography paper. The chromatography paper is rolled up and the bottom is dipped into a small amount of a suitable solvent. As the solvent moves up the chromatography paper, the dyes in the colourings separate. After a suitable time the paper is removed from the solvent, dried and analysed.

As the solvent moves up the chromatography paper, the dyes are carried along with the solvent. The dyes move up the paper at different rates. The rate depends on their solubility in the solvent and how strongly they are attracted to the paper. Those that are more soluble in the solvent and are not attracted strongly to the paper travel a long distance up the paper. Those that are less soluble in the solvent and are strongly attracted to the paper travel only a short distance up the paper. From the chromatogram in Figure 10, we can see that the orange drink contained two permitted colourings 2 and 3.

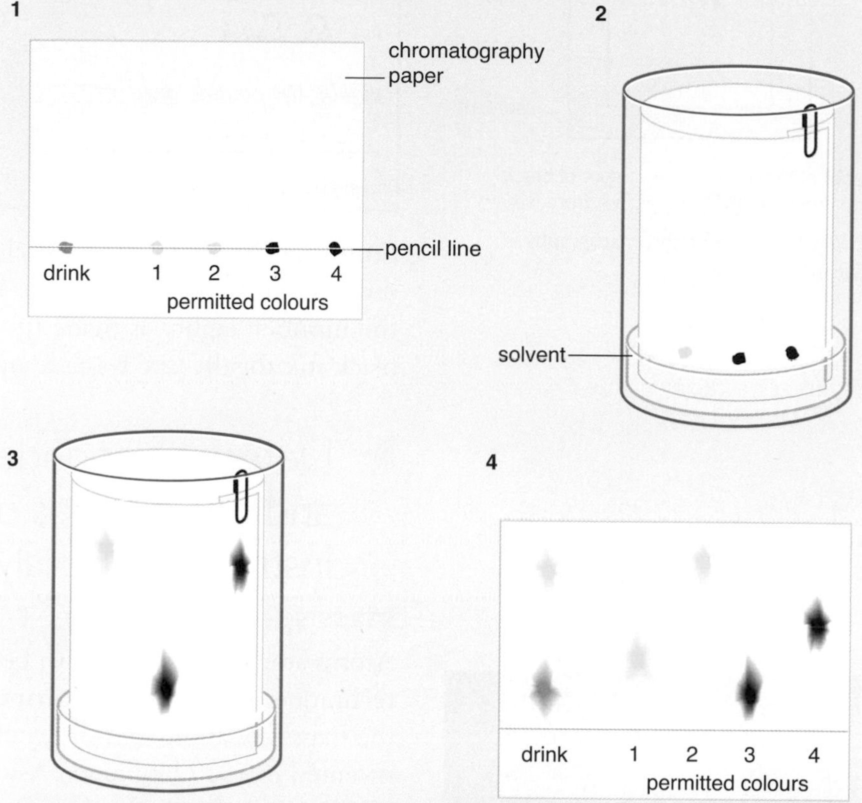

Figure 10 Chromatography can be used to check the food colours in a drink

A mixture of colourless substances can also be separated using chromatography. To show where the individual substances in the mixture have moved to, a locating agent is sprayed on the paper. The spray reacts with the separated substances forming coloured products allowing the mixture to be analysed. Mixtures of colourless amino acids can be separated using chromatography. The chemical spray ninhydrin is used to show up the different amino acids that are contained in the mixture.

Using chromatography to overcome forgery

An example of personal forgery is when someone writes a signature on a cheque which is not their own. It could also be where someone changes the figures or wording on a cheque or on another document. In many instances this is so well done that a forensic scientist is called in to provide evidence that a forgery has been committed. For example, a forensic scientist can show that the word 'eighty' has been added to a cheque. To do this the forensic scientist uses chromatography to analyse the black inks that appear on the cheque. They can tell it is a forgery when the black inks on the cheque are different for different parts of the cheque.

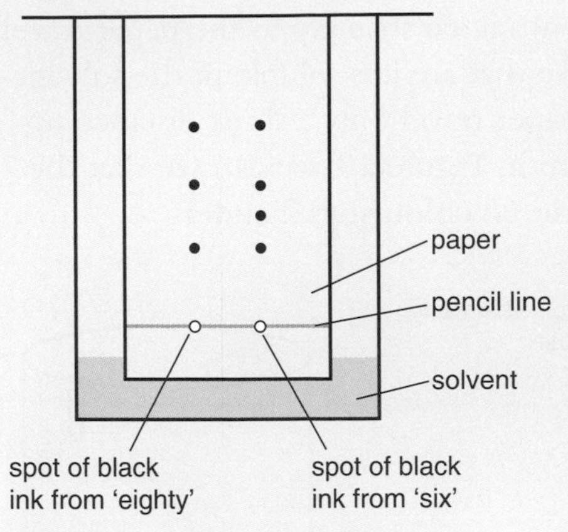

Figure 11 Use of chromatography in forensic science

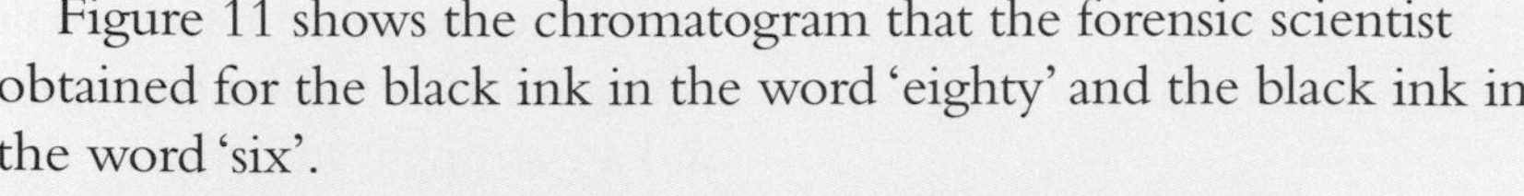
Figure 11 shows the chromatogram that the forensic scientist obtained for the black ink in the word 'eighty' and the black ink in the word 'six'.

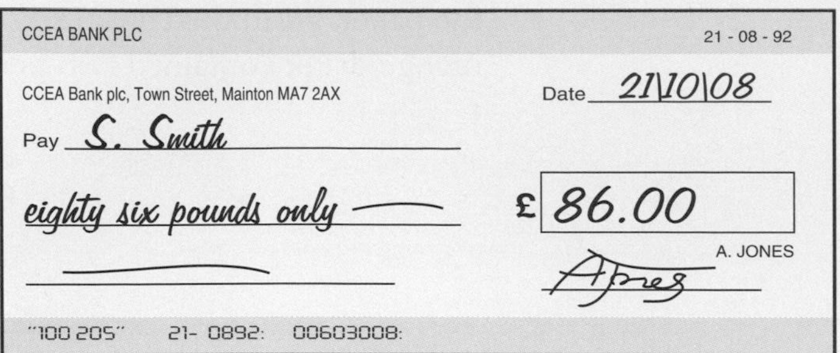
CCEA BANK PLC 21 - 08 - 92

CCEA Bank plc, Town Street, Mainton MA7 2AX Date 21\10\08

Pay S. Smith

eighty six pounds only £ 86.00

A. JONES

"100 205" 21- 0892: 00603008:

From the chromatogram it is clear that the two black inks are different and that a forgery has been committed. The black ink for the number 'eighty' is made up of three different dyes while the black ink for the 'six' is made up of four dyes.

Detection and identification of elements and compounds using modern instrumental analysis

Mass spectrometer

Atoms are much too small to be weighed; however, using the technique of **mass spectrometry**, chemists can accurately compare the masses of atoms and molecules. The mass spectrometer was invented in 1919 by Francis Aston who later won the Nobel Prize in Chemistry for his work on isotopes. The relative masses of atoms are called **relative atomic masses (RAM)** while the relative masses of molecules are called **relative molecular masses (RMM)**. The masses of all atoms and molecules are measured relative to one twelfth the mass of a carbon-12 atom, $^{12}_{6}C$ (see Chapter 8, page 107). Figure 12 shows a photograph of a mass spectrometer.

Figure 13 Francis Aston

Figure 12 Mass spectrometer

Figure 14 shows a mass spectrum of chlorine. The mass spectrum shows two peaks, one with relative atomic mass 35 and the other with relative atomic mass 37. The heights of the two peaks show that the relative proportions of chlorine-35 and chlorine-37 are in the ratio 3:1 and this means that for every four chlorine atoms there are always three chlorine-35 atoms to one chlorine-37 atom. Chlorine-35 and chlorine-37 are called the two isotopes of chlorine (see page 108).

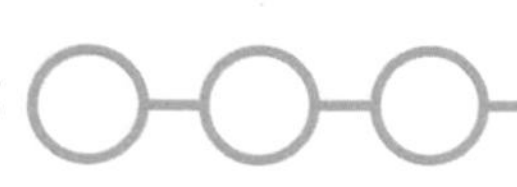

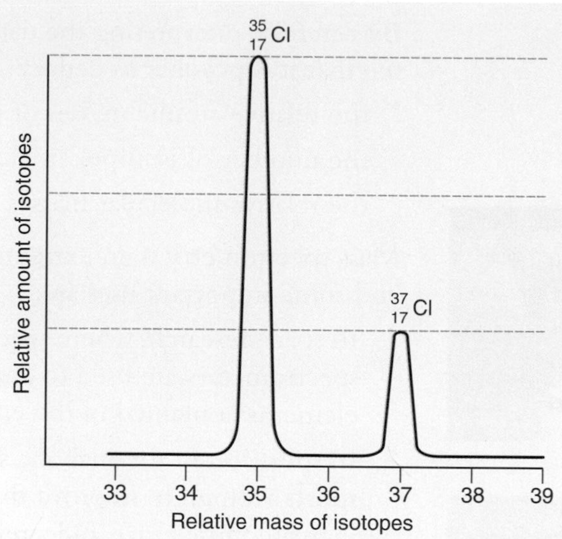

Figure 14 Mass spectrum of chlorine

The occurrence of isotopes accounts for the fact that the relative atomic mass of chlorine is not a whole number. The average mass of a chlorine atom on the ^{12}C scale (the relative atomic mass) is:

$$[(3 \times 35) + (1 \times 37)]/4 = 35.5$$

Using mass spectrometry, it is seen that not all atoms of an element have the same mass; for example, magnesium has three different types of atoms (isotopes), ^{24}Mg, ^{25}Mg and ^{26}Mg. The mass spectrometer shows that most elements have more than one isotope, and some have as many as 20 isotopes.

The mass spectrometer is also used to obtain the relative molecular mass of molecules. A molecule such as methane, CH_4, will have a mass spectrum with a peak at 16 which corresponds to its relative molecular mass:

Relative molecular mass (RMM), $CH_4 = 12 + (4 \times 1) = 16$

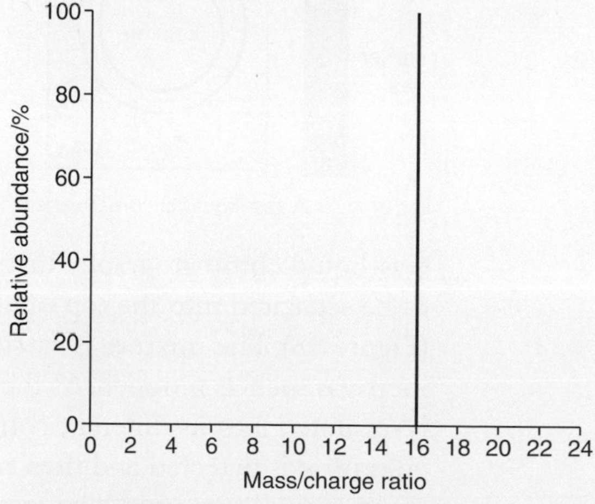

Figure 15 Mass spectrum of methane

For a molecule like ethanol, C_2H_5OH, we can predict that its mass spectrum will show a peak at 46 as the relative molecular mass is:

$$\text{RMM, } C_2H_5OH = (2 \times 12) + (5 \times 1) + 16 + 1 = 46$$

By carefully interpreting the data from mass spectrometry we can see that it is possible to deduce:

* the relative atomic masses of elements
* the number of isotopes an element contains
* the relative molecular masses of compounds and molecules.

Figure 16 Space probe

Figure 17 Men's 100 metres final in the Olympics

Mass spectrometry is an extremely important method of analysis and some important uses are:

1. In space research, where space probes containing mass spectrometers are used to analyse and identify compounds and elements contained in the environment of planets;
2. In sport to test for anabolic steroids used by sports men and sports women to improve their performance. Anabolic steroids increase muscle size and strength and thus increase an athlete's chance of winning. Drugs such as anabolic steroids are also very harmful and can lead to heart disease, cancer and depression. Sporting bodies have banned the use of anabolic steroids in sporting competitions and athletes are regularly tested for their use. Samples of their urine are tested using mass spectrometry. Chemists can identify the particular drug from its mass spectrum.

Gas–liquid chromatography

Gas-liquid chromatography is a powerful and important method in chemical analysis. It is particularly suitable for separating mixtures of volatile liquids.

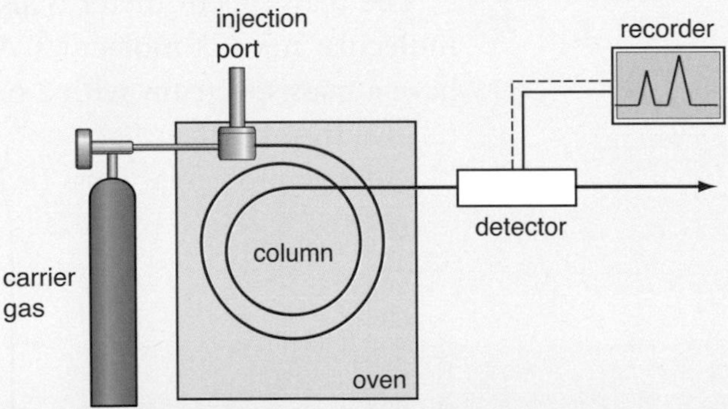

Figure 18 A gas–liquid chromatograph

Gas-liquid chromatography involves injecting a sample of the mixture to be separated into the top of a heated chromatography column (Figure 18). The mixture is carried through the column by a flow of inert gas such as nitrogen. As the mixture passes through the column it is separated into its different compounds. As each substance leaves the column it is detected and then recorded. Each peak on the recorder represents a compound. The area under each peak is proportional to the amount of that compound in the mixture. If there are four compounds in the mixture to be separated then the gas-liquid chromatograph will show four distinct peaks. The following gas-liquid chromatogram was obtained in the separation of two amino acids.

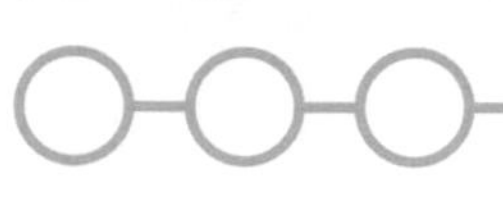

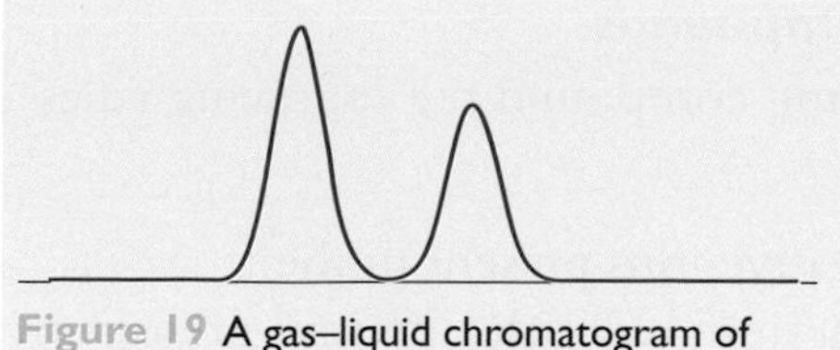

Figure 19 A gas–liquid chromatogram of the separation of two amino acids

When the detector is showing a peak, some of the compound passing through may be diverted to a mass spectrometer. The mass spectrum of the compound is then obtained and compared against a computer database of known compounds. This allows for the compounds in the mixture to be identified. Gas-liquid chromatography is widely used in the petrochemical industry, environmental monitoring and in chemical research.

Advantages and disadvantages of mass spectrometry and gas–liquid chromatography

The main disadvantage of these instrumental techniques is that the equipment is very expensive and also to analyse and interpret the results requires the expertise of trained analytical chemists. It is also important when handling the chemicals to be analysed that care is taken to observe the necessary health and safety procedures.

There are many advantages but the main ones are that only small samples are required for analysis and that results are obtained fairly quickly. It is also very beneficial that gas-liquid chromatography and mass spectrometry can be combined to separate and identify compounds. This allows chemists to determine exactly what compounds are contained in a sample of an unknown mixture.

Chemical formulae of compounds

Formulae of ionic compounds

The charges on the different cations, anions and molecular ions as given in Table 6 will be used to work out the formulae of ionic compounds. The charge on cations and anions is also related to the element's valency or combining power. A calcium ion, Ca^{2+}, with a charge of 2+ has a valency of 2 while the aluminium ion, Al^{3+}, with a charge of 3+ has a valency of 3.

Name (charge 1+)	Symbol	Name (charge 2+)	Symbol	Name (charge 3+)	Symbol
Lithium	Li^+	Magnesium	Mg^{2+}	Aluminium	Al^{3+}
Sodium	Na^+	Calcium	Ca^{2+}	Iron(III)	Fe^{3+}
Potassium	K^+	Barium	Ba^{2+}		
Ammonium	NH_4^+	Copper(II)	Cu^{2+}		
Silver	Ag^+	Zinc	Zn^{2+}		
Hydrogen	H^+	Lead	Pb^{2+}		
		Iron(II)	Fe^{2+}		

Name (charge 1−)	Symbol	Name (charge 2−)	Symbol	Name (charge 3−)	Symbol
Fluoride	F^-	Carbonate	CO_3^{2-}	Phosphate	PO_4^{3-}
Chloride	Cl^-	Sulfate	SO_4^{2-}	Nitride	N^{3-}
Bromide	Br^-	Sulfide	S^{2-}		
Iodide	I^-	Oxide	O^{2-}		
Hydroxide	OH^-				
Hydrogen carbonate	HCO_3^-				
Hydrogen sulfate	HSO_4^-				
Nitrate	NO_3^-				

Table 6 Ion charges for a number of cations, anions and molecular ions

Writing the formulae of ionic compounds

When writing the formula of an ionic compound the following rules must be used:

* Write down the positive and negative ions present in the compound; for example, in magnesium chloride, the ions present are Mg^{2+} and Cl^-.
* Because ionic compounds are neutral, the charges must cancel out; for example, for magnesium chloride we must take $\mathbf{Mg^{2+}}$ **and** $\mathbf{2Cl^-}$ as the 2+ charge is cancelled out by the 2− charge from the two chloride ions.
* The formula is now written without the charges: $\mathbf{MgCl_2}$.

Example 1 Sodium chloride
Ions present are $\mathbf{Na^+}$ **and** $\mathbf{Cl^-}$, charges are the same and cancel out so the formula is **NaCl**.

Example 2 Calcium oxide
Ions present are $\mathbf{Ca^{2+}}$ **and** $\mathbf{O^{2-}}$, charges are the same and cancel out so the formula is **CaO**.

Example 3 Potassium oxide
Ions present are $\mathbf{K^+}$ **and** $\mathbf{O^{2-}}$, the charges do not cancel out so we must take $\mathbf{2K^+}$ to balance the 2− charge on $\mathbf{O^{2-}}$. The formula is $\mathbf{K_2O}$.

Example 4 Magnesium bromide
Ions present are $\mathbf{Mg^{2+}}$ **and** $\mathbf{Br^-}$, the charges do not cancel each other out so we must take $\mathbf{2Br^-}$ to balance the 2+ charge on $\mathbf{Mg^{2+}}$. The formula is $\mathbf{MgBr_2}$.

Example 5 Aluminium oxide
Ions present are $\mathbf{Al^{3+}}$ **and** $\mathbf{O^{2-}}$, the charges do not cancel each other out so we must take $\mathbf{2Al^{3+}}$ **and** $\mathbf{3O^{2-}}$ to balance the charges, i.e. $(2 \times 3+) = 6+$ and $(3 \times 2-) = 6-$; overall these charges now cancel out. The formula is $\mathbf{Al_2O_3}$.

Example 6 Calcium nitrate
Ions present are $\mathbf{Ca^{2+}}$ **and** $\mathbf{NO_3^-}$, the charges do not cancel each other out so we must take $\mathbf{2NO_3^-}$ to balance the 2+ charge on $\mathbf{Ca^{2+}}$. The formula is $\mathbf{Ca(NO_3)_2}$. Note the use of brackets when using the molecular ion, NO_3^-.

Group	Valency
I	1
II	2
III	3
IV	4
V	3
VI	2
VII	1
O	–

Table 7 Valency for the different groups in the Periodic Table

Formulae of covalent compounds

To work out the formula of a covalent compound you need to use valency. Valency is the combining power of an atom or ion. Table 7 gives the valency for the different groups in the Periodic Table.

Note the elements in Group O do not form compounds, so these elements have no valency. Hydrogen has a valency of one.

Writing the formulae of covalent compounds

Example 1 Methane

Methane has a formula CH_4, as carbon has a valency of **4** and hydrogen has a valency of **1**. This means that it takes four hydrogen atoms to combine with one atom of carbon.

Example 2 Ammonia

Ammonia has the formula NH_3, as nitrogen has a valency of **3** and hydrogen has a valency of **1**. This means that it takes three hydrogen atoms to combine with one atom of nitrogen.

Example 3 Carbon dioxide

Carbon dioxide has the formula CO_2, as carbon has a valency of **4** and oxygen has a valency of **2**. This means it takes two atoms of oxygen to combine with one atom of carbon.

Example 4 Water

Water has the formula H_2O, as hydrogen has a valency of **1** and oxygen has a valency **2**. This means it takes two atoms of hydrogen to combine with one atom of oxygen.

Questions

9 Using silicon dioxide, SiO_2, as an example, explain the meaning of the term valency.

10 Write the formula for the following ionic compounds:

a) potassium chloride
b) magnesium oxide
c) calcium bromide
d) zinc sulfate
e) sodium carbonate
f) copper(II) hydroxide
g) magnesium hydrogen carbonate
h) aluminium sulfate
i) iron(II) oxide.

11 Use valency to work out the formulae for the following covalent molecules:

a) silicon dioxide
b) hydrogen chloride
c) carbon tetrachloride
d) ammonia
e) phosphorus trichloride
f) methane.

12 Write out the formulae for the cations, anions and molecular ions in the following compounds:

a) LiI **b)** $Mg(NO_3)_2$ **c)** PbS **d)** $CuSO_4$ **e)** Al_2O_3

Hazardous chemicals

Many chemicals or materials have harmful properties and their containers must be labelled with hazard symbols to identify the dangers. Hazard symbols are used because they have been internationally agreed and are easily recognised. Words beside or below the symbols indicate the type of hazard. Figure 20 shows diagrams of the different hazard symbols used to identify harmful chemical substances:

Explosive

A substance likely to explode.
e.g. ammonium dichromate

Toxic

Substances which can cause death. They may cause problems if swallowed, inhaled or absorbed through the skin.
e.g. chlorine, sulfur dioxide

Harmful

Substances similar to toxic substances but not as harmful
e.g. aspirin, iodine, ethanol

Corrosive

Substances which attack and destroy living tissues, including eyes and skin.
e.g. concentrated sulfuric acid, concentrated sodium hydroxide

Irritant

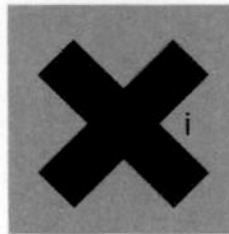

Substances which are not corrosive but can cause reddening or blistering of the skin
e.g. dilute sulfuric acid, iodine solution

Highly flammable

Substances which can catch fire easily
e.g. petrol, ethanol

Figure 20 Hazard symbols

States of matter and the kinetic theory

We have seen that matter is made up of solids, liquids and gases. Scientists use the kinetic theory to explain the behaviour of solids, liquids and gases, for example **why**:

* does water freeze when it is cooled?
* do metals expand on heating?
* can we smell food cooking in a restaurant?

The kinetic theory states that:

* All matter is made up of tiny, invisible particles. The particles can be atoms, ions or molecules.
* The particles are continually moving and if the temperature is raised the particles gain energy and move faster.
* At a given temperature, the lighter particles move faster than heavier ones.

In Figure 21, the kinetic theory is used to explain the differences between solids, liquids and gases:

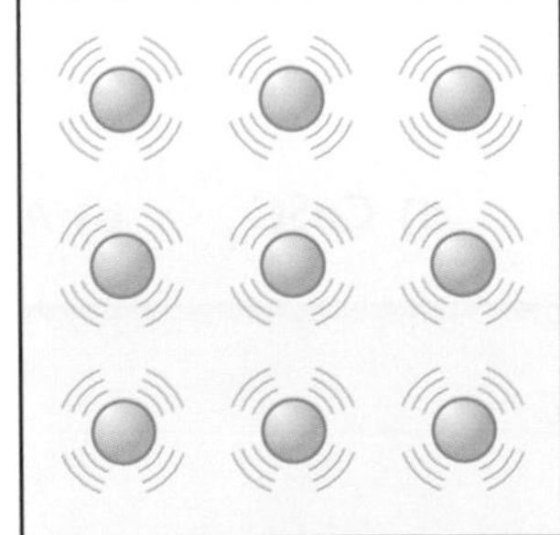

Solid
The particles are close together, and are held in place by strong attractive forces between them. So solids are more dense than liquids and gases and cannot be compressed. The particles can only vibrate about fixed points. So solids have a fixed volume and shape and cannot flow.

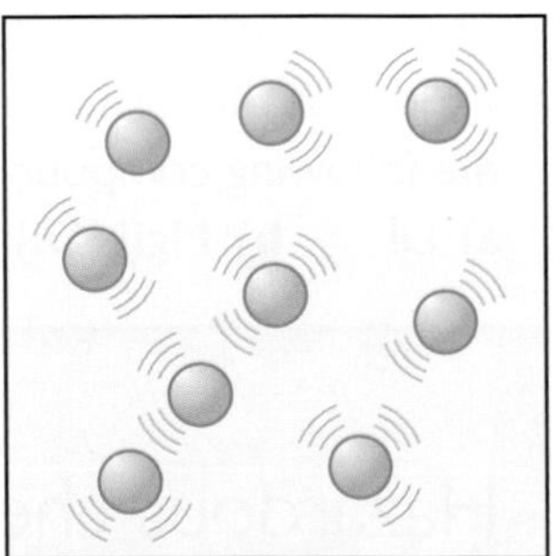

Liquid
The particles are a little further apart and the attractive forces between them are not as strong as those in solids. So liquids are not as dense as solids and can be compressed slightly. The particles can roll around each other so they flow easily. They can change their shape but have a fixed volume.

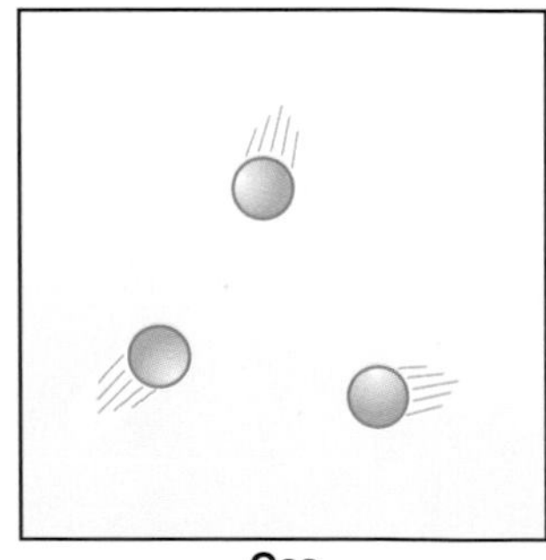

Gas
The particles are very far apart and there are no attractive forces between them. So the densities of gases are very low and they can be easily compressed. The particles move around very fast in all the space available, so they fill their whole container and flow easily.

Figure 21 Particles in solids, liquids and gases

The different changes of state are shown in Figure 22, while Figure 23 represents the changes of state for water.

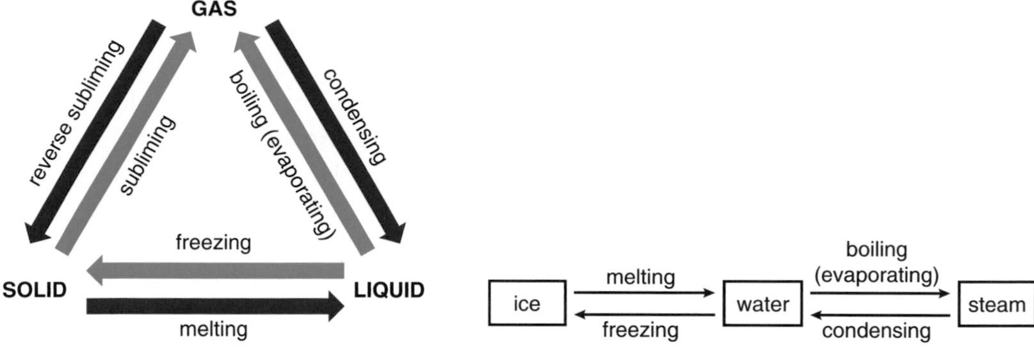

Figure 22 Changes of state

Figure 23 Changes of state for water

Melting

When a solid is heated, the particles gain energy causing them to vibrate faster and faster about their fixed positions. When sufficient energy is gained the particles break away from their fixed positions and the solid melts and a liquid forms. The particles can now move around each other as shown in Figure 24. The temperature at which this occurs is called the melting point of the solid. **The melting point is the temperature at which a solid is changed to a liquid.**

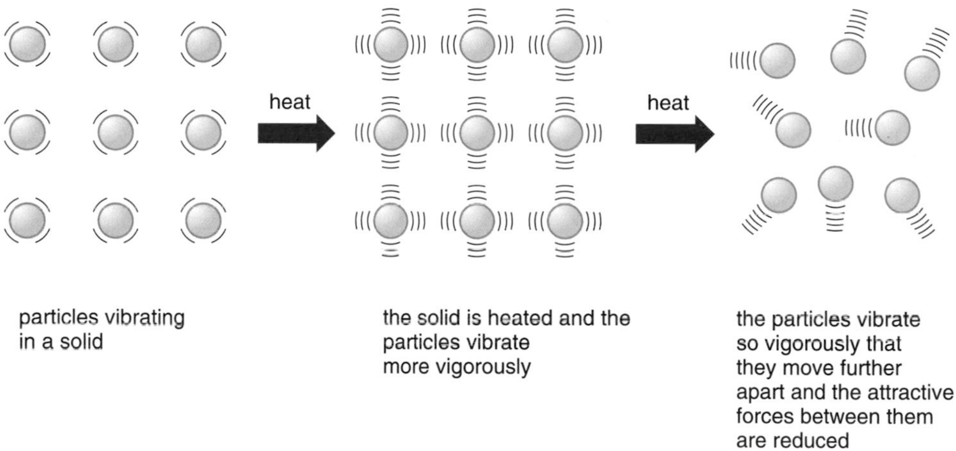

Figure 24 What happens when a solid melts

During the melting process heat energy is taken in by the particles and this energy is used to overcome the bonds or the attractions between the particles. Melting is described as an **endothermic** process because energy has been taken in to melt the solid. Solids with high melting points have strong bonds between the particles and require a lot of energy to break the strong bonds. Solids with low melting points have weak attractive forces between the particles and require little energy to overcome the weak attractive forces.

Boiling and evaporation

When a liquid is heated the particles gain energy and move faster. Before reaching the boiling temperature, some of the higher energy particles will have sufficient energy to overcome the attractions between themselves and other particles in the liquid. These particles are able to escape and form a gas. This is known as evaporation. **Evaporation is the change of state from a liquid to a gas below the boiling point.**

On further heating all particles gain sufficient energy to overcome the attractive forces between particles and the liquid boils. **The boiling point is the temperature at which a liquid turns to a gas.** Due to the large number of particles escaping at the boiling point, bubbles of vapour are formed throughout the liquid. Liquids with strong attractive forces between the particles have high boiling points while those with weaker attractive forces have lower boiling points. Like melting, boiling and evaporation are endothermic processes, where energy is absorbed or taken in.

While melting, boiling and evaporating take in energy, condensation and freezing give out energy i.e. they are **exothermic** processes. **Condensation is the change of state from a gas to a liquid.** When the gas is cooled, the particles lose energy and are able to move closer and closer together until a liquid forms. The formation of attractive forces between the particles of the liquid causes energy to be given out. Similarly, when the particles of a liquid are cooled, the particles move closer and closer together until the attractive forces between the particles are strong enough for a solid to form. The bonds or attractive forces which form when a liquid freezes to form a solid cause energy to be given out i.e. the process is **exothermic**. **Freezing is the change of state from a liquid to a solid.**

Sublimation

Sublimation is the direct change from a solid to a gas. This is an unusual change because on heating the solid, the substance does not pass through the liquid state. The compound dry ice or solid carbon dioxide and the element iodine are two examples of substances that sublime. Dry ice is a solid at −79 °C and above this temperature it sublimes to form carbon dioxide gas. The sublimation of carbon dioxide has commercial properties in that it can be used for special effects on stage and it can also be used as a coolant. Iodine is a grey-black solid at room temperature and when it is gently heated it produces a deep purple vapour. Figure 25 shows the effect of heating dry ice and iodine.

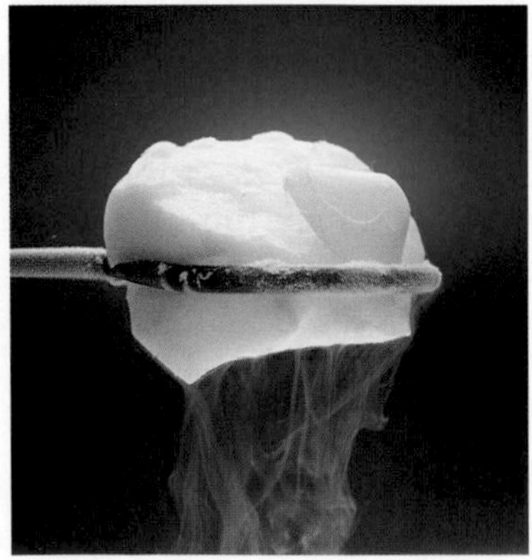

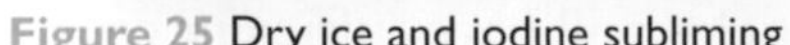
Figure 25 Dry ice and iodine subliming

Questions

13 What do you understand by the following terms?
a) boiling **b)** freezing **c)** evaporation

14 Name the processes involved in the following changes of state:
a) a liquid changing to a gas **b)** a solid changing to a liquid
c) liquid changing to a solid **d)** a gas going to a liquid
e) steam going to water
f) carbon dioxide gas going to dry ice.

15 For each part of Question 14 state if the change taking place is exothermic or endothermic.

16 Use diagrams to explain what happens to:
a) The particles of steam as they are cooled down to form water and then cooled further to form ice.
b) Particles of gaseous iodine as it is cooled down.

17 Explain why water has a higher boiling point than alcohol.

Exam questions

1 Some dyes and food flavourings such as tartrazine and monosodium glutamate have been linked with health issues.
A student carried out an experiment to separate the food dyes in four different orange juice drinks, **A, B, C** and **D**, to decide if tartrazine was present. The results are shown below.

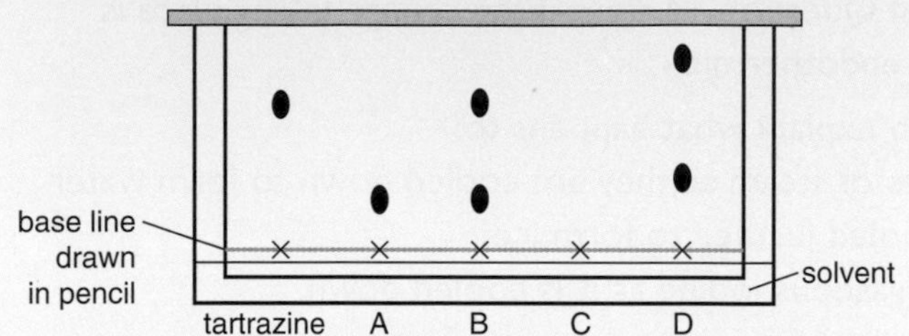

a) What name is given to this method of separating food dyes? *(1 mark)*

b) Why is the base line drawn in pencil? *(1 mark)*

c) Which orange drink (**A, B, C** or **D**) contains food dyes which do not dissolve in the solvent? *(1 mark)*

d) Which orange juice drink (**A, B, C** or **D**) contains tartrazine? *(1 mark)*

e) Which orange juice drink (**A, B, C** or **D**) contains only one food dye? *(1 mark)*

f) Name an instrumental method which could be used to separate the food dyes in an orange juice drink. *(1 mark)*

2 a) Many chemicals have harmful properties and their containers must be labelled with hazard symbols. Copy the diagram below, and match the chemicals with the correct hazard symbol. One has been done for you. *(3 marks)*

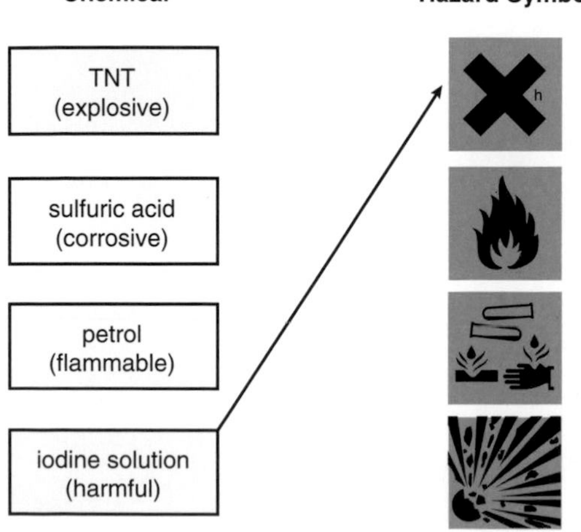

b) Give **two** reasons why hazard **symbols** are used rather than words. *(2 marks)*

3 Substances may be classified as elements, compounds or mixtures.

a) Copy and complete the table below by using a tick (✓) to classify each substance as an element, compound or mixture. The first one has been done for you.

Substance	Element	Compound	Mixture
crude oil			✓
nitrogen			
copper oxide			
brass			
pure water			

(4 marks)

b) Draw a diagram to show how the particles are arranged in a solid element such as copper. *(1 mark)*

c) One of the statements below describes what a compound is.

A It is made of different elements chemically joined together.
B It is made up of different elements mixed together.
C It is made up of one type of atom only.
D It is made up of metals only.

Which is the correct statement, A, B, C or D? *(1 mark)*

4 a) The graph shows the melting points and the boiling points of the first four elements in the same group of the Periodic Table, against their atomic number.

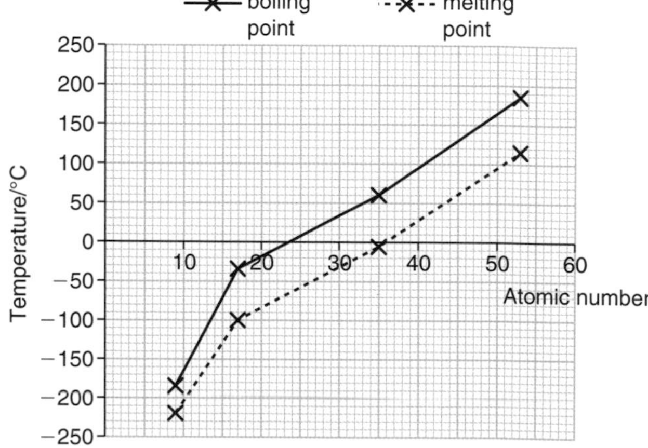

i) State the electronic configuration of the element with the lowest melting point. *(1 mark)*

ii) Use the graph to find the melting point and boiling point of the elements with atomic number 17 and 35 and use this information to work out the states of these elements at room temperature and pressure (20 °C).

	Element with atomic number 17	Element with atomic number 35
Melting point/°C		
Boiling point/°C		
Physical state at room temperature		

(6 marks)

iii) Draw a diagram to show how the particles are arranged at 20 °C in the element with atomic number 17. *(1 mark)*

iv) The graph on the previous page shows data for the first four elements in this group. The fifth element in this group is a solid at room temperature and pressure. Explain what happens, in terms of particles, when this solid is heated and changes to a liquid. *(3 marks)*

v) One of the elements in this group sublimes when heated. What is meant by the term sublimation? *(1 mark)*

b) The diagrams below represent elements, compounds and mixtures.

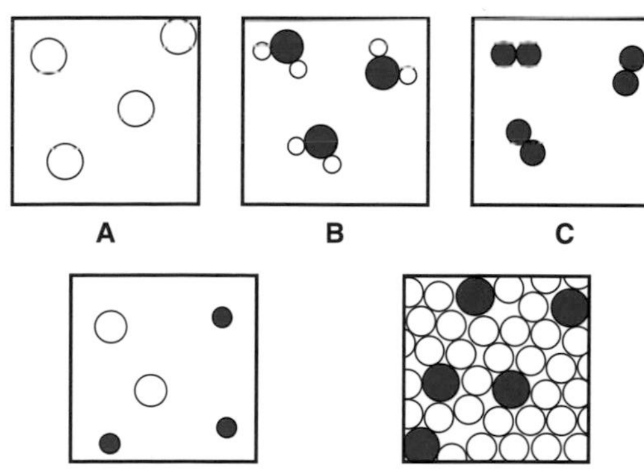

Use the letters A, B, C, D or E to answer the questions below. Each letter may be used once, more than once, or not at all.

State which of the diagrams could represent:

i) a gaseous mixture of argon and neon
ii) a mixture of two solids
iii) oxygen gas O_2
iv) a gas such as helium
v) a compound which is a gas. *(5 marks)*

5 Hazard symbols are used to warn about the dangers of chemicals.

a) Give two reasons why hazard symbols are used instead of words to warn about the dangers of chemicals. *(2 marks)*

b) Five chemicals and their hazard symbols are shown below.

Irritant

Barium nitrate

Highly flammable

Ethanol

Explosive

Ammonium dichromate

Toxic

Barium chloride

Corrosive

Sulfuric acid

From the chemicals shown:

i) Name a toxic chemical. *(1 mark)*
ii) Name a chemical which is flammable. *(1 mark)*
iii) Why could it be dangerous to store ammonium dichromate in your garden shed? *(1 mark)*

6 Copy and complete the table below to show whether the chemical is an element, a compound or a mixture. One has been done for you.

Chemical	Element	Compound	Mixture
Silver	✓		
Salt solution			
Aluminium			
Sulfur dioxide			
Water			
Crude oil			

(5 marks)

7 Explain how a mixture of sand and salt can be separated to produce sand and a sample of salt crystals.

In this question you will be assessed on using your written communication skills including the use of specialist science terms. *(6 marks)*

8 The table below gives information about four substances, A, B, C and D.

Substance	Melting point/ °C	Conductor of electricity	Effect of heating in air using a Bunsen burner
A	150	No	Melts and burns forming a black solid and water
B	1536	Yes	Melts to form a shiny silver liquid
C	200	No	Forms a black solid and a colourless gas
D	1083	Yes	Slowly forms a black solid

a) Which of the substances A, B, C or D could be a compound? *(1 mark)*

b) Which **two** of the substances A, B, C or D are metals? *(1 mark)*

c) Describe another test you could carry out, other than the tests in the table, to prove these substances were metals. *(1 mark)*

9 Names and symbols are used to describe chemicals. You may find your Data Leaflet helpful when answering some parts of this question.

For each of the questions below, three answers are given. Only **one** is correct. Choose the correct answer.

a) The correct chemical symbol for iron is:
i) Ir **ii)** Fe **iii)** I *(1 mark)*

b) The compound with the formula $Mg(OH)_2$ is:
i) magnesium oxide
ii) magnesium hydride
iii) magnesium hydroxide *(1 mark)*

c) The correct chemical formula for calcium sulfate is:
i) $CaSO_4$
ii) $CaSo_4$
iii) $Ca(SO)_4$ *(1 mark)*

d) The formula SO_2 means:
i) 2 **S** atoms and 2 **O** atoms
ii) 1 **S** atom and 2 **O** atoms
iii) 2 **S** atoms and 1 **O** atom *(1 mark)*

e) There is a gas with the formula CO. A correct name for this gas is:
i) cobalt
ii) carbon dioxide
iii) carbon monoxide *(1 mark)*

10 Use your Data Leaflet to help you answer this question. Choose the correct answer in each part.

a) The chemical symbol for sodium is:
i) K **ii)** So **iii)** Na *(1 mark)*

b) The formula for the nitrate ion is:
i) NO_3^- **ii)** NO_3 **iii)** N^{3-} *(1 mark)*

c) Sb is the chemical symbol for:
i) tin **ii)** antimony **iii)** sulfur *(1 mark)*

d) The formula for the chlorine molecule is:
i) Cl **ii)** Cl_2 **iii)** Cl_3 *(1 mark)*

e) Which one of the following statements is true?
i) all nitrates are soluble
ii) all nitrates are insoluble
iii) some nitrates are soluble *(1 mark)*

11 A student wanted to find out if black food colouring was a mixture of dyes or just a single substance. He set up an experiment as shown below.

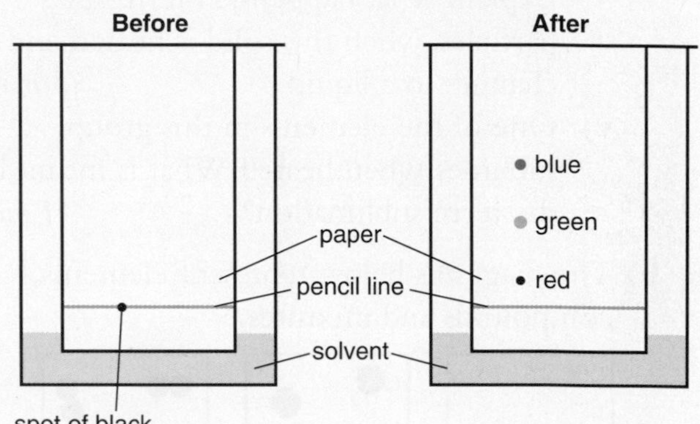

a) i) What name is given to this method of separating dyes? *(1 mark)*

ii) What dyes were mixed to form the black food colouring? *(1 mark)*

iii) Which dye is the most soluble in the solvent? *(1 mark)*

iv) The black food colouring has the numbers 122, 102 and 142 on the label. What letter of the alphabet comes before each number? *(1 mark)*

b) The student also had a bottle of blue food colouring. How could he find out if the blue dye in the black colouring was the same as the blue dye in the second bottle? You may wish to use a diagram. *(3 marks)*

Chemical Equations

During the 2012 Olympic Games the athletes will not be the only thing the world will be watching with interest. The English manufacturer of sports and racing cars, Lotus Cars, have announced that they are perfecting a fleet of taxis which will be fuelled by hydrogen. The large American company General Motors have made public their intention to introduce hydrogen powered vehicles to the public in 2015. Hydrogen has been used as a fuel since the 1800s but difficulties handling an inflammable gas prevented its widespread use. However, in the search for energy sources which are not based on ever dwindling stocks of fossil fuels and do not produce greenhouse gases, hydrogen is once again taking centre stage. (See Chapter 14, page 183.)

Consider the reaction happening in the combustion engine or in the fuel cell which provides the energy to allow the car to move. Hydrogen reacts with oxygen to produce water and energy.

Figure 1 Proudly proclaiming its use of hydrogen, this car fills up with the environmentally friendly fuel

Chemists communicate information about reactions by using **chemical equations**. The substances which react together, **the reactants**, are placed on the left hand side. The substances which are formed, **the products**, are placed on the right hand side. Both sides of the equation are connected by **an arrow**.

Chemists use ***equations*** to write down what happens during a reaction.

reactants —(react to form)→ **products**

the chemicals which are reacted together	the substances formed in the reaction

There are different types of equations:

1. **A word equation**
   The names of the reactants and products are used.

2. **A balanced chemical equation**
   The chemical formulae of the reactants and products are used.

3. **An ionic equation**
   This is similar to the balanced chemical equation where some or all of the chemical formulae are formulae of ions.

4. **A half equation**
   A half equation illustrates the movement of electrons in a chemical reaction.

Word equations

Try to write a **word equation** for the reaction of hydrogen with oxygen.

hydrogen + oxygen → water

Try writing the word equations for the reactions below which produce the hydrogen fuel for the environmentally friendly cars.

Reaction one
Hydrogen is produced by the reaction of methane with steam. Carbon dioxide is also formed.

Reaction two
In this reaction the hydrogen and carbon dioxide are formed by the reaction of carbon monoxide with water.

Reaction one

methane + steam → carbon dioxide + hydrogen

Reaction two

carbon monoxide + water → carbon dioxide + hydrogen

Word equations can be written to describe any chemical reaction.

Questions

Try writing word equations for the following chemical reactions, some of which you will study as part of this GCSE course.

1. Hydrogen reacts with nitrogen to form ammonia in the Haber process.
2. In the contact process, sulfur dioxide is oxidised to produce sulfur trioxide.
3. Hydrochloric acid is neutralised by sodium hydroxide to produce sodium chloride and one other product.
4. Calcium carbonate reacts with hydrochloric acid to form a gas, calcium chloride and water.
5. Potassium sulfate is produced by the action of sulfuric acid on potassium oxide. The second product is water.
6. Copper oxide and carbon dioxide are produced when copper carbonate is heated.
7. Heating hydrated copper sulfate produces anhydrous copper sulfate and water.
8. Copper oxide is reduced by hydrogen to form copper and water.
9. Sulfur burns in air with a blue flame to form sulfur dioxide.
10. Iron will rust when exposed to water and air. (The full chemical name for rust is hydrated iron(III) oxide.)

State symbols

State symbols can be added to all types of equations to add some more information. The state symbol shows the reader if the reactants used or the products formed are solids, liquids or gases, or dissolved in water.

We can add state symbols to the equations from Questions 4 and 8 on page 54.

calcium carbonate$_{(s)}$ + hydrochloric acid$_{(aq)}$ → carbon dioxide$_{(g)}$ + water$_{(l)}$ + calcium chloride$_{(aq)}$

copper oxide$_{(s)}$ + hydrogen$_{(g)}$ → copper$_{(s)}$ + water$_{(g)}$

State symbol	Represents
(s)	solid
(l)	liquid
(g)	gas
(aq)	aqueous solution (the substance is dissolved in water)

In the first of the word equations above, it can be inferred from the state symbols that a solution is added to a solid and as the reaction proceeds bubbles will be observed in the reaction vessel (the beaker).

In the second word equation above, it can be seen that water vapour is formed rather than liquid water.

Balanced chemical equations

A **balanced chemical equation** gives even more information about a chemical reaction.

Writing balanced chemical equations

Consider again the reaction between hydrogen and oxygen to form water.

Draw a molecule of hydrogen, a molecule of oxygen and a molecule of water using dot-and-cross diagrams. (See Chapter 2, page 19.)

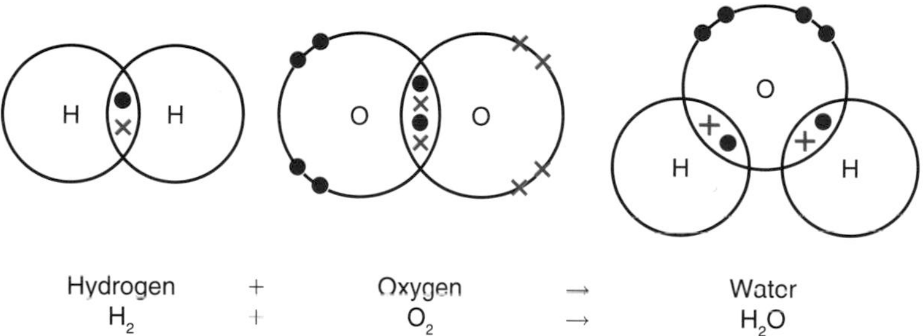

Figure 2 Molecules of hydrogen, oxygen and water

Look carefully at the drawings of the molecules.

* How many hydrogen atoms are there on the LHS, the reactant side?
* How many hydrogen atoms are there on the RHS, the product side?
* How many oxygen atoms are there on the LHS, the reactant side?
* How many oxygen atoms are there on the RHS, the product side?

There are two atoms of hydrogen on the left hand side of the equation and two on the right hand side. The hydrogen atoms have simply rearranged themselves. There are two oxygen atoms on the LHS of the equation but only one on the RHS. An oxygen atom cannot have simply disappeared. There seems to be an extra atom of oxygen. The following diagram seems to solve the problem. There are now the same number of oxygen atoms on each side of the equation.

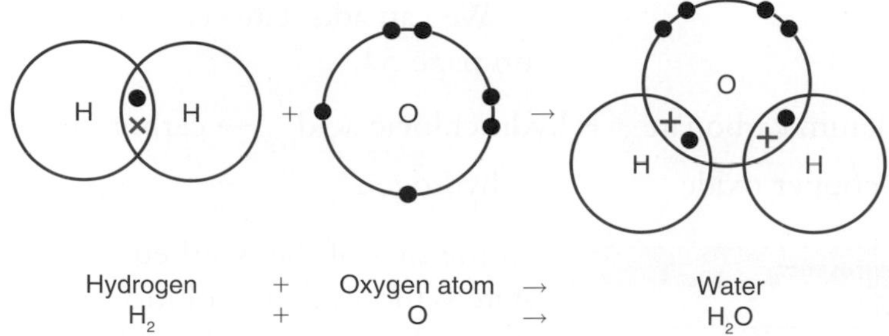

Figure 3

However, oxygen naturally occurs as a diatomic molecule, two atoms joined together by a covalent bond.

This may solve the problem.

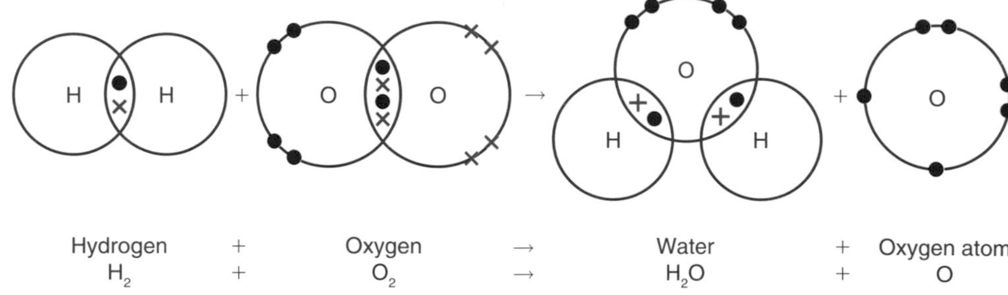

Figure 4

There are now the same number of oxygen atoms on each side of the equation. But the equation now does not describe the actual chemical reaction. The reaction between oxygen and hydrogen produces only water, not oxygen atoms as well.

There is one more solution to the problem.

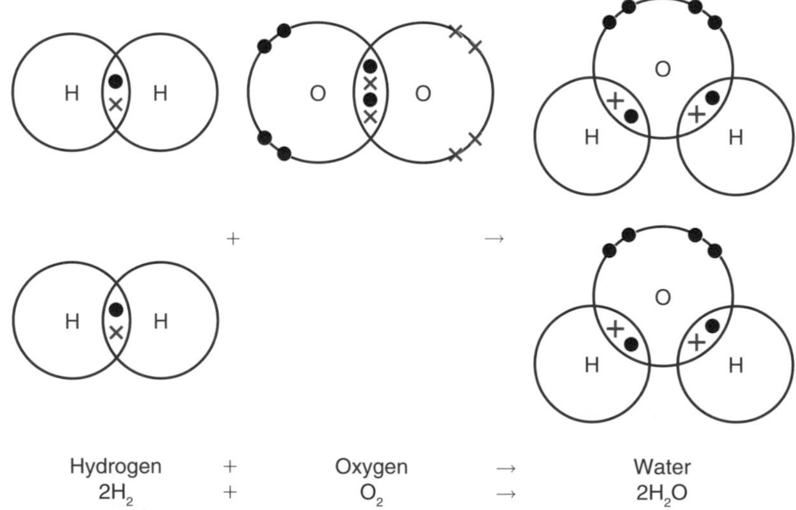

Figure 5

If another molecule of hydrogen is added, two molecules of water will be formed.

* How many hydrogen atoms are there now on the LHS, the reactant side?
* How many hydrogen atoms are there now on the RHS, the product side?

* How many oxygen atoms are there now on the LHS, the reactant side?
* How many oxygen atoms are there now on the RHS, the product side?

This diagram illustrates that two molecules of hydrogen react with one molecule of oxygen to produce two molecules of water. Chemists write this information in a **balanced chemical equation**.

$2H_2 + O_2 \rightarrow 2H_2O$

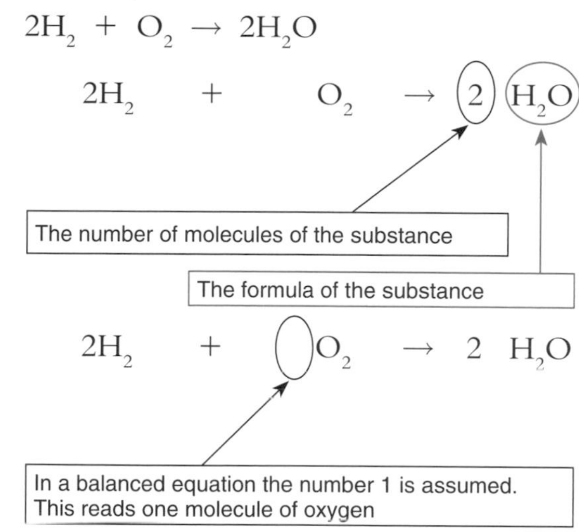

Figure 6

Example 1

Write a balanced chemical equation for the reaction between aluminium and oxygen to form aluminium oxide.

Step 1 *write the word equation*
aluminium + oxygen → aluminium oxide

Step 2 *write the individual formula for each species in the reaction*
$Al + O_2 \rightarrow Al_2O_3$

Step 3 *balance the equation*
When learning how to balance equations it can be helpful to add in boxes in front of each of the species in the equation. The numbers placed in the boxes are known as the balancing numbers (or more correctly, the stoichiometry of the equation). The boxes also help to remind you **not to place numbers into the formulae** of the chemicals.

Consider Al:
1 on LHS and 2 on RHS

Place a 2 in the box in front of Al on the LHS

$\boxed{2}Al + \Box O_2 \rightarrow \Box Al_2O_3$

Now there are 2 Al atoms on each side of the equation.

Consider O:
2 on LHS and 3 on RHS

Place a 3 in the box in front of oxygen and a 2 in the box in front of Al_2O_3. This gives 6 O atoms on each side of the equation.

$\boxed{2}Al + \boxed{3}O_2 \rightarrow \boxed{2}Al_2O_3$

Remember the following substances occur naturally as diatomic molecules. The molecule exists as a pair of atoms.

H_2 hydrogen
N_2 nitrogen
O_2 oxygen
F_2 fluorine
Cl_2 chlorine
Br_2 bromine
I_2 iodine

Consider Al again:

2 on LHS and 4 on RHS

Place a 4 in the box in front of the Al

$\boxed{4}\,Al + \boxed{3}\,O_2 \rightarrow \boxed{2}\,Al_2O_3$

4 Al on LHS and 4 Al on the RHS

6 O on the LHS and 6 O on RHS

The equation is balanced.

$4Al + 3O_2 \rightarrow 2Al_2O_3$

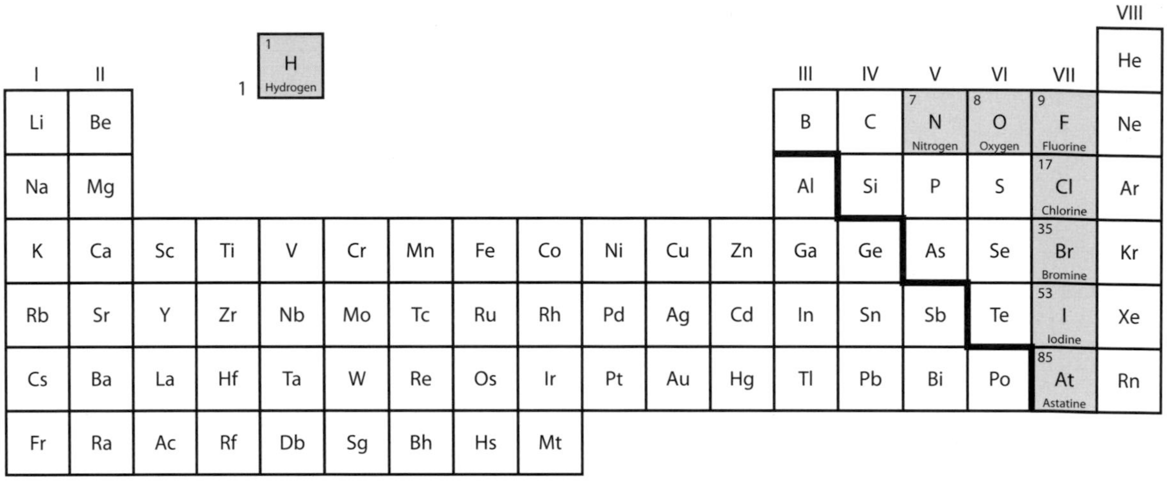

I	II											III	IV	V	VI	VII	VIII
				1 H Hydrogen													He
Li	Be											B	C	7 N Nitrogen	8 O Oxygen	9 F Fluorine	Ne
Na	Mg											Al	Si	P	S	17 Cl Chlorine	Ar
K	Ca	Sc	Ti	V	Cr	Mn	Fe	Co	Ni	Cu	Zn	Ga	Ge	As	Se	35 Br Bromine	Kr
Rb	Sr	Y	Zr	Nb	Mo	Tc	Ru	Rh	Pd	Ag	Cd	In	Sn	Sb	Te	53 I Iodine	Xe
Cs	Ba	La	Hf	Ta	W	Re	Os	Ir	Pt	Au	Hg	Tl	Pb	Bi	Po	85 At Astatine	Rn
Fr	Ra	Ac	Rf	Db	Sg	Bh	Hs	Mt									

The elements which naturally occur as diatomic molecules are in the shape of the number 7 on the Periodic Table. The vertical part of the number 7 is through Group 7. It can be useful to mark this out on your copy of the Periodic Table. It can help when it comes to writing balanced chemical equations.

Figure 7

Example 2

Write a balanced chemical equation for the reaction between phosphorus(V) chloride and water to form two acids, hydrochloric acid and phosphoric acid.

Step 1 *write the word equation*

phosphorus(V) chloride + water → hydrochloric acid + phosphoric acid

Step 2 *write the individual formula for each species in the reaction*

$$PCl_5 + H_2O \rightarrow HCl + H_3PO_4$$

Step 3 *balance the equation*

Consider the P atom:

1 P atom on the LHS and 1 P atom on the RHS

Consider the Cl atom:

5 Cl on the LHS and 1 Cl on the RHS

Place a 5 in the box in front of the HCl

$\boxed{}\,PCl_5 + \boxed{}\,H_2O \rightarrow \boxed{5}\,HCl + \boxed{}\,H_3PO_4$

Consider the H atom:

2 H atoms on the LHS and 8 H atoms on the RHS

Place a 4 in the box in front of the H_2O

☐ PCl_5 + [4] $H_2O \rightarrow$ [5] HCl + ☐ H_3PO_4

Consider the O atom:

4 O atoms on the LHS and 4 O atoms on the RHS

Check all of the atoms once again to check if any of the added numbers affected other atoms.

The equation is balanced.

$PCl_5 + 4H_2O \rightarrow 5HCl + H_3PO_4$

Questions

Practise balancing the following equations.

11 **Step 1** *write the word equation*

aluminium + copper oxide → aluminium oxide + copper

Step 2 *write the individual formula for each species in the reaction*

$Al + CuO \rightarrow Al_2O_3 + Cu$

Step 3 *balance the equation*

☐ Al + ☐ CuO → ☐ Al_2O_3 + ☐ Cu

12 **Step 1** *write the word equation*

sodium oxide + water → sodium hydroxide

Step 2 *write the individual formula for each species in the reaction*

$Na_2O + H_2O \rightarrow NaOH$

Step 3 *balance the equation*

☐ Na_2O + ☐ H_2O → ☐ NaOH

13 **Step 1** *write the word equation*

magnesium + phosphorus → magnesium phosphide

Step 2 *write the individual formula for each species in the reaction*

$Mg + P_4 \rightarrow Mg_3P_2$

Step 3 *balance the equation*

14 **Step 1** *write the word equation*

iron + chlorine → iron(III) chloride

Step 2 *write the individual formula for each species in the reaction*

$Fe + Cl_2 \rightarrow FeCl_3$

Step 3 *balance the equation*

15 **Step 1** *write the word equation*

vanadium(V) oxide + calcium chloride → calcium oxide + vanadium(V) sulfide

Step 2 *write the individual formula for each species in the reaction*

V_2O_5 + ______ → ______ + V_2S_5

Step 3 *balance the equation*

16 **Step 1** *write the word equation*

phosphorus + oxygen → phosphorus(III) oxide

Step 2 *write the individual formula for each species in the reaction*

P_4 + ________ → P_4O_6

Step 3 *balance the equation*

17 **Step 1** *write the word equation*

aluminium + hydrogen chloride → aluminium chloride + hydrogen

Step 2 *write the individual formula for each species in the reaction*

________ + HCl → $AlCl_3$ + ________

Step 3 *balance the equation*

18 chlorine + sodium iodide → sodium chloride + iodine

The following examples contain some combustion equations.

Handy Hint 1: when balancing these equations balance the oxygen atom last.

19 propane + oxygen → carbon dioxide + water

C_3H_8 + O_2 → CO_2 + H_2O

20 ethanol + oxygen → carbon dioxide + water

C_2H_5OH +

Remember: when fuels containing carbon and hydrogen are burned in oxygen, carbon dioxide and water are always formed.

Handy Hint 2: for these combustion reactions use a fraction, e.g. $2\frac{1}{2}$, or a decimal, e.g. 2.5, to balance the oxygen atoms then multiply all the balancing numbers by 2.

21 Write a balanced chemical reaction for the combustion of ethane (C_2H_6). (Stick to the three step process.)

22 Write a balanced chemical equation for the reaction of butane (C_4H_{10}) with oxygen.

23 iron(II) sulfide + oxygen → iron(III) oxide + sulfur dioxide

FeS + → Fe_2O_3 +

24 ammonia + oxygen → water + nitrogen(II) oxide

NH_3 + → + NO

Handy Hint 3: Some compound ions may be treated as a group of atoms rather than individual atoms.

The formulae of the compound ions which you are expected to be familiar with are given on the back page of the Data Leaflet supplied by the examination board. A list of compound ions which can be treated as a group when balancing equations is given to the RHS of this paragraph. However, as you get used to using them you will probably remember the names and formulae quite easily eventually.

Name of compound ion	Formula of compound ion
nitrate	NO_3^-
ammonium	NH_4^+
carbonate	CO_3^{2-}
sulfate	SO_4^{2-}
phosphate	PO_4^{3-}

25 aluminium sulfate + potassium sulfate → potassium aluminium sulfate

$Al_2(SO_4)_3 + K_2SO_4 \rightarrow KAl(SO_4)_2$

26 lead(II) nitrate + aluminium chloride → lead(II) chloride + aluminium nitrate

$Pb(NO_3)_2 + AlCl_3 \rightarrow PbCl_2 + Al(NO_3)_3$

27 Copper and silver nitrate react to produce silver crystals and a solution of copper nitrate.

28 Sodium hydroxide will neutralise sulfuric acid to form a salt and water.

29 Hydrogen will react with iodine to form hydrogen iodide.

30 The reaction between solutions of calcium chloride and silver nitrate produces a white solid (silver chloride) and a solution of calcium nitrate. (Try adding state symbols to the balanced chemical equation.)

Questions

Further practice

31 Balance the following equations. The individual formulae have been written for you.

a) $Zn + HCl \rightarrow ZnCl_2 + H_2$
b) $NCl_3 \rightarrow N_2 + Cl_2$
c) $Mg + O_2 \rightarrow MgO$
d) $Br_2 + NaI \rightarrow NaBr + I_2$
e) $C_5H_{12} + O_2 \rightarrow CO_2 + H_2O$
f) $C_3H_6O_3 + O_2 \rightarrow CO_2 + H_2O$
g) $NaNO_3 + PbO \rightarrow Pb(NO_3)_2 + Na_2O$
h) $Fe + AgNO_3 \rightarrow Fe(NO_3)_2 + Ag$
i) $(NH_4)_2CO_3 \rightarrow NH_3 + CO_2 + H_2O$
j) $AgBr + AlPO_4 \rightarrow Ag_3PO_4 + AlBr_3$

32 Write balanced chemical equations for the following reactions. Follow the three step process.

a) Chlorine bubbled into sodium iodide produces iodine in a solution of sodium chloride.
b) Hydrogen reduces carbon dioxide forming methane and water.
c) Carbon monoxide will burn in oxygen to form carbon dioxide.
d) Nitrogen and hydrogen react to form ammonia.
e) Iron(III) oxide is reduced in the blast furnace by carbon monoxide to produce iron. Carbon dioxide is also formed.
f) Sulfuric acid is used to produce nitric acid by reacting it with sodium nitrate. A solution of sodium sulfate is formed.
g) Sodium chloride and water are formed by the neutralisation of sodium hydroxide and hydrochloric acid.

h) Zinc is more reactive than copper, therefore zinc can displace copper from a solution of copper sulfate.

i) When sulfuric acid is added to copper carbonate, bubbles of carbon dioxide are released and copper sulfate and water are formed.

j) Sulfur dioxide is oxidised to sulfur trioxide by burning it in oxygen.

33 The formulae of the species in these reactions may look a little unusual; however, these reactions provide good practice in balancing equations.

a) $I_2 + Na_2S_2O_3 \rightarrow NaI + Na_2S_4O_6$

b) $HCl + Na_2S_2O_3 \rightarrow SO_2 + S + NaCl + H_2O$

c) $N_2O_5 + H_2O \rightarrow HNO_3$

d) $NO + Cl_2 \rightarrow NOCl$

e) $K + B_2O_3 \rightarrow K_2O + B$

f) $FeS_2 + O_2 \rightarrow Fe_2O_3 + SO_2$

g) $CH_3COOH + Mg \rightarrow (CH_3COO)_2Mg + H_2$

h) $CuCO_3 + HCl \rightarrow CuCl_2 + H_2O + CO_2$

i) $K_2CO_3 + HCl \rightarrow KCl + H_2O + CO_2$

j) $NO_2 + H_2O + O_2 \rightarrow HNO_3$

k) $C_4H_8S_2 + O_2 \rightarrow CO_2 + H_2O + SO_3$

l) $PCl_3 + H_2O \rightarrow H_3PO_3 + HCl$

m) $Ca_3P_2 + H_2O \rightarrow Ca(OH)_2 + PH_3$

Ionic equations

In some cases chemists find it useful to focus on certain ions in a reaction rather than on all of the compounds involved.

Consider the following balanced chemical equations describing the reactions between three different sodium halides and silver nitrate.

$$AgNO_3 + NaCl \rightarrow NaNO_3 + AgCl$$

$$AgNO_3 + NaBr \rightarrow NaNO_3 + AgBr$$

$$AgNO_3 + NaI \rightarrow NaNO_3 + AgI$$

Focusing on the silver halides that are formed, the equations can be written in the form of an ionic equation.

$$Ag^+ + Cl^- \rightarrow AgCl$$

$$Ag^+ + Br^- \rightarrow AgBr$$

$$Ag^+ + I^- \rightarrow AgI$$

Examples of ionic equations can be found in Chapters 6 and 10.

Half equations

A half equation concentrates on the movement of electrons in a chemical reaction.

Consider the diagrams in Chapter 2 showing the formation of ionic bonds when a metal element reacts with a non-metal element. The diagram below illustrates the formation of the ionic bond formed when calcium reacts with oxygen.

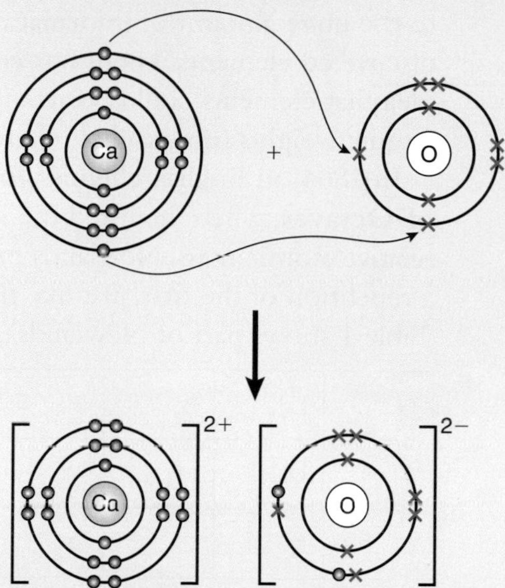

Figure 8 Calcium oxide

The calcium atom loses two electrons from the outer shell and forms a calcium ion which has a charge of 2+. The oxygen atom gains two electrons to form an oxide ion which has a charge of 2−. The diagram above illustrates this process well but it can be time consuming for chemists to draw such diagrams for all the chemical reactions they study. The process can be illustrated using two half equations.

Half equation 1: calcium loses the two electrons on its outer shell.

$$Ca - 2e^- \rightarrow Ca^{2+}$$

The loss of the electrons can be written in this form; however, chemists conventionally write half equations where the reactant loses electrons in this form:

$$Ca \rightarrow Ca^{2+} + 2e^-$$

Half equation 2: oxygen gains two electrons to obtain a full outer shell.

$$O + 2e^- \rightarrow O^{2-}$$

Other examples of half equations can be found in Chapter 9, pages 125–127.

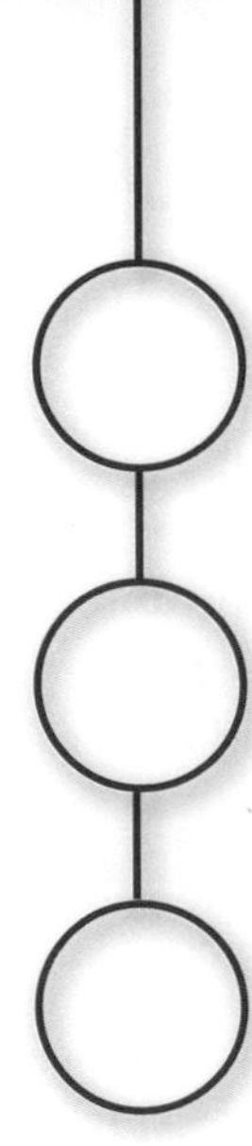

The Periodic Table

▶ Newlands and Mendeleev

Around the mid-nineteenth century many chemists were researching and publishing information on the properties of elements. More and more they realised that it was necessary to bring some type of order to the huge amount of information that was available on the already discovered elements. There was considerable attention given to the idea that elements could be arranged in terms of their properties and atomic weights (now called relative atomic mass).

In 1864, an English chemist, **John Newlands**, published the **Law of Octaves**, where he listed the known elements in order of their relative atomic mass. Newlands proposed that the eighth element was a repetition of the first, just like the eight notes in an octave of music. Table 1 shows part of Newlands' arrangement.

H	Li	Be	B	C	N	O
F	Na	Mg	Al	Si	P	S
Cl	K	Ca	Cr	Ti	Mn	Fe

Table 1 Part of Newlands' arrangement of elements in octaves

Starting with lithium, Li, and moving on eight places we arrive at sodium, Na, an element with very similar properties to lithium. In the same way we can show this eighth relationship of Newlands' for a number of other elements, for example, magnesium and calcium or fluorine and chlorine. Although Newlands had made a significant contribution to the classification of the elements, his work was rejected by other scientists because:

* His classification assumed that all elements had been discovered, even though a number of new elements had only been recognised a few years prior to his publication. No gaps were left for undiscovered elements. The discovery of new elements would immediately destroy his arrangement of octaves.
* Newlands grouped some elements together which were not similar in their properties. For example manganese was grouped with phosphorus and nitrogen while titanium was grouped with carbon and silicon.
* In forming the octaves, Newlands found it necessary to place two elements into one position. This happened for cobalt and nickel.

Although Newlands had identified important periodic properties between certain elements based on his Law of Octaves, it was a Russian chemist **Dmitri Mendeleev**, in 1869, who received the main credit for arranging the elements in the Periodic Table. Like Newlands he arranged the elements in order of their increasing relative atomic mass. He also placed elements with similar properties in the same vertical group as shown in Figure 1; however, Mendeleev realised that there were elements that had not been discovered and he **left gaps** for them. The gaps also allowed him to keep similar elements in the same vertical columns. Figure 1 shows that the vertical columns of elements were called **groups** and the horizontal rows of elements were called **periods**.

	Group							
	I	II	III	IV	V	VI	VII	VIII
Period 1	H							
Period 2	Li	Be	B	C	N	O	F	
Period 3	Na	Mg	Al	Si	P	S	Cl	
Period 4	K Cu	Ca Zn	* *	Ti *	V As	Cr Se	Mn Br	Fe Co Ni
Period 5	Rb Ag	Sr Cd	Y In	Zr Sn	Nb Sb	Mo Te	* I	Ru Rh Pd

Figure 1 Part of Mendeleev's Periodic Table

Mendeleev predicted that, through time, elements would be discovered that would fill the gaps he had left in his **Periodic Table**. He also predicted the properties of many of the unknown elements with amazing accuracy; for example, in the gaps below aluminium and silicon he predicted the properties of two unknown elements, eka-aluminium and eka-silicon. Later these two elements were discovered (1875 and 1886 respectively); they were called gallium and germanium and had properties almost identical to those predicted by Mendeleev. Confidence in the Periodic Table soared. The accuracy of Mendeleev's predictions influenced other scientists and it soon became accepted that the Periodic Table was a suitable way of ordering the elements and their properties.

▶ The modern Periodic Table

The modern Periodic Table (Figure 2 and Appendix 1) is based on that of Mendeleev; however, there are a number of changes.

* Mendeleev placed the elements in order of relative atomic mass; however, in the modern Periodic Table elements are placed in order of their **atomic number**. When Mendeleev placed elements in order of relative atomic mass he found that in some instances he had to reverse the order of the elements, for example, tellurium, Te = 128 and iodine, I = 127. According to ordering by relative atomic mass, Mendeleev should have placed iodine before tellurium. However, he realised that for iodine and tellurium to fit into their proper groups he had to reverse the order. This problem is now overcome using atomic number where tellurium = 52 and iodine = 53.
* A family of very unreactive elements, called the noble gases or **Group 0** elements, has been discovered and inserted.
* The **transition metals** have been taken out and placed in a block of metals between Group II and Group III.

Key: H (symbol), hydrogen (name), 1 (atomic number)

Group → / Period ↓	1 Alkali metals	2 Alkaline-earth metals					transition elements						3	4	5	6	7 Halogens	0 Noble gases
1								H hydrogen 1										He helium 2
2	Li lithium 3	Be beryllium 4											B boron 5	C carbon 6	N nitrogen 7	O oxygen 8	F fluorine 9	Ne neon 10
3	Na sodium 11	Mg magnesium 12											Al aluminium 13	Si silicon 14	P phosphorus 15	S sulfur 16	Cl chlorine 17	Ar argon 18
4	K potassium 19	Ca calcium 20	Sc 21	Ti 22	V 23	Cr chromium 24	Mn manganese 25	Fe iron 26	Co 27	Ni 28	Cu copper 29	Zn zinc 30	Ga 31	Ge 32	As 33	Se 34	Br bromine 35	Kr krypton 36
5	Rb 37	Sr 38	Y 39	Zr 40	Nb 41	Mo 42	Tc 43	Ru 44	Rh 45	Pd 46	Ag silver 47	Cd 48	In 49	Sn tin 50	Sb 51	Te 52	I iodine 53	Xe 54
6	Cs 55	Ba 56	57–71 see below	Hf 72	Ta 73	W 74	Re 75	Os 76	Ir 77	Pt platinum 78	Au gold 79	Hg mercury 80	Tl 81	Pb lead 82	Bi 83	Po 84	At 85	Rn 86
7	Fr 87	Ra 88	89–103 see below	Ku 104	Ha 105	106	107	108	Mt 109									

lanthanides	La lanthanum 57	Ce 58	Pr 59	Nd 60	Pm 61	Sm 62	Eu 63	Gd 64	Tb 65	Dy 66	Ho 67	Er 68	Tm 69	Yb 70	Lu 71
actinides	Ac actinium 89	Th 90	Pa 91	U uranium 92	Np 93	Pu 94	Am 95	Cm 96	Bk 97	Cf 98	Es 99	Fm 100	Md 101	No 102	Lr 103

Figure 2 Modern Periodic Table

Elements in the Periodic Table

Figure 3 Photographs of mercury, bromine, sulfur, copper and chlorine

There are just over 100 elements in the Periodic Table and these elements may be solids, liquids or gases. Of these elements there are 11 that are gases, two that are liquids and 90 that are solids. Figure 4 highlights the physical state of all 103 elements in the Periodic Table.

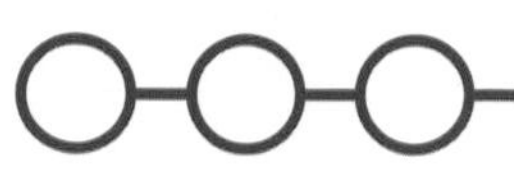

I	II											III	IV	V	VI	VII	VIII
				1 H Hydrogen													2 He Helium
7 Li Lithium	9 Be Berylium											5 B Boron	6 C Carbon	7 N Nitrogen	8 O Oxygen	9 F Fluorine	10 Ne Neon
11 Na Sodium	12 Mg Magnesium											13 Al Aluminium	14 Si Silicon	15 P Phosphorus	16 S Sulfur	17 Cl Chlorine	18 Ar Argon
19 K Potassium	20 Ca Calcium	21 Sc Scandium	22 Ti Titanium	23 V Vanadium	24 Cr Chromium	25 Mn Magnesium	26 Fe Iron	27 Co Cobalt	28 Ni Nickel	29 Cu Copper	30 Zn Zinc	31 Ga Gallium	32 Ge Germanium	33 As Arsenic	34 Se Selenium	35 Br Bromine	36 Kr Krypton
37 Rb Rubidium	38 Sr Strontium	39 Y Yttrium	40 Zr Zirconium	41 Nb Niobium	42 Mo Molybdenum	43 Tc Technetium	44 Ru Ruthenium	45 Rh Rodium	46 Pd Palladium	47 Ag Silver	48 Cd Cadmium	49 In Indium	50 Sn Tin	51 Sb Antimony	52 Te Tellurium	53 I Iodine	54 Xe Xenon
55 Cs Caesium	56 Ba Barium	57 La Lanthanum	72 Hf Hafnium	73 Ta Tantalum	74 W Tungsten	75 Re Rhenbium	76 Os Osmium	77 Ir Iridium	78 Pt Platinum	79 Au Gold	80 Hg Mercury	81 Tl Thallium	82 Pb Lead	83 Bi Bismuth	84 Po Polonium	85 At Astatine	86 Rn Radon
87 Fr Francium	88 Ra Radium	89 Ac Actinium	104 Rf Rutherfordium	105 Db Dubnium	106 Sg Saaborgium	107 Bh Bohrium	108 Hs Hassium	109 Mt Meitnerium									

58 Ce Cerium	59 Pr Praseodymium	60 Nd Neodymium	61 Pm Promethium	62 Sm Samarium	63 Eu Europium	64 Gd Gadolinium	65 Tb Terbium	66 Dy Dysprosium	67 Ho Holmium	68 Er Erbium	69 Tm Thulium	70 Yb Ytterbium	71 Lu Lutetium
90 Th Thorium	91 Pa Protactinium	92 U Uranium	93 Np Neptunium	94 Pu Plutonium	95 Am Americum	96 Cm Curium	97 Bk Berkelium	98 Cf Californium	99 Es Einsteinium	100 Fm Fermium	101 Md Mendelevium	102 No Nobelium	103 Lr Lawrencium

Solids
Liquids
Gases

Figure 4 The modern Periodic Table. Elements can be metals or non-metals. They can be solids, liquids or gases

It is seen that:

* All the metal elements are solids apart from mercury which is a liquid.
* The only liquid non-metal is bromine.
* The eleven gases are all non-metal elements and these are hydrogen, nitrogen, oxygen, fluorine, chlorine and the noble gases (helium, neon, argon, krypton, xenon and radon).
* There are several non-metal elements that are solids, for example, carbon, phosphorus, sulfur and iodine.

The metal elements are separated from the non-metal elements in the modern Periodic Table. The black zig-zag line on Figure 4 shows this separation. The non-metal elements lie to the right of the black zig-zag line. There are many more metallic elements. These lie to the left of the black line. Some elements which are positioned directly on either side of this dividing line are not true metals nor true non-metals. Silicon and germanium are good examples of this. They are known as semi-metals. A semi-metal shares some of the properties of metals and of non-metals. Silicon is positioned with the non-metals in the Periodic Table, yet it has the appearance of a shiny grey metal and will conduct electricity to a small extent.

Group names, position in the Periodic Table and electronic structure

Some of the groups have been given common names as well as group numbers. These are shown in the table below.

Group number	Name	Elements
I	Alkali metals	Lithium, sodium, potassium, caesium and francium
II	Alkaline earth metals	Beryllium, magnesium, calcium, strontium, barium and radium
VII	Halogens	Fluorine, chlorine, bromine, iodine and astatine
0	Noble gases	Helium, neon, argon, krypton, xenon and radon

The arrangement of the elements in the modern Periodic Table is closely related to their electronic structures. Elements with similar properties appear in the same group and this is summarised in Table 2.

Element	Electronic structure	Number of electrons in outer shell	Group number	Reactivity	Metal or non-metal
Sodium	2,8,1	1	I	Very reactive	Metal
Potassium	2,8,8,1	1	I	Very reactive	Metal
Fluorine	2,7	7	VII	Very reactive	Non-metal
Chlorine	2,8,7	7	VII	Very reactive	Non-metal
Neon	2,8	8	VIII or 0	Unreactive	Non-metal
Argon	2,8,8	8	VIII or 0	Unreactive	Non-metal

Table 2 Elements with similar electronic structure and properties are in the same group

The elements in Group I have one electron in their outer shell, for example, sodium has an electronic structure 2,8,**1** while potassium is 2,8,8,**1**. This outermost electron is lost easily, so these **Group I metals are very reactive** and form ions with one positive charge, for example Na^+ and K^+.

Moving into Group II metals we find that these metals have all got two electrons in the outer shell. Magnesium has an electronic structure 2,8,**2** while calcium has an electronic structure of 2,8,8,**2**. **Group II metals are not quite as reactive as Group I** and lose their two outermost electrons to form ions with a charge of 2+, for example Mg^{2+} or Ca^{2+}.

Moving over to the halogens, Group VII, we find that the elements in this group of non-metals have seven electrons in their outer shell. Fluorine has an electronic structure of 2,**7** while chlorine has an electronic structure of 2,8,**7**. These elements can easily gain one electron to gain a filled outer shell and so the halogens are **a group of very reactive non-metals.**

Next to the halogens in the Periodic Table is Group VIII or 0. This group of gases, also known as the noble gases, have filled outer shells of electrons, for example, neon 2,**8** and argon 2,8,**8**. **These gases are very unreactive** and stable as they do not have to transfer or share electrons to fill their outer shell. As the noble gases are unreactive and very stable they have several important uses.

* Helium is used in balloons and airships because it is non-flammable and has a low density.
* As argon is very unreactive it is used in light bulbs to prolong the lifetime of the filament and also to reduce tungsten atoms evaporating from the filament. A vacuum cannot be used as too many tungsten atoms evaporate from the extremely hot tungsten filament.
* Neon is used in discharge tubes to create fluorescent advertising signs as it is unreactive and produces a coloured glow when its atoms are bombarded by a stream of electrons.

Questions

1 Copy this paragraph and fill in the blanks.

Perhaps the greatest contributor to the development of the Periodic Table was the Russian scientist _______________ in 1869. He stated that 'when elements are arranged in order of increasing _______________________________ similar properties recur at intervals'. He wrote down what he knew about each element on a separate card and then sorted the cards into 'piles of elements' with similar _____________. His inspiration was to leave gaps for _________________________ elements. Nowadays, the elements are arranged in order of increasing _____________________.

2 From your Periodic Table give the symbol for an element which is:

a) a noble gas
b) an alkaline earth metal
c) a halogen
d) an alkali metal.

3 Use your Periodic Table to name:

a) a metal in Period 3 with three electrons in its outer shell
b) a non-metal in Period 2 which belongs to Group VII
c) a noble gas with two electrons in its outer shell
d) an element which forms a stable ion by gaining two electrons.

4 **a)** Give three features of the Periodic Table developed by Mendeleev.
b) Give three ways in which the modern Periodic Table differs from that developed by Mendeleev.

5 Use the following list of elements to answer the questions below:

carbon, sulfur, aluminium, sodium, magnesium, chlorine and potassium

a) name an element which has a giant covalent structure
b) give the symbol for the most reactive metal in the list
c) name the element which forms diatomic molecules
d) what type of bonding exists in sodium?

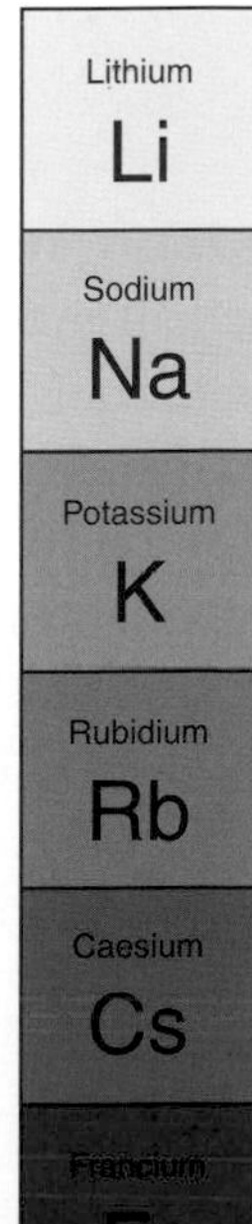

Figure 5 The alkali metals in Group I

▶ Properties of Groups I, II and VII elements

Group I: alkali metals

Group I or alkali metals are a group of very reactive metals. Due to their high reactivity they must be stored under oil to prevent them from reacting with oxygen or water vapour in the air. The metals are all soft and when freshly cut give a silver lustre but tarnish rapidly in air. Although they are all reactive metals, the **reactivity increases down the group**.

Owing to their high reactivity, great care must be taken when using the alkali metals. Your teacher may demonstrate the reactions of lithium, sodium and potassium with water but you will not use rubidium or caesium because they are too reactive and explode violently in water. It is important that when the reaction is being carried out, a safety screen is used and students wear safety goggles. In addition a small sample of each metal is used to minimise any dangers of an explosion.

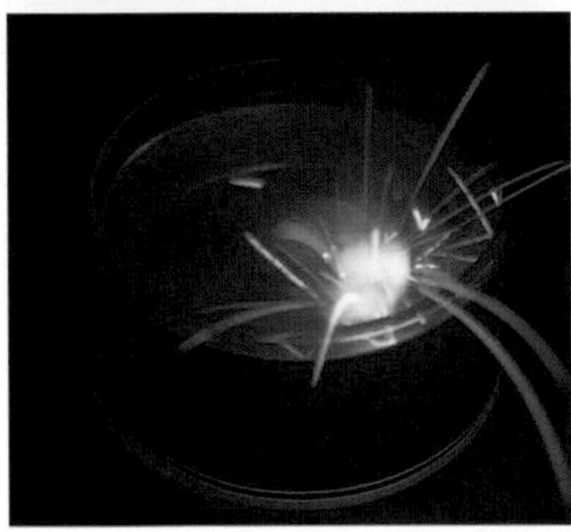

Figure 6 The reactions of a) lithium, b) sodium and c) potassium with water

Chemical reactions of the alkali metals

Reaction with water

This group of metals is called the alkali metals as they react with water to form hydrogen and a colourless **alkaline** solution of the metal hydroxide (Figure 6). For Li, Na and K, all three metals float and move around on the surface of the water and eventually disappear. Sodium and potassium both melt when they react with water (see page 142).

Lithium reacts with water forming a steady stream of hydrogen gas and a colourless alkaline solution of lithium hydroxide.

lithium + water → lithium hydroxide + hydrogen

$$2Li_{(s)} + 2H_2O_{(l)} \rightarrow 2LiOH_{(aq)} + H_{2(g)}$$

Sodium reacts vigorously with water, forming a molten metal sphere and producing hydrogen gas and sometimes the hydrogen ignites and burns with a yellow flame.

sodium + water → sodium hydroxide + hydrogen

$$2Na_{(s)} + 2H_2O_{(l)} \rightarrow 2NaOH_{(aq)} + H_{2(g)}$$

Potassium reacts violently with water and the hydrogen ignites spontaneously, burning with a lilac flame. The reaction is very fast and highly exothermic.

potassium + water → potassium hydroxide + hydrogen

$$2K_{(s)} + 2H_2O_{(l)} \rightarrow 2KOH_{(aq)} + H_{2(g)}$$

Reaction with halogens

Alkali metals react vigorously with halogens to form **ionic metal halides**. The vigour of the reaction depends on the alkali metal and the halogen used. The reactivity of the alkali metals increases down the group while the reactivity of the halogens increases up the group. This means lithium is the least reactive alkali metal and fluorine is the most reactive halogen. Thus, when Li, Na and K react with chlorine we can predict that the reaction between potassium and chlorine will be the most vigorous reaction as potassium is lower in Group I than lithium or sodium.

The general equation for an alkali metal reacting with a halogen is:

$$2M + X_2 \rightarrow 2MX$$

For example sodium and chlorine react vigorously at room temperature to form sodium chloride:

sodium + chlorine → sodium chloride

$$2Na + Cl_2 \rightarrow 2NaCl$$

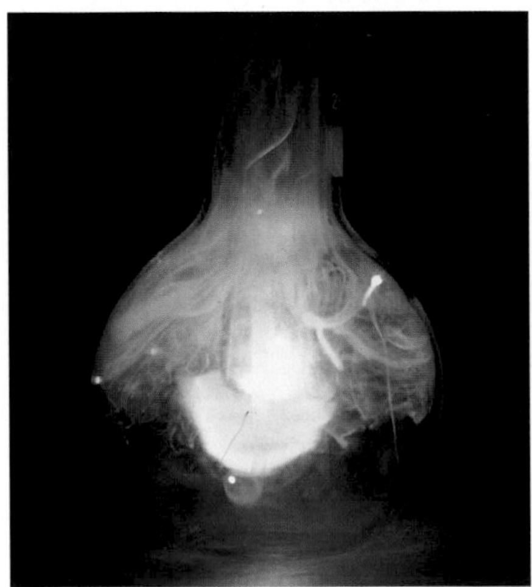

Figure 7 Reaction between sodium and chlorine

It is possible to write **half equations** to show the formation of sodium chloride from sodium and chlorine (see Chapter 4, page 62).

In this reaction sodium gives up an electron to form a positive sodium ion:

$$Na \rightarrow Na^{+} + e^{-}$$

While each chlorine atom in the chlorine molecule accepts an electron to form a chloride ion:

$$Cl_2 + 2e^{-} \rightarrow 2Cl^{-}$$

Sodium chloride is an ionic metal halide and it is a white crystalline solid.

All alkali metals have **similar chemical properties** because when they react their atoms lose one electron to form positive ions with a stable electronic structure as shown in Table 3.

From Table 3 we can see that all Group I metals form ions with a stable noble gas electron structure.

Formation of ion (half equation)	Electronic structure of ion
$Li \rightarrow Li^{+} + e^{-}$	2
$Na \rightarrow Na^{+} + e^{-}$	2,8,
$K \rightarrow K^{+} + e^{-}$	2,8,8

Table 3 Half equations for the formation of Group I ions

Questions

6 This question is about Group I metals.

a) What is the common name of Group I metals?

b) Show how the electrons are arranged in a sodium atom.

c) Name the metal in Group I which has the smallest atom.

d) Give the name of the most reactive metal in Group I.

e) Why is lithium stored under oil?

f) Why should caesium never be added to water?

7 A small piece of potassium was added to water in a large trough.

a) Give four things you would observe in this reaction.

b) Write a word equation to show what happens when potassium reacts with water.

c) How would you show that the final solution contained potassium hydroxide?

8 a) Write a balanced equation to show how sodium reacts with chlorine.

b) Use a half equation to show how sodium forms a sodium ion.

c) Explain why all Group I metals have similar chemical properties.

9 Balance the following equations.

a) $K + Cl_2 \rightarrow KCl$

b) $Na + H_2O \rightarrow NaOH + H_2$

c) $Li + O_2 \rightarrow Li_2O$

d) $Cl_2 + e^{-} \rightarrow Cl^{-}$

Group 6	Group 7	Group 0
		He
O	F	Ne
S	Cl	Ar
	Br	Kr
	I	Xe
	At	Rn

Figure 8 The halogens

Group VII: halogens

The elements of Group VII are similar to each other, but their properties gradually change as you go down the group from fluorine to iodine. Some of the physical properties of the halogens are highlighted in the table below.

Element	Relative atomic mass	State at room temperature	Colour	Structure	Melting point/ °C	Boiling point/ °C
Fluorine	19	gas	pale yellow	F_2 molecules	−220	−188
Chlorine	35.5	gas	pale green	Cl_2 molecules	−101	−35
Bromine	80	liquid	red-brown	Br_2 molecules	−7	58
Iodine	127	solid	dark grey solid which sublimes to give a purple vapour	I_2 molecules	114	183

Table 4 Some physical properties of the halogens

From Table 4 it is seen that:

* Descending the group the elements change colour from yellow (fluorine) to green (chlorine) to red/brown (bromine) to grey/black (iodine).

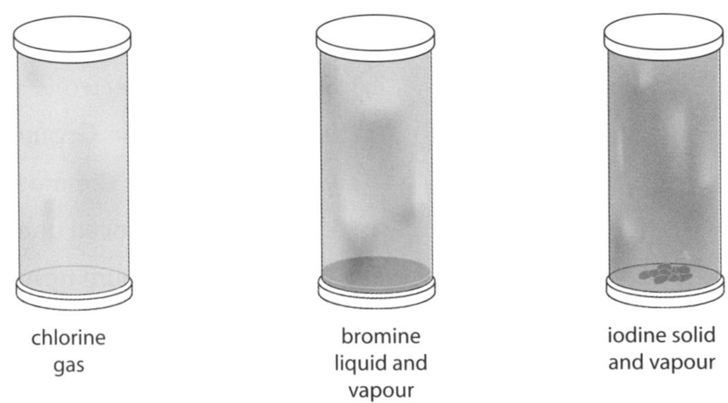

Figure 9 Gas jars of fluorine, chlorine, bromine and iodine

* Descending the group the melting and boiling points increase. Although the diatomic molecules have strong covalent bonds **between the atoms**, there are only weak attractive forces **between the molecules** (van der Waals' attractive forces). This explains why the melting and boiling points are low; however, to explain the increase in melting points and boiling points it is important to realise that the size of the molecules increases as you move down from fluorine to iodine. As the size of the molecules increases so too does the attractive forces between the molecules. Due to the increased attraction between the molecules the melting points and boiling points increase moving down the group.

* Elements change state as the atomic number and relative atomic mass increase. Fluorine and chlorine are gases, bromine is a liquid and iodine is a solid. For fluorine and chlorine the forces of attraction between the molecules are very weak and there is little or no attraction between the gaseous molecules. Thus the molecules

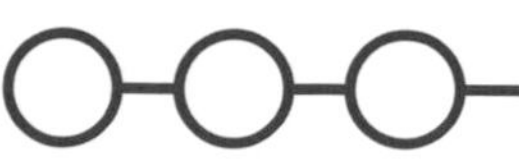

are far apart and these two halogens are gases. For bromine, the molecules increase in size and the attractive forces between them are sufficiently strong to bring the molecules close together to form a liquid. For iodine the attractive forces are sufficiently strong to hold the molecules closely together in an orderly arrangement and as a result iodine is a solid. It is an unusual solid in that it sublimes on heating to give thick purple vapours.

Chemical reactions of the halogens

Displacement reactions

The halogens are a reactive group of non-metals and their reactivity decreases down the group. Fluorine is the most reactive halogen and it is also the most reactive of all non-metals. The reactivity of the halogens can be demonstrated using **displacement reactions**. These are the reactions of halogens with solutions of metal halides and are summarised in Table 5 for chlorine, bromine and iodine.

Reaction	Chlorine	Bromine	Iodine
With sodium chloride solution	No reaction	No reaction	No reaction
With sodium bromide solution	Chlorine displaces orange/brown bromine	No reaction	No reaction
With sodium iodide solution	Chlorine displaces brown iodine	Bromine displaces brown iodine	No reaction

Table 5 Displacement reactions of the halogens

Consider the reaction of chlorine water (water with dissolved chlorine gas) with colourless sodium bromide solution. Since chlorine is more reactive than bromine, the following reaction takes place:

chlorine + sodium bromide (colourless solution) → sodium chloride + bromine (orange/brown solution)

$$Cl_{2(aq)} + 2NaBr_{(aq)} \rightarrow 2NaCl_{(aq)} + Br_{2(aq)}$$

The solution turns an orange/brown colour as bromine has been displaced by the more reactive chlorine.

In the same way bromine is more reactive than iodine and will react with sodium iodide to displace iodine and produce sodium bromide:

bromine (orange/brown solution) + sodium iodide → sodium bromide + iodine (dark brown solution)

$$Br_{2(aq)} + 2NaI_{(aq)} \rightarrow 2NaBr_{(aq)} + I_{2(aq)}$$

These displacement reactions clearly show that a more reactive halogen will displace a less reactive halogen from an aqueous solution of its salt.

Chemical properties of the halogens

Halogens have similar chemical properties because when they react their atoms gain an electron to form a negative ion which has a stable electronic structure like a noble gas. Consider the displacement reaction above where a chlorine molecule reacts to form two chloride ions. During the reaction each chlorine atom gains an electron to form a chloride ion with a filled outer shell of electrons, 2,8,8. The following half equation shows how this takes place:

$$Cl_2 + 2e^- \rightarrow 2Cl^-$$

Each chloride ion has an electronic structure of 2,8,8.

In the same way fluorine reacts to form the fluoride ion with a stable electronic structure of 2,8.

$$F_2 + 2e^- \rightarrow 2F^-$$

The above equations show that the halogens have similar chemical reactions. In the reactions their atoms gain an electron to achieve a noble gas electron structure.

Questions

10 This question is about the halogens.

a) To which group in the Periodic Table do the halogens belong?

b) Give two physical properties of bromine.

c) What would you observe if chlorine was bubbled into an aqueous solution of potassium iodide? Write a symbol equation for the reaction taking place.

d) Give a reason why the reaction in **c)** should be carried out in a fume cupboard.

11 a) Draw a diagram to show how the electrons are arranged in a chlorine atom.

b) Use your diagram to explain how a chlorine molecule forms.

c) Explain why chlorine has a low boiling point.

d) From your knowledge of trends in physical properties explain why bromine is a liquid and iodine is a solid.

12 a) Draw electron diagrams to show how the electrons are arranged in atoms of lithium and fluorine. Use your diagrams to show how the compound lithium fluoride forms.

b) Give two properties of the compound lithium fluoride.

13 Balance the following equations:

a) $K + I_2 \rightarrow KI$

b) $NaBr + Cl_2 \rightarrow NaCl + Br_2$

c) $Cl_2 + H_2 \rightarrow HCl$

Exam questions

1 In 1864, after many years of work, the chemist John Newlands noticed a regular pattern in the properties of some elements. He called this pattern the Law of Octaves and presented the elements in a table.
Despite being a great breakthrough, Newlands' table was limited and only five years later a Russian chemist, Dmitri Mendeleev, produced a more complete table of elements. He called this table the Periodic Table.

H	Li	Be	B	C	N	O
F	Na	Mg	Al	Si	P	S
Cl	K	Ca	Cr	Ti	Mn	Fe

Newlands' table of the elements from his Law of Octaves

	Group I	II	III	IV	V	VI	VII	VIII
Period 1	H = 1							
Period 2	Li = 7	Be = 9.4	B = 11	C = 12	N = 14	O = 16	F = 19	
Period 3	Na = 23	Mg = 24	Al = 27.3	Si = 28	P = 31	S = 32	Cl = 35.5	
Period 4	K = 39	Ca = 40	? = 44	Ti = 48	V = 51	Cr = 52	Mn = 55	Fe = 56, Co = 59, Ni = 59
Period 5	Cu = 63	Zn = 65	? = 68	? = 72	As = 75	Se = 78	Br = 80	
Period 6	Rb = 85	Sr = 87	?Yt = 88	Zr = 90	Nb = 94	Mo = 96	? = 100	Ru = 104, Rn = 104, Pd = 106
Period 7	Ag = 108	Cd = 112	In = 113	Sn = 118	Sb = 122	Te = 125	J = 127	
Period 8	Cs = 133	Ba = 137	?Di = 138	?Ce = 104				
Period 9								
Period 10			?Er = 178	?La = 180	Ta = 182	W = 184		Os = 195, Ir = 197, Pt = 198
Period 11	Au = 199	Hg = 200	Tl = 204	Pb = 207	Bi = 208			
Period 12				Th = 231		U = 240		

Mendeleev's Periodic Table of the elements

a) Compare Newlands' table of the elements with Mendeleev's Periodic Table shown above.

Why was Mendeleev's Periodic Table of the elements considered to be better than the work of Newlands? *(4 marks)*

b) In Mendeleev's Periodic Table of the elements, one element is labelled

J = 127

i) What do you understand by the number 127? *(1 mark)*

ii) What symbol do we now use for this element? (You may find the Periodic Table, on page 246, useful.) *(1 mark)*

c) i) What name is given to Group II in the **modern** Periodic Table? *(1 mark)*

ii) In what group of the **modern** Periodic Table would you find a group of unreactive gases called the noble gases? *(1 mark)*

iii) What is the name of the element in Group I and Period III of the **modern** Periodic Table? *(1 mark)*

2 The Periodic Table is a tool used by chemists to understand the behaviour of the elements.

a) The table below is part of the table of elements devised by the English chemist John Newlands in 1864. Repeating patterns of properties were observed in the elements.

H	Li	Be	B	C	N	O
F	Na	Mg	Al	Si	P	S
Cl	K	Ca	Cr	Ti	Mn	Fe

i) What name did Newlands give to the repeating pattern observed in the properties of the elements? *(1 mark)*

ii) Which group of elements, present in the modern Periodic Table, is missing from Newlands' table above? Explain your answer. *(2 marks)*

b) Dmitri Mendeleev produced a more comprehensive table of elements in 1869. The table below shows part of his Periodic Table in which elements were arranged in order of increasing atomic mass.

H							
Li	Be	B	C	N	O	F	
Na	Mg	Al	Si	P	S	Cl	
K Cu	Ca Zn		Ti	V As	Cr Se	Mn Br	Fe Co Ni

i) Suggest why Mendeleev placed zinc in the same group as calcium. *(1 mark)*

ii) Suggest **one** way in which Mendeleev used creative thought to improve on Newlands' table. *(1 mark)*

iii) Describe how Mendeleev's table is different from the modern Periodic Table.

In this question, you will be assessed on using your written communication skills including the use of specialist science terms. *(6 marks)*

c) The following diagram shows part of the modern Periodic Table divided into five sections: A, B, C, D and E.

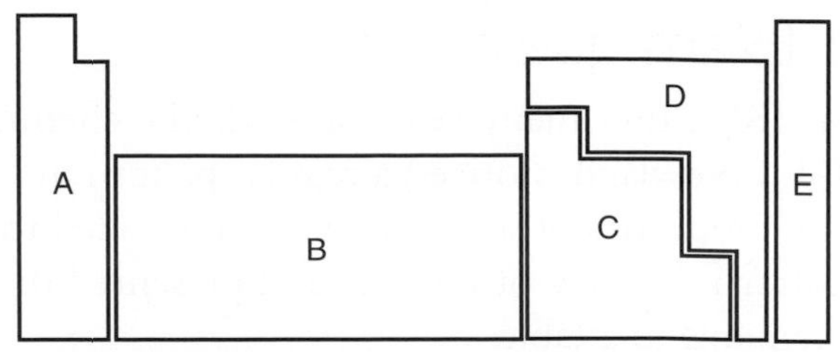

Select from A–E the section in which you would find:

i) an unreactive gas which forms no compounds *(1 mark)*

ii) a metal which reacts with cold water *(1 mark)*

iii) a coloured gas. *(1 mark)*

d) The melting points of the first eighteen elements of the Periodic Table are shown in the graph.

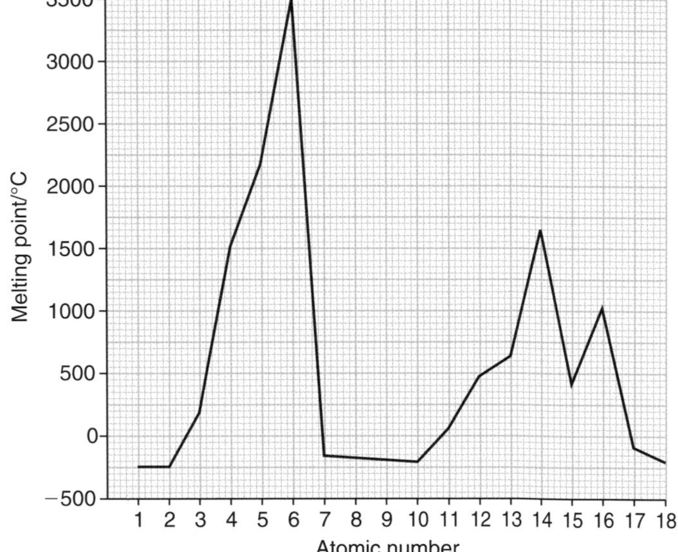

Use the graph and your knowledge of the Periodic Table to answer the following questions.

i) Name the element with the highest melting point and state the group to which it belongs. *(2 marks)*

ii) Complete the table below.

Atomic number	Name of element	State at room temperature (20 °C)
4		
9		

(4 marks)

iii) Write the electronic structure of the element with melting point 1380 °C. *(1 mark)*

3 The Periodic Table is a tool used by chemists to understand the behaviour of the elements.

a) The table below is part of the table of elements devised by the English chemist John Newlands in 1864. Repeating patterns of properties were observed in the elements up to calcium.

H	F	Cl
Li	Na	K
Be	Mg	Ca
B	Al	
C	Si	
N	P	
O	S	

i) What name did Newlands give to the repeating pattern observed in the properties of the elements? *(1 mark)*

ii) Which group of elements, present in the modern Periodic Table, is missing from Newlands' table above? *(1 mark)*

iii) Explain why this group was missing from Newlands' classification of elements. *(1 mark)*

b) Dmitri Mendeleev produced a more comprehensive table of elements in 1869 which he called the Periodic System of Elements. The table below shows part of this arrangement of elements together with their 'atomic weights'.

H 1						
Li 7	Be 9.4	B 11	C 12	N 14	O 16	F 19
Na 23	Mg 24	Al 27.4	Si 28	P 31	S 32	Cl 35.5
K 39	Ca 40		**Element A**	As 75	Se 79.4	Br 80
Rb 85.4	Zn 65.2					

i) Suggest two reasons why zinc, Zn, could be grouped with magnesium and calcium. *(2 marks)*

ii) Mendeleev gave Element A the name eka-silicon and predicted its properties. What name was given to this element when it was discovered? *(1 mark)*

iii) State two features of Mendeleev's table of elements which are different from the modern Periodic Table. *(2 marks)*

c) The elements of Group VII of the modern Periodic Table exhibit trends in many different physical and chemical properties.

F
Cl
Br
I

i) What is the name given to Group VII of the Periodic Table? *(1 mark)*

ii) Group VII elements exist as diatomic molecules. What is meant by the term diatomic? *(1 mark)*

iii) Name **two other** elements apart from those in Group VII which are diatomic. *(2 marks)*

iv) Fluorine and chlorine are gases at room temperature and pressure. Name **one other** non-metal element which is a gas at room temperature and pressure. *(1 mark)*

v) Bromine is a liquid at room temperature and pressure. Name one other element which is a liquid at room temperature and pressure. *(1 mark)*

vi) Which is the most reactive of the Group VII elements shown above? *(1 mark)*

vii) Iodine, when heated, undergoes sublimation. What is meant by the term sublimation? *(2 marks)*

4 The Periodic Table contains all known elements. It evolved from the study of the trends and patterns in the physical and chemical properties of the elements.

a) i) Name the Russian chemist who devised a Periodic Table very similar to the modern Periodic Table used today. *(1 mark)*

ii) Fill in the blanks in the following passage.

The modern Periodic Table arranges the elements in order of increasing atomic ________ whereas early versions of the Periodic Table arranged them in order of increasing atomic ________. *(2 marks)*

iii) State one other difference between the modern Periodic Table and early versions of the Periodic Table. *(1 mark)*

iv) Name the English chemist who devised 'a law of octaves' for the elements. *(1 mark)*

b) The Periodic Table groups together elements with similar properties.

i) How many groups are there in the Periodic Table? *(1 mark)*

ii) In which group would you find the most reactive metals? *(1 mark)*

iii) Name the group that contains only non-metals which are unreactive. *(1 mark)*

iv) How does the reactivity of the elements in Group II change on descending the group? *(1 mark)*

c) There are many patterns and trends in the Periodic Table.

i) What is the name given to the horizontal rows in the Periodic Table? *(1 mark)*

ii) What is the relationship between the position of an element in the Periodic Table and the number of electrons in the outer shell of an atom of the element? *(1 mark)*

iii) Describe the trend in atomic size on moving across the Periodic Table from sodium to argon. *(1 mark)*

iv) Most elements may be classified as metals or non-metals. Name one element which is classified as a semi-metal and state one reason why it may be classified in this way. *(2 marks)*

5 a) Complete the blanks in the paragraph below about the Periodic Table.

In 1869, a Russian chemist called ____________ produced a Periodic Table very similar to the one we use today. The elements of the modern Periodic Table are arranged in order of increasing ________ number. In the Periodic Table, the horizontal rows are called periods and the vertical columns of elements are called ________. Moving across a period, the size of the atoms ________ and the non-metallic character of the elements ________. *(5 marks)*

b) Sodium and potassium are both in Group I of the Periodic Table.

i) Give another name for the Group I elements. *(1 mark)*

ii) Name another element found in Group I. *(1 mark)*

iii) Which element in Group I is least reactive? *(1 mark)*

iv) In terms of electronic configuration, what do the elements of Group I have in common? Illustrate your answer giving the full electronic configuration of sodium and potassium. *(3 marks)*

c) Use your Periodic Table to answer the following questions.

i) Give the symbol of a noble gas. *(1 mark)*

ii) Give the symbol of an element which has five electrons in its outer shell. *(1 mark)*

iii) Give the symbol of a non-metal which is solid at room temperature and pressure. *(1 mark)*

iv) Give the symbol of an element which forms an ion with a charge of 2+. *(1 mark)*

v) Give the symbol of an element in Period 3 which is best described as a semi-metal. *(1 mark)*

6 a) Calcium is a Group II metal which reacts with water.

i) Give one safety precaution which must be taken when carrying out this reaction in the laboratory. *(1 mark)*

ii) Describe three things you would observe happening when calcium is added to water. *(3 marks)*

iii) Complete the word equation for the reaction of calcium with water.

calcium + water ⟶

_______ + _______ *(2 marks)*

iv) Would you expect the solution formed when calcium reacts with water to be acidic, alkaline or neutral? *(1 mark)*

v) Name a Group II element which is more reactive than calcium when added to water. *(1 mark)*

b) i) Describe two things you would observe happening when magnesium burns in air. *(2 marks)*

ii) Write a balanced symbol equation to show how magnesium reacts with oxygen. *(3 marks)*

c) i) Complete the diagrams below to show the arrangement of all the electrons in a calcium atom and an oxygen atom. *(2 marks)*

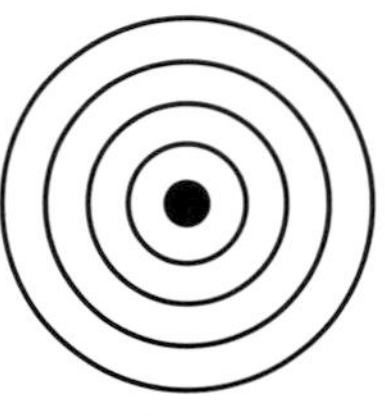
calcium atom

oxygen atom

ii) How does the arrangement of the electrons in a calcium atom and an oxygen atom change when calcium oxide is formed? *(3 marks)*

d) Calcium oxide reacts with water to give a solution known as limewater. What is the name and the formula of the calcium compound present in limewater? *(2 marks)*

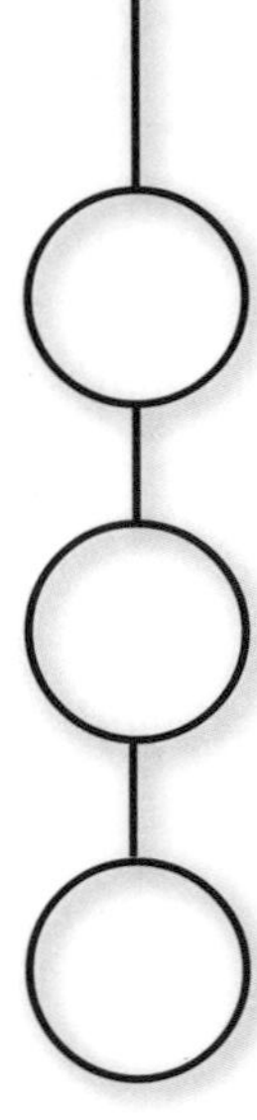

6 Acids, Bases and Salts – Tests for Ions

The substances in the groups below can be easily found in the home.

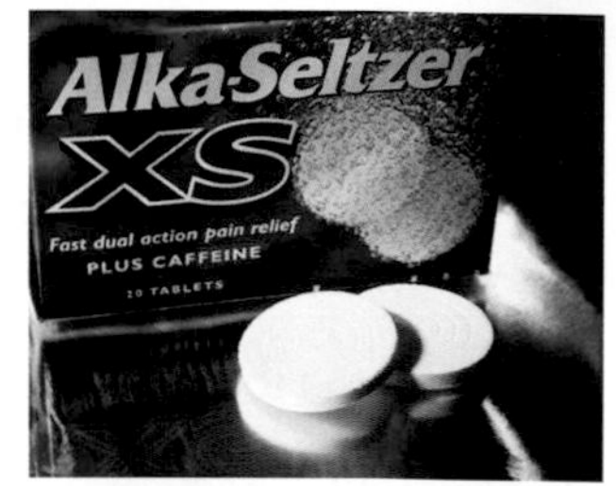

DISTILLED MALT VINEGAR

SARSONS Malt

Group 1

Group 2

Note the correct way to write pH.

pH

This is because the letter 'p' in this instance is a mathematical symbol similar to '+' and '×'. (It means $-\log_{10}$.)

Look carefully at the two groups of substances.

* What have the substances in Group 1 got in common with each other?
* What have the substances in Group 2 got in common with each other?

Among other things, Group 1 all have a sour taste. The Latin word for sour is *acidus*. Group 1 are acidic substances. Group 2 are basic substances. The examples in Group 2 are soluble in water. A base which is soluble in water is called an alkali. An indicator is a chemical which will change colour when it reacts with an acid or an alkali. Acids, bases, alkalis and indicators have been studied in KS3.

The names of four different indicators are given in the first column of the table on the next page. In the second column of the table the observations made when the indicator is added to an acid or an alkali are recorded.

An alkali is a soluble base.

Name of indicator	Observations in acidic, neutral and alkaline solutions	
Red litmus paper	Turns blue when in alkaline solution. Remains red in acidic and neutral solutions.	
Blue litmus paper	Turns red in acidic solution. Remains blue in alkaline and neutral solutions.	
Phenolphthalein	A colourless liquid which is pale pink in alkaline solution. Remains colourless in neutral and weakly acidic solutions.	
Universal indicator	A dark green liquid which changes to several different colours in different strengths of acids and alkalis. The colour of the liquid can be compared to the colours on a chart and the pH of the liquid inferred.	
Universal indicator paper	A peach coloured strip of paper which changes to different colours in different strengths of acids and alkalis. The colour of the paper can be compared to the colours on a chart and the pH of the liquid found.	

To view all the colours of universal indicator as a 'rainbow':

* Place 60 cm^3 of 1 mol/dm^3 hydrochloric acid into a 100 cm^3 measuring cylinder.
* Add five drops of universal indicator.
* Prepare a saturated solution of sodium carbonate, Na_2CO_3.
* Tilting the cylinder carefully, add 5 cm^3 of the saturated solution of sodium carbonate to the measuring cylinder, using a dropping pipette.
* The saturated sodium carbonate solution is more dense than the dilute acid and will sink to the bottom of the cylinder. As the acid reacts with the alkali, carbon dioxide is evolved and the bubbles of gas help to mix the solution. The universal indicator produces a rainbow of colours as the alkaline nature of the solution gradually changes to acidic from the bottom to the top of the cylinder.

These indicators are useful in different laboratory and field situations. Choose the **best** indicator from the table above to use in each of the following situations.

1. A gardener wishes to know whether the soil in the garden is alkaline. A sample of soil is mixed with water and filtered. The filtrate is tested with an indicator.
2. A chef requires a vinegar for the preparation of a marinade. The chef has three different vinegars to choose from. Which indicator could be used to find the strongest vinegar?
3. A chemist needs an acid which has a pH of 2.5 to complete a reaction. Will any of the indicators in the table be accurate enough to measure a pH of 2.5?

The gardener could use red litmus paper.

The chef could use universal indicator paper. A drop of each vinegar could placed onto the paper and the colour observed. The redder the colour the stronger the acid. (The chef could also use universal indicator solution.)

The chemist could use universal indicator solution but it would be difficult to say that the pH was exactly 2.5. A more accurate method of measuring pH would be needed for this situation.

Figure 1 Two different types of pH meter

The photographs show two different types of pH meters. These meters can record a pH to two decimal places. There are also solutions of strong acids which have a negative pH. A 2 mol/dm^3 solution of sulfuric acid has a pH of −0.6. The pH of such strong acids cannot be measured accurately by any indicator but can be measured accurately using a pH meter.

▶ Strong and weak acids and alkalis

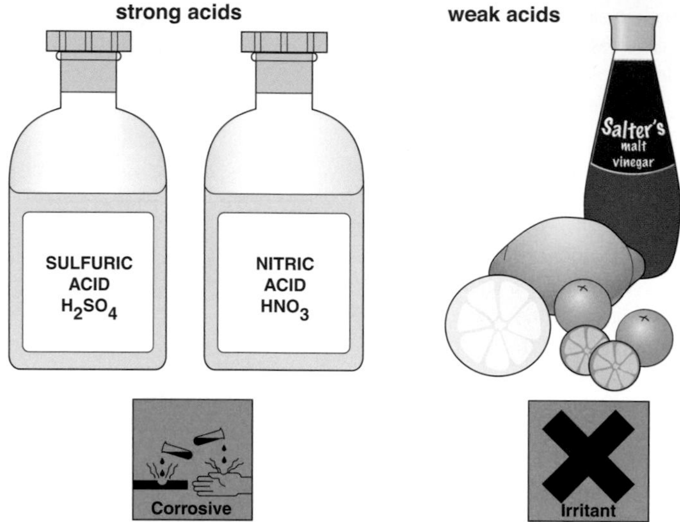

Figure 2 Strong and weak acids

Acids which can be found in the laboratory

Strong acids	
Hydrochloric acid	HCl
Nitric acid	HNO_3
Sulfuric acid	H_2SO_4
Weak acids	
Ethanoic acid	CH_3COOH
Carbonic acid	H_2CO_3

Soluble acids dissolve in water to produce hydrogen ions, $H^+_{(aq)}$.

The strength of an acid depends on the number of hydrogen ions, $H^+_{(aq)}$, dissolved in water.

A strong acid is one which is completely ionised in water. A weak acid is one which is only partially ionised in water.

For example, when hydrogen chloride gas, $HCl_{(g)}$, is dissolved in water, all the molecules are ionised into hydrogen ions and chloride ions.

$$HCl_{(aq)} \rightarrow H^+_{(aq)} + Cl^-_{(aq)}$$

The resulting solution contains only two species, hydrogen ions, $H^+_{(aq)}$, and chloride ions, $Cl^-_{(aq)}$. Hydrochloric acid is a strong acid.

In a dilute solution where 100 molecules of hydrogen chloride are added to water, all 100 molecules will ionise to produce 100 hydrogen ions and 100 chloride ions.

Consider a weak acid like ethanoic acid, CH_3COOH.

$$CH_3COOH_{(aq)} \rightarrow CH_3COO^-_{(aq)} + H^+_{(aq)}$$

In a dilute solution where 100 molecules of CH_3COOH are added to water approximately 33 molecules will ionise to form 33 hydrogen ions, $H^+_{(aq)}$, and 33 ethanoate ions, $CH_3COO^-_{(aq)}$; 67 molecules of CH_3COOH will remain combined. The resulting mixture will contain all three species, CH_3COOH and CH_3COO^- and H^+.

Acids dissolve in water to produce hydrogen ions, $H^+_{(aq)}$.

Alkalis dissolve in water to produce hydroxide ions, $OH^-_{(aq)}$.

Therefore, the solution of hydrochloric acid made by dissolving 100 molecules of hydrogen chloride in water will be a stronger acid than a solution of ethanoic acid made by dissolving 100 molecules of CH_3COOH in the same volume of water, because the 100 molecules of HCl produce 100 hydrogen ions while 100 molecules of CH_3COOH produce only 33 hydrogen ions.

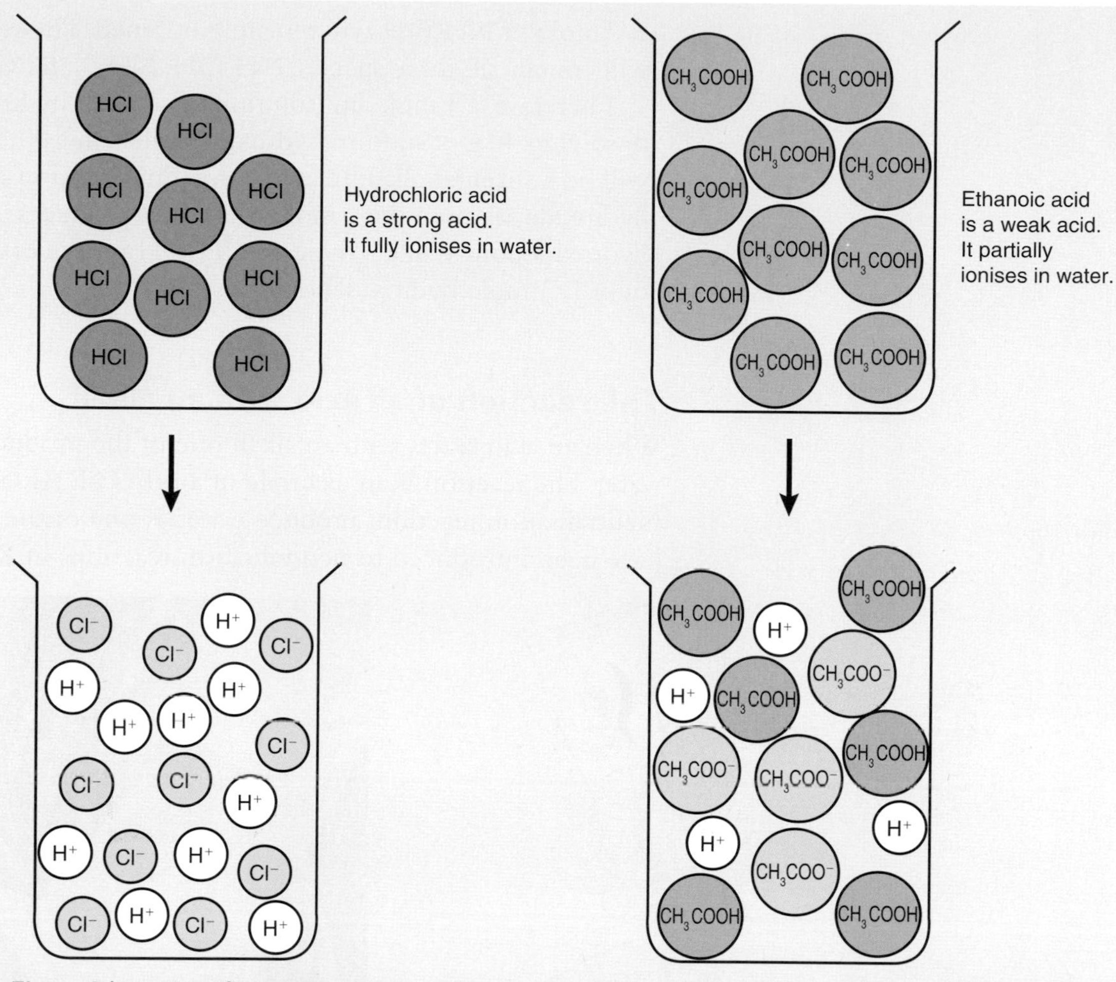

Figure 3 Ionisation of a strong acid and a weak acid

All alkalis produce hydroxide ions, $OH^-_{(aq)}$, when dissolved in water. The strength of an alkali depends on the number of hydroxide ions, $OH^-_{(aq)}$, dissolved in water.

A strong alkali is one which is completely ionised in water. A weak alkali is one which is only partially ionised in water.

For example, when sodium hydroxide pellets, $NaOH_{(s)}$, are dissolved in water, the compound forms sodium ions and hydroxide ions.

$$NaOH_{(aq)} \rightarrow Na^+_{(aq)} + OH^-_{(aq)}$$

The resulting solution contains only two species, hydroxide ions ($OH^-_{(aq)}$) and sodium ions ($Na^+_{(aq)}$). Sodium hydroxide is a strong alkali.

In a dilute solution where 1 mole of sodium hydroxide pellets are added to sufficient water all of the pellets will dissolve to produce 1 mole of aqueous hydroxide ions and 1 mole of aqueous sodium ions.

Consider a weak alkali such as ammonium hydroxide, NH_4OH.

$$NH_4OH_{(aq)} \rightarrow NH_4{}^+_{(aq)} + OH^-_{(aq)}$$

In a dilute solution of 1 mol/dm^3 of ammonium hydroxide approximately 1/3 mole will ionise to form 1/3 mole of hydroxide ions ($OH^-_{(aq)}$) and 1/3 mole of ammonium ions ($NH_4{}^+_{(aq)}$).

Alkalis which can be found in the laboratory

Strong alkalis	
Sodium hydroxide	NaOH
Potassium hydroxide	KOH
Weak alkalis	
Ammonium hydroxide	NH_4OH

2/3 mole of NH_4OH will remain combined. The resulting mixture will contain all three species, NH_4OH, NH_4^+ and OH^-.

Therefore, a 1 mol/dm^3 solution of sodium hydroxide made by dissolving 40 g of sodium hydroxide pellets in 1000 cm^3 of water will be a stronger alkali than a 1 mol/dm^3 solution of ammonium hydroxide, because the 1 mole of NaOH produces 1 mole of hydroxide ions while 1 mole of NH_4OH produces approximately only 1/3 mole hydroxide ions.

The reaction of an acid with an alkali

When an acid reacts with an alkali one of the products formed is water. The reaction is an example of a NEUTRALISATION reaction. Neutralisation reactions produce water as one of the products. You have been introduced to neutralisation reactions in KS3.

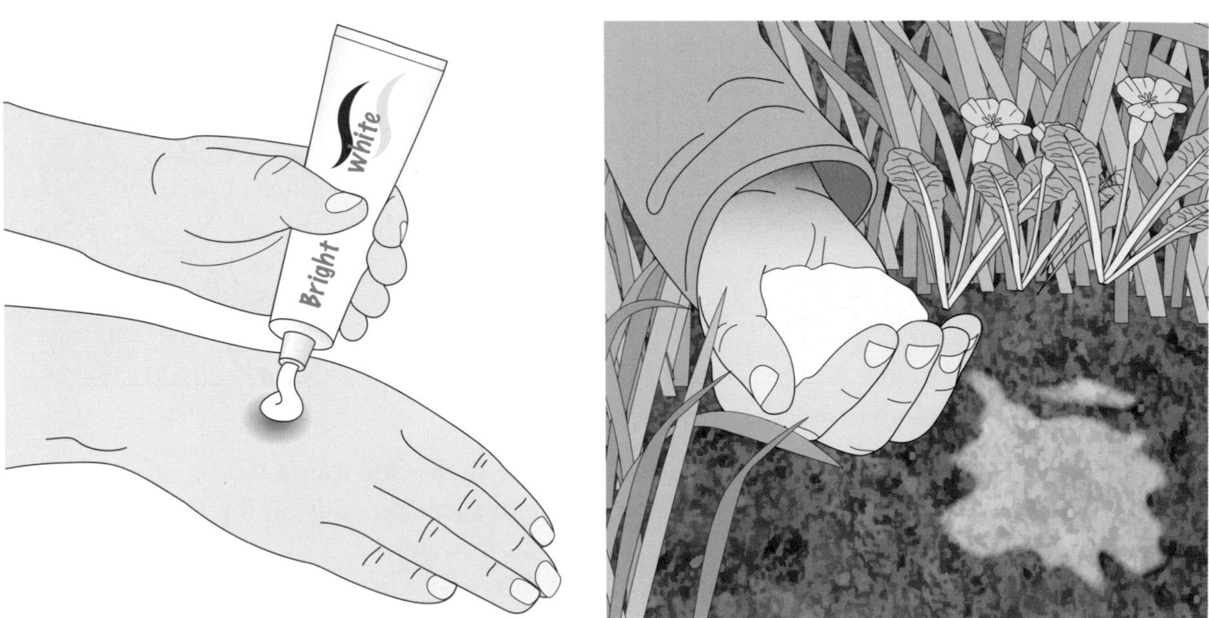

Figure 4 Neutralisation reactions

The ionic equation for neutralisation:

$$H^+_{(aq)} + OH^-_{(aq)} \rightarrow H_2O_{(l)}$$

Consider the balanced chemical equations given below which are examples of neutralisation reactions between acids and alkalis.

$$HCl + NaOH \rightarrow NaCl + H_2O$$
$$HCl + KOH \rightarrow KCl + H_2O$$
$$HCl + LiOH \rightarrow LiCl + H_2O$$

The formation of water can be written in the following ionic equation.

$$H^+_{(aq)} + OH^-_{(aq)} \rightarrow H_2O_{(l)}$$

The hydrogen ions from the acid react with the hydroxide ions from the alkali to produce water.

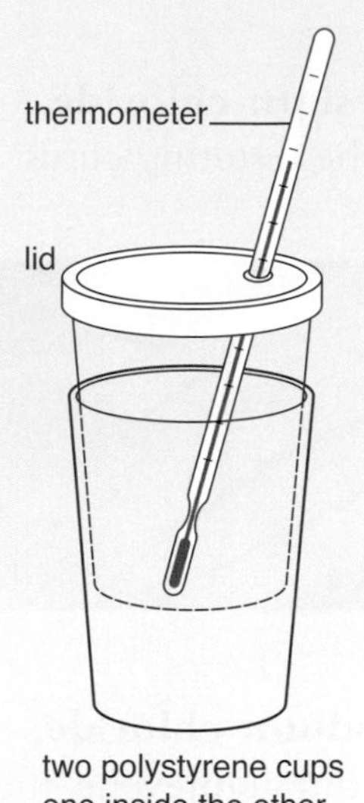

Figure 5 A simple calorimeter

A chemical reaction which releases energy is known as an **exothermic** reaction.

In an exothermic reaction the temperature of the surroundings increases, and the reading on the thermometer goes up.

A chemical reaction which requires energy is known as an **endothermic** reaction.

In an endothermic reaction the temperature of the surroundings decreases, and the reading on the thermometer goes down.

Investigating the temperature change during a neutralisation reaction

A calorimeter is an experimental apparatus which can be used to measure temperature changes in a chemical reaction.

A simple calorimeter can be made from two polystyrene cups, a lid and a thermometer, similar to the one shown on the left.

The chemical reaction occurs in solution.

Temperature may increase or decrease.

The insulating cup traps the heat or prevents heat from entering from the surroundings.

1. Prepare two simple calorimeters as described above.
2. Pipette 25 cm^3 of 0.5 mol/dm^3 sodium hydroxide into one calorimeter.
3. Pipette 25 cm^3 of 0.5 mol/dm^3 hydrochloric acid into the second calorimeter.
4. Measure the temperature of the acid and the alkali every 30 seconds for 5 minutes. Record the temperature in a table.
5. Pour the 25 cm^3 sodium hydroxide into the acid in the calorimeter rapidly with care.
6. Replace the lid and the thermometer quickly.
7. Swirl gently.
8. Measure the temperature every 30 seconds from 5 minutes 30 seconds to 10 minutes. Record the temperatures in a table.
9. Draw a graph of temperature against time.
10. Is the neutralisation reaction endothermic or exothermic?

The simple calorimeter used in this experiment may be improved by increasing the insulation, preventing the heat of the reaction being lost to the surroundings or heat from the surroundings increasing the temperature inside the reaction chamber. An improved calorimeter is shown below. Can you suggest two more improvements which may be made to this calorimeter?

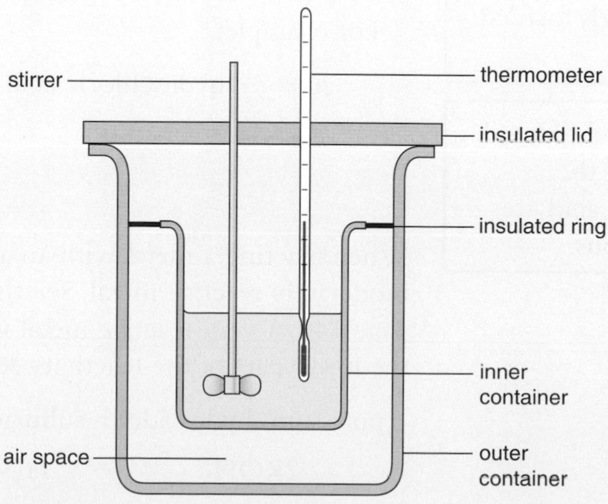

Figure 6 An improved calorimeter

▶ Salts

Tofu is made by coagulating soy milk with **magnesium chloride**, $MgCl_2$, or **calcium sulfate**, $CaSO_4$, and pressing the resulting curds into soft white blocks.

Figure 7 Production of tofu

Bacon is made by curing the flesh of a pig with **sodium chloride**, NaCl, and **sodium nitrate**, $NaNO_3$. The sodium nitrate prevents the growth of *Clostridium botulinum,* which is a bacterium that can cause serious illness.

Figure 8 Curing of bacon

Name of salt	Formula	Example of use of the salt
Silver nitrate	$AgNO_3$	High speed photographic film
Magnesium sulfate	$MgSO_4$	Tomato fertiliser Rose fertiliser
Copper sulfate	$CuSO_4$	Dyeing industry In anti-fungal paints for boats As an anti-bacterial agent in sheep dip
Magnesium chloride	$MgCl_2$	Added to flooring materials to help to prevent dust Fire proofing textiles
Aluminium sulfate	$Al_2(SO_4)_3$	Purification of water Manufacture of paper

Magnesium chloride, calcium sulfate, sodium chloride and sodium nitrate all belong to a class of compounds known as **salts**. These salts are used in food preservation and food preparation. There are, however, hundreds of salts with thousands of uses. Some like sodium chloride are naturally occurring and can be mined or remain after sea water has evaporated but the vast majority are man-made.

Salt is the general name given to certain compounds formed when an acid reacts.

A salt is a compound formed when some or all of the hydrogen ions in an acid are replaced by metal ions.

> **Salt** is the general name given to certain compounds formed when an acid reacts.

> A **salt** is a compound formed when some or all of the hydrogen ions in an acid are replaced by metal ions.

For example:

zinc + hydrochloric acid → zinc chloride + hydrogen

$$Zn + 2HCl \rightarrow \boxed{ZnCl_2} + H_2$$

a salt

When reacting a metal with an acid to produce a salt, choose a moderately reactive metal. See the reactivity series in Chapter 11, page 140. A very reactive metal will be dangerous, while a metal from the lower part of the reactivity series will not react at all to form a salt.

potassium hydroxide + sulfuric acid → potassium sulfate + water

$$2KOH + H_2SO_4 \rightarrow \boxed{K_2SO_4} + 2H_2O$$

a salt

Reactions which produce salts

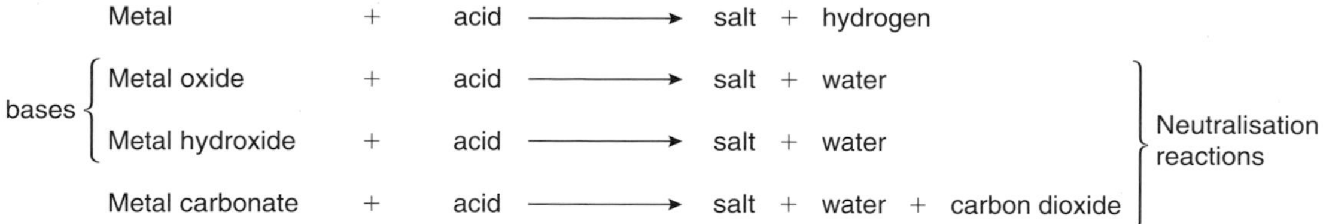

Examples

1. magnesium + hydrochloric acid → magnesium chloride + hydrogen

$Mg + 2HCl \rightarrow MgCl_2 + H_2$

2. magnesium oxide + sulfuric acid → magnesium sulfate + water

$MgO + H_2SO_4 \rightarrow MgSO_4 + H_2O$

3. magnesium hydroxide + ethanoic acid → magnesium ethanoate + water

$Mg(OH)_2 + 2CH_3COOH \rightarrow (CH_3COO)_2Mg + 2H_2O$

4. magnesium carbonate + nitric acid → magnesium nitrate + water + carbon dioxide

$MgCO_3 + 2HNO_3 \rightarrow Mg(NO_3)_2 + H_2O + CO_2$

Neutralisation reactions

Reactions 2, 3 and 4 above are **neutralisation** reactions.

You have been introduced to neutralisation reactions in KS3. Neutralisation reactions produce water as one of the products (see page 84).

Naming salts

A salt is named in two parts. The first part of the name is the name of the metal ion or ammonium ion. The second part of the name is derived from the acid from which the salt was produced.

Name of acid	Name of salt produced when the acid reacts
Hydrochloric acid	chloride
Nitric acid	nitrate
Sulfuric acid	sulfate
Phosphoric acid	phosphate
Ethanoic acid	ethanoate

Example:

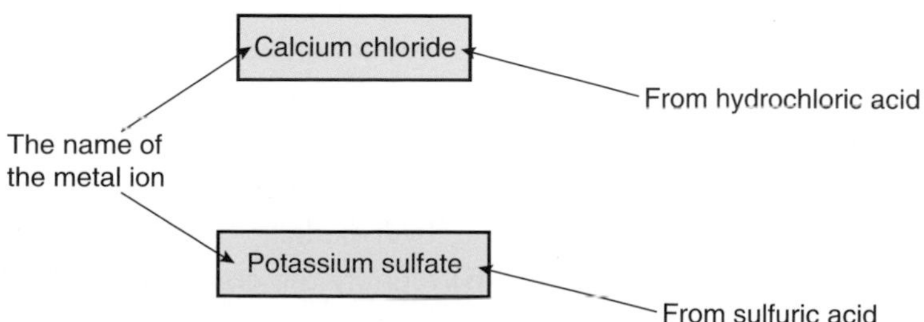

Questions

Complete the following equations describing reactions which produce salts.

1 a) calcium oxide + hydrochloric acid →
b) magnesium hydroxide + sulfuric acid →
c) potassium carbonate + nitric acid →
d) zinc carbonate + hydrochloric acid →
e) calcium + ethanoic acid →

2 a) lithium oxide + ___________ → lithium sulfate + ___________
b) ___________ + ___________ → sodium sulfate + water
c) ________ + ________ → sodium sulfate + water + carbon dioxide
d) ________ + ________ → aluminium sulfate + hydrogen
e) copper(II) carbonate + ________ → copper(II) sulfate + ________ + ________

3 Write balanced chemical equations for all of the reactions in **1** and **2** above.

The solubility of salts

The preparation and use of a salt is dependent on whether the salt is soluble or insoluble. A list of soluble and insoluble compounds is given on the final page of the Data Leaflet supplied for use during your examination. The information is reproduced below.

Solubility in cold water of common salts, hydroxides and oxides

Soluble
All sodium, potassium and ammonium salts
All nitrates
Most chlorides, bromides, iodides EXCEPT Silver and lead chlorides, bromides and iodides
Most sulfates EXCEPT lead and barium sulfates Calcium sulfate is slightly soluble

Insoluble
Most carbonates EXCEPT sodium, potassium and ammonium carbonates
Most hydroxides EXCEPT sodium, potassium and ammonium hydroxides Calcium hydroxide is slightly soluble
Most oxides EXCEPT sodium, potassium and calcium oxides, which react with water

Questions

4 Using the information in the tables above:

a) State whether the following compounds are soluble or insoluble. Sodium carbonate, silver bromide, lead nitrate, copper sulfate, lithium oxide, aluminium sulfate, magnesium hydroxide, silver iodide, copper oxide, magnesium nitrate, ammonium phosphate, potassium ethanoate, calcium hydroxide, calcium chloride, barium sulfate, strontium nitrate, copper carbonate, potassium oxide, sodium hydroxide.

b) Identify the compounds which are salts.

The preparation of soluble salts

Consider the four general acid reactions which produce salts. Look carefully at the state symbols of the reactants.

1. metal + acid → salt + hydrogen

   zinc$_{(s)}$ + hydrochloric acid$_{(aq)}$ → zinc chloride$_{(aq)}$ + hydrogen$_{(g)}$

2. metal oxide + acid → salt + water

   copper oxide$_{(s)}$ + sulfuric acid$_{(aq)}$ → copper sulfate$_{(aq)}$ + water$_{(l)}$

3. metal hydroxide + acid → salt + water

   sodium hydroxide$_{(aq)}$ + ethanoic acid$_{(aq)}$ → sodium ethanoate$_{(aq)}$ + water$_{(l)}$

4. metal carbonate + acid → salt + water + carbon dioxide

   magnesium carbonate$_{(s)}$ + nitric acid$_{(aq)}$ → magnesium nitrate$_{(aq)}$ + water$_{(l)}$ + carbon dioxide$_{(g)}$

For examples number 1, 2 and 4 above, a solid is added to an aqueous solution/liquid to produce a salt.

For example number 3 above, two different aqueous solutions/liquids are added together to produce a salt.

Therefore, you only need two practical techniques to prepare salts in the laboratory. Each technique prepares a salt which is not contaminated with excess acid or base.

Technique 1: adding a solid to an aqueous solution/liquid

Excess solid/filtration

Figure 9 Preparation of salt: adding a solid to an aqueous solution/liquid

The reaction is complete when no more of the base will dissolve.

If the reaction produces a gas, the reaction is complete when no more bubbles of gas are released.

1. Place dilute acid into a beaker.
2. Slowly add an excess of the solid base, stirring and/or heating gently if necessary.
3. Filter the mixture.
4. Dispose of the residue, the excess solid base.
5. Keep the filtrate, the solution of the salt in water.

The base is added to excess to ensure all of the acid has reacted. The salt formed will not be contaminated by any remaining acid.

Technique 2: mixing two different aqueous solutions/liquids

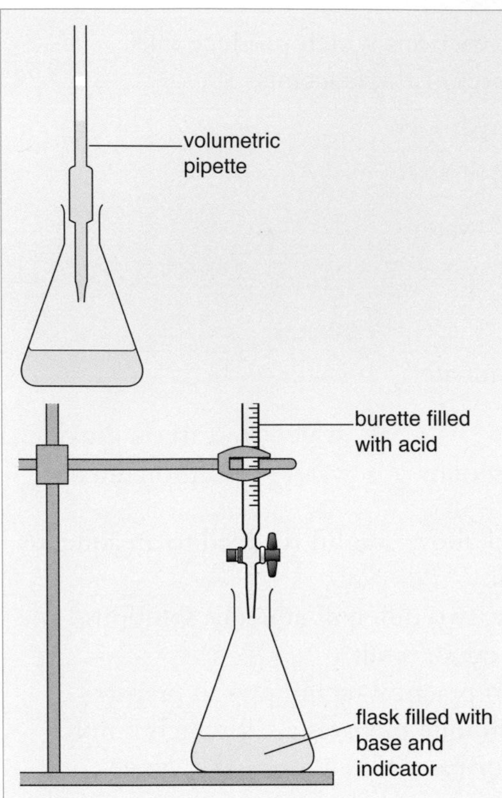 	**1.** Prepare the burette and fill with dilute acid. **2.** Pipette 25 cm^3 of aqueous alkali into a conical flask, using a pipette filler.	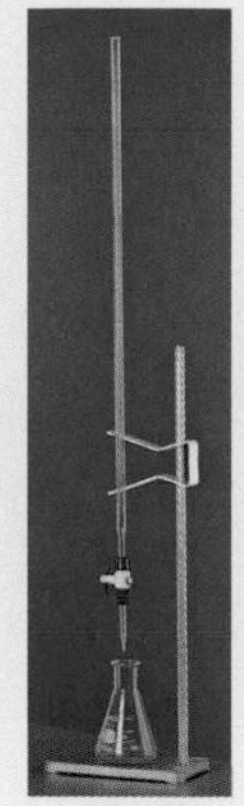
The reaction is complete when the end point is reached.	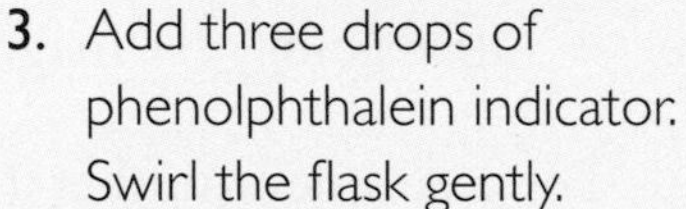 **3.** Add three drops of phenolphthalein indicator. Swirl the flask gently. **4.** Add the acid from the burette, swirling gently to mix the solutions.	The indicator is added to signal the exact point when all of the acid has reacted. 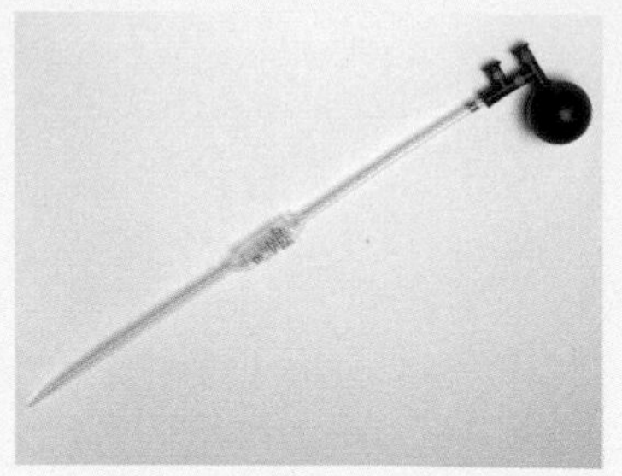
	5. Stop adding the acid at the end point. (At the end point of this titration the indicator will change from pink to colourless.) **6.** Record the volume of acid added.	
Alternatively the indicator may be removed by passing the solution through a cylinder containing charcoal.	**7.** Repeat the titration with fresh samples of aqueous alkali until two concordant results are obtained. **8.** Repeat the titration without the indicator.	(Concordant results are ones which differ by less than 0.1 cm^3.) Add the volume of acid found when carrying out the previous titrations using the indicator.
	The conical flask now contains a solution of the salt in water.	This means the solution of the salt formed in the reaction is not contaminated with the indicator.

Preparation and use of the pipette

* rinse with deionised water
* using a pipette filler rinse with solution
* fill with solution
* hold the pipette vertically with the volume line at eye level
* run out the solution until the bottom of the meniscus is on the line.

Preparation of the burette

* rinse with deionised water
* rinse with the solution
* fill with solution
* allow the solution to run out until the bottom of the meniscus is on the zero line
* ensure the tip is full and there are no air bubbles.

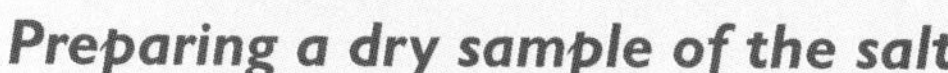

Preparing a dry sample of the salt

Techniques 1 and 2 prepare a solution of the salt in water.

1. Pour the solution of the salt in water into an evaporating dish.
2. Evaporate 2/3 of the liquid slowly using a Bunsen burner.
3. Transfer the remaining liquid to a crystallising dish and leave in a cool place to crystallise.
4. Filter off any remaining liquid, if necessary.
5. Dry the crystals in a low temperature oven or in a desiccator or between two pieces of absorbent paper.

Questions

5 Which technique would you use to prepare the salts produced by the chemical reactions below?
(Hint: use the information given about the solubilities of compounds on page 88.)

a) Copper sulfate from copper oxide and sulfuric acid

b) sodium hydroxide + hydrochloric acid → sodium chloride + water

c) calcium carbonate + hydrochloric acid → calcium chloride + water + carbon dioxide

d) The reaction of sulfuric acid with potassium oxide produces an aqueous solution of potassium sulfate.

▶ Tests for ions

Cation: a positive ion
Anion: a negative ion

A salt contains at least two ions, a positive ion (the cation) and a negative ion (the anion). The name and formula of an unknown salt can be determined using a series of simple chemical tests.

Tests for cations

1 A flame test

* clean a nichrome wire (a nickel-chromium alloy) by dipping it into concentrated hydrochloric acid
* hold the wire in a hot Bunsen flame. Repeat until the wire does not produce any colour in the flame
* dip the clean nichrome wire into the concentrated hydrochloric acid again and dip it into a small amount of the unknown solid. (A small sample of the solid will stick to the wire)
* place the wire in the Bunsen flame
* observe the colour of the flame.

> Nichrome wire will produce a slight orange tinge in a Bunsen flame. You will soon be able to distinguish this from the colour imparted to the flame by the salt.
>
> Dilute hydrochloric acid may be used for safety reasons. However, the colour is not so intense.

Colour of flame	Cation/metal ion/positive ion
yellow (persistent)	sodium ion, Na^+
lilac	potassium ion, K^+
brick red	calcium ion, Ca^{2+}
apple green	barium ion, Ba^{2+}
green/blue	copper ion, Cu^{2+}

> Flame test rods made from a high melting point ceramic material may be used instead of a nichrome wire. These rods are usually for one use only and do not need to be cleaned in the same way as a nichrome wire.

2 Using sodium hydroxide solution

* dissolve a small sample of the solid salt in water
* place approximately 10 cm³ of the solution into a test-tube
* add sodium hydroxide solution drop by drop
* observe the colour of the precipitate if one is produced
* for any white precipitate produced, continue to add sodium hydroxide solution, drop by drop
* observe what happens to the precipitate.

> The precipitates formed are gelatinous precipitates. A gelatinous precipitate has the appearance of a jelly.

Colour of the precipitate produced by the reaction of sodium hydroxide solution with salt solution	Cation/positive ion/metal ion present in the salt	
blue	copper(II) ion, Cu^{2+}	
	$Cu^{2+}_{(aq)} + 2OH^-_{(aq)} \rightarrow Cu(OH)_{2(s)}$	
green	iron(II) ion, Fe^{2+}	
	$Fe^{2+}_{(aq)} + 2OH^-_{(aq)} \rightarrow Fe(OH)_{2(s)}$	
red-brown	iron(III) ion, Fe^{3+}	
	$Fe^{3+}_{(aq)} + 3OH^-_{(aq)} \rightarrow Fe(OH)_{3(s)}$	
white	magnesium ion, Mg^{2+}	
	$Mg^{2+}_{(aq)} + 2OH^-_{(aq)} \rightarrow Mg(OH)_{2(s)}$	
	aluminium ion, Al^{3+} zinc ion, Zn^{2+}	precipitate will re-dissolve in excess sodium hydroxide solution
	$Al^{3+}_{(aq)} + 3OH^-_{(aq)} \rightarrow Al(OH)_{3(s)}$ $Zn^{2+}_{(aq)} + 2OH^-_{(aq)} \rightarrow Zn(OH)_{2(s)}$	

The precipitates formed in these reactions are powdery.

Tests for anions

1 Tests for halide ions

* dissolve a small sample of the solid salt in water
* place approximately 10 cm^3 of the solution into a test-tube
* add four drops of nitric acid
* add silver nitrate solution drop by drop
* observe the colour of the precipitate if one is produced.

Colour of the precipitate produced by the reaction of silver nitrate solution with salt solution	Anion/negative ion present in the salt
white	chloride ion, Cl^-
	$Ag^+_{(aq)} + Cl^-_{(aq)} \rightarrow AgCl_{(s)}$
cream	bromide, Br^-
	$Ag^+_{(aq)} + Br^-_{(aq)} \rightarrow AgBr_{(s)}$
yellow	iodide, I^-
	$Ag^+_{(aq)} + I^-_{(aq)} \rightarrow AgI_{(s)}$

2 Tests for sulfate ions

* dissolve a small sample of the solid salt in water
* place about 10 cm^3 of the solution into a test-tube
* add barium chloride solution drop by drop
* observe the colour of the precipitate if one is produced.

Colour of the precipitate produced by the reaction of barium chloride solution with salt solution	Anion/negative ion present in the salt
white	sulfate ion, SO_4^{2-}
	$Ba^{2+}_{(aq)} + SO_4^{2-}{}_{(aq)} \rightarrow BaSO_{4(s)}$

3 Tests for carbonate ions

* add hydrochloric acid to the solid salt
* collect and test any gas formed with limewater
* if the limewater becomes cloudy/milky the gas evolved is carbon dioxide and the salt is a carbonate.

$$CO_3^{2-}{}_{(aq)} + 2H^+_{(aq)} \rightarrow H_2O_{(l)} + CO_{2(g)}$$

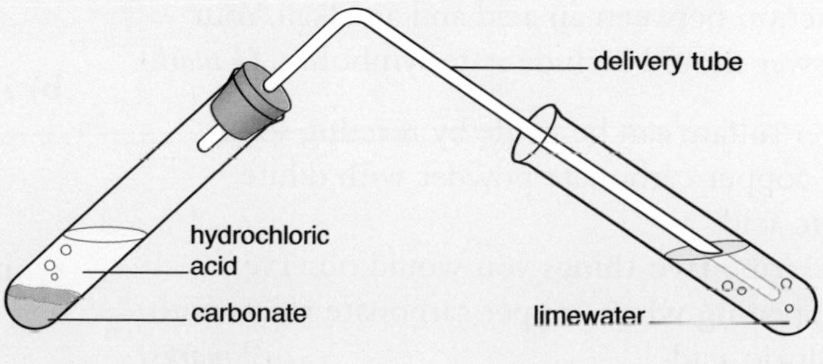

Questions

6 A series of tests were carried out on four unknown salts, A, B, C and D. The observations were recorded in the table below.
Use the observations to deduce the names of the ions in each salt.
Name and write the formula of each salt.

Salt	Observations on the addition of					Flame test
	Water	$NaOH_{(aq)}$	$AgNO_{3(aq)}$ + HNO_3	$BaCl_{2(aq)}$	$HCl_{(aq)}$	
A	dissolves		white powdery precipitate			intense yellow colour remaining in the flame for 1 minute
B	insoluble	green gelatinous precipitate			bubbles of gas evolved, gas turns limewater milky	
C	dissolves	white gelatinous precipitate re-dissolves in excess $NaOH_{(aq)}$		white powdery precipitate		
D	dissolves	blue gelatinous precipitate		white powdery precipitate		

▶ Exam questions

1 Indigestion is often caused by excess acid in the stomach.

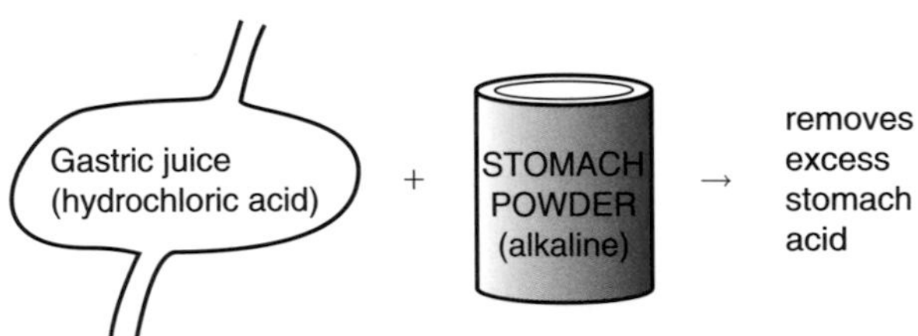

a) What name is given to the reaction which removes acidity? *(1 mark)*

b) Write an ionic equation to represent the reaction between an acid and an alkali. Your answer should include state symbols. *(1 mark)*

2 Copper sulfate can be made by reacting solid green copper carbonate powder with dilute sulfuric acid.

a) Describe **two** things you would observe happening when copper carbonate reacts with sulfuric acid. *(2 marks)*

b) Why can copper sulfate not be prepared by adding dilute sulfuric acid directly to copper? *(1 mark)*

3 Potassium and sodium are alkali metals.

a) How are these metals stored in the school laboratory? *(1 mark)*

b) What type of base is an alkali? *(1 mark)*

4 a) Complete the table below which gives some information about two metal elements. *(4 marks)*

Element	Group	Period	Electronic structure
Magnesium	II		
		4	2,8,8,1

b) i) Beryllium, magnesium and calcium belong to Group II in the Periodic Table. Which of these three metals is the most reactive? *(1 mark)*

ii) Give **two** things you would observe when dilute hydrochloric acid is added to calcium carbonate. *(2 marks)*

iii) Complete the word equation for the reaction of calcium carbonate with dilute hydrochloric acid. *(2 marks)*

calcium carbonate + hydrochloric acid = ____ + ____ + ____

c) Many metal compounds are coloured solids. Others are white. Give the correct colour for each of the four compounds below. Choose from the list of colours.

white green red brown blue black

i) copper(II) carbonate
ii) magnesium oxide
iii) hydrated copper(II) sulfate
iv) anhydrous copper(II) sulfate *(2 marks)*

5 a) Describe **two** things you would observe happening when magnesium reacts with dilute sulfuric acid. *(2 marks)*

b) Write a balanced **symbol equation** to show how magnesium reacts with dilute sulfuric acid. *(2 marks)*

c) Indigestion is caused when there is too much hydrochloric acid in the stomach. It can be neutralised by taking indigestion tablets which contain a base such as magnesium carbonate.

i) Explain what happens during a neutralisation reaction. *(2 marks)*

ii) Balance the symbol equation between magnesium carbonate and hydrochloric acid. *(1 mark)*

$$MgCO_3 + HCl \rightarrow MgCl_2 + CO_2 + H_2O$$

iii) How could you show that the gas given off in this neutralisation reaction is carbon dioxide? (Note: you will **not** be given credit for answers which involve putting out a flame because this test works for several gases.) *(2 marks)*

6 a) Gunpowder is an explosive material which contains the salt potassium nitrate. In the 15th and 16th centuries potassium nitrate was obtained from urine. Nowadays potassium nitrate can be manufactured by neutralisation.

i) What do you understand by the term **salt**? *(2 marks)*

ii) Write the formula for potassium nitrate. *(1 mark)*

iii) Name two compounds which would react together to form potassium nitrate. *(2 marks)*

b) Copper(II) chloride is a soluble salt which may be prepared by adding excess copper(II) carbonate to hydrochloric acid.

i) What would you observe when solid copper(II) carbonate is added to dilute hydrochloric acid? *(3 marks)*

ii) Write a balanced symbol equation for the reaction of copper(II) carbonate with hydrochloric acid? *(3 marks)*

iii) How would you remove the excess copper(II) carbonate from the solution of the salt? *(1 mark)*

iv) Hydrated copper(II) chloride contains 2 moles of water of crystallisation. Write the formula of hydrated copper(II) chloride. *(1 mark)*

c) i) A pure solution of the copper(II) chloride was tested as shown in the diagram below. Complete the boxes to state what you would observe when the two tests are carried out. *(3 marks)*

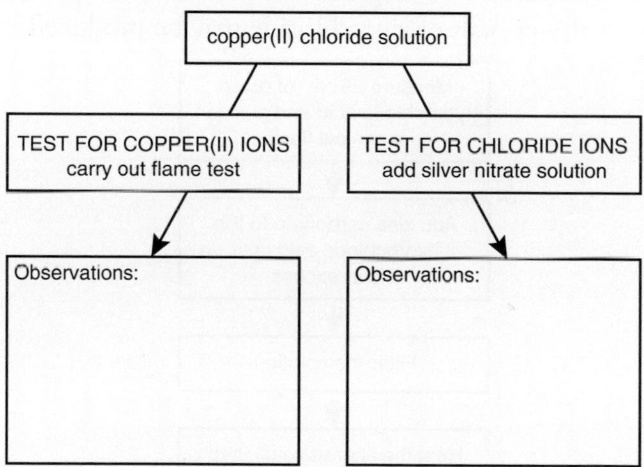

ii) Describe how you would carry out a flame test. **Quality of written communication will be assessed in this question.** *(6 marks)*

d) A large sample of permanent hard water was heated until all the water was evaporated. A white solid remained. This **white solid** was left on a watch glass for a few days and it changed to a **colourless liquid**.
A small sample of the colourless liquid was tested with silver nitrate solution and a white precipitate was observed.

A flame test was carried out on a small sample of the colourless liquid and a brick-red flame colour was observed.

i) Explain why the **white solid** changed to a **colourless liquid** over a few days. *(3 marks)*

ii) What is the name of the white precipitate formed when silver nitrate solution was added. *(1 mark)*

iii) Using the result of the flame test, write the formula of the metal ion which is present in the **colourless liquid**. *(1 mark)*

iv) Name the **white solid**. *(1 mark)*

7 a) Hydrochloric acid reacts with zinc hydroxide and potassium hydroxide. These reactions produce salts. Zinc hydroxide is a base. Potassium hydroxide is an alkali.

i) Name **one other** base. *(1 mark)*

ii) What is meant by the term alkali? *(1 mark)*

b) The reaction between zinc carbonate and hydrochloric acid produces the salt zinc chloride. The diagram below details how pure, dry crystals of zinc chloride may be produced.

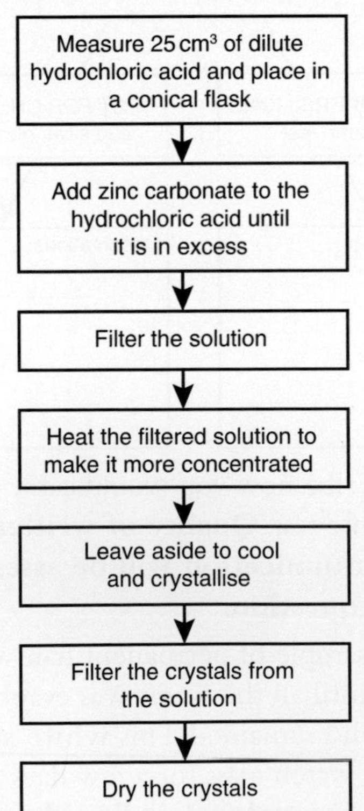

i) What piece of apparatus would you use to measure 25 cm^3 of hydrochloric acid? *(1 mark)*

ii) Explain why the zinc carbonate is added until it is in excess. *(1 mark)*

iii) Give **one** way in which you would know the zinc carbonate is in excess. *(1 mark)*

iv) What is the **general** name given to the solid trapped by the filter paper? *(1 mark)*

v) What is the general name given to the filtered solution? *(1 mark)*

vi) Explain why the crystals form as the solution is cooled. *(2 marks)*

vii) Give **two** methods of drying the crystals. *(2 marks)*

c) Zinc chloride consists of zinc ions and chloride ions. The table below describes a chemical test for zinc ions.

	Zinc ions
Test	add sodium hydroxide solution to a solution of zinc chloride
Observations	

i) Complete the table giving the observations for the test for zinc ions. *(2 marks)*

ii) Write a balanced ionic equation for the reaction between the zinc ions in zinc chloride and the hydroxide ions in sodium hydroxide. *(3 marks)*

8 Potassium sulfate is a white crystalline solid used in the manufacture of glass and as a fertiliser.

a) Describe in detail how you would prepare a pure, dry sample of potassium sulfate from potassium hydroxide and sulfuric acid solutions. Your answer should include the following: *(10 marks)*

- apparatus used
- suitable volumes of solutions
- indicator used and colour change observed
- method of drying the crystals.

b) Write a balanced symbol equation for the reaction between potassium hydroxide and sulfuric acid. *(3 marks)*

c) Name another **compound** that would react safely with sulfuric acid to produce potassium sulfate. *(1 mark)*

d) Write a balanced ionic equation for a neutralisation reaction. **Include state symbols.** *(3 marks)*

7 Solubility

Water is a simple covalent molecule, consisting of two atoms of hydrogen and one atom of oxygen. It is described by the formula H_2O. However, even though the molecule contains only three atoms it is one of the most important substances on Earth.

Water makes up almost 70% of the mass of the human body. The human brain is 95% water. Blood contains 82% water and human lungs consist of 90% water. A drop of only 1 or 2% in the volume of water in your body can trigger signs of dehydration: fuzzy short-term memory, small amounts of dark coloured urine, flushed face and lack of energy.

Figure 1 Water is essential for a healthy body

O—H
H
H_2O

Figure 2 Molecule of water

Much of the Earth is covered in water. About 70% of the Earth's surface is covered in water but water also exists in the air as water vapour and in the ground as ground water.

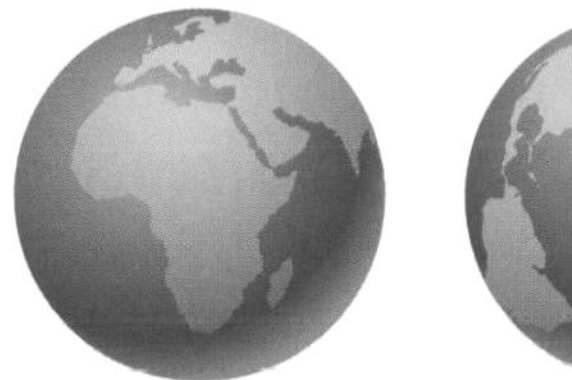

Figure 3 Much of the Earth's surface is covered in water

► The physical properties of water

Colour	State at room temperature and pressure	Melting point	Boiling point
colourless	liquid	0 °C	100 °C

Figure 4 shows the changes of state of water in several different ways.

When ice (solid water) is heated the molecules of water gain energy and move further apart to form a liquid (water). This change of state is called melting.

When water is heated the molecules gain energy and move further apart to form a gas (steam). This change of state is called boiling. Water boils when it reaches 100 °C.

When steam is cooled the molecules lose energy and become closer together to form water. This change of state is called condensation.

When water is cooled the molecules lose energy and become closer together and form a regular pattern. This change of state is called freezing. Water freezes at 0 °C.

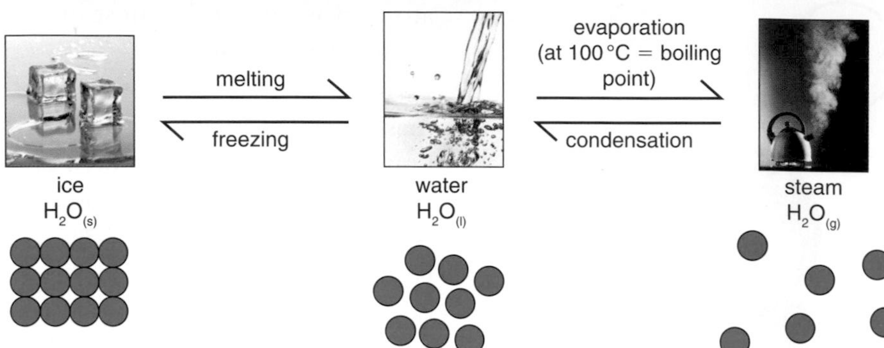

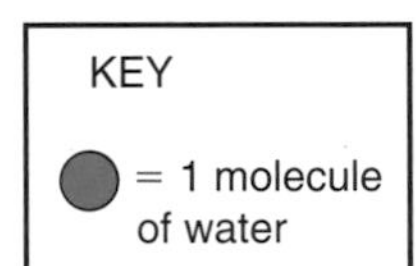

Figure 4 The changes of state of water

► Testing for water

Chemical tests for water

Anhydrous copper(II) sulfate

Figure 5 Anhydrous copper(II) sulfate test

> White copper(II) sulfate turns blue when water is added.

A few drops of the unknown liquid are added to white anhydrous copper(II) sulfate. If the colour of the white copper(II) sulfate changes to blue the liquid is water.

anhydrous copper(II) sulfate + water → copper(II) sulfate solution

$CuSO_4$	$+ H_2O \rightarrow$	$CuSO_{4(aq)}$
white		blue

Cobalt chloride paper

Dip cobalt chloride paper into the unknown colourless liquid. If the cobalt chloride paper changes colour from blue to pink the liquid is water.

anhydrous cobalt chloride + water → cobalt chloride solution

$CoCl_4$	$+ H_2O \rightarrow$	$CoCl_{4(aq)}$
blue		pink

Physical tests for water

1. Pure water will boil at 100 °C at 1 atmosphere pressure.
2. Pure water will freeze at 0 °C at 1 atmosphere pressure.

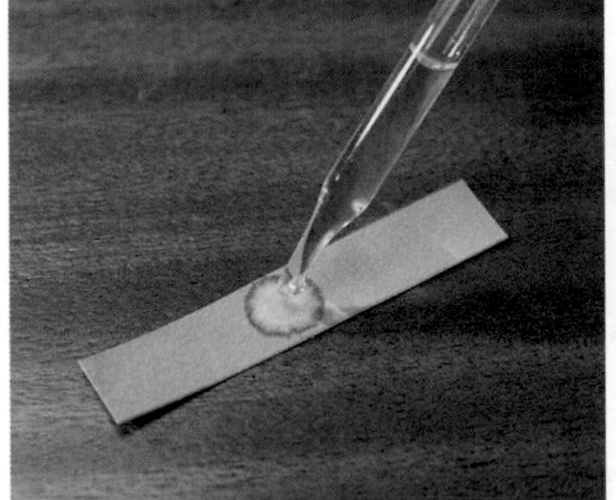

Figure 6 Cobalt chloride paper

Solubility

Pure water cannot be found naturally as water is an extremely good solvent. This is advantageous whenever we wash and whenever we eat, as all living things rely on water to dissolve their food and oxygen. However, the ability of water to dissolve substances can be a major disadvantage. Harmful waste from farms and factories may get dissolved in rivers, lakes and streams making them polluted. (A pollutant is a substance which causes harm to any living organism.)

Some substances will dissolve in water better than others. The table below shows the solubility of some solids and gases at two different temperatures.

Solvent: a substance that does the dissolving

Solute: a substance that is dissolved

Solution: a substance dissolved in a solvent; a mixture of a solute and a solvent

Saturated: a solution which cannot dissolve any more solute

Substance	State at room temperature and pressure	Solubility in 100 g of water at	
		25 °C	40 °C
copper(II) sulfate	solid	32	45
potassium chlorate	solid	7.3	13.9
potassium chloride	solid	34.2	40.1
oxygen	gas	0.0091	0.0065
carbon dioxide	gas	0.01782	0.0973
methane	gas	0.0023	0.0016

The table illustrates the pattern of solubility for solids and gases.

The solubility of solids *increases* with increase in temperature.

The solubility of gases *decreases* with increase in temperature.

This explains the danger of the thermal pollution of water resources to the aquatic life the resource supports.

Some industrial processes use water as a coolant. The cool water taken into the industrial plant is heated and disposed of by allowing it to drain into rivers and lakes. The warm water increases the temperature of the river or lake. This is known as **thermal pollution**. The mass of oxygen dissolved in the water will decrease as the temperature of the water increases. Thus the mass of oxygen available for aquatic life will decrease. Eventually, the water resource will not have sufficient oxygen to sustain life.

Increasing the temperature of a body of water is one way of decreasing the mass of oxygen available for aquatic life; the presence of certain dissolved solids in the water is another.

Nitrates contain the very soluble NO_3^- ion. They are used in artificial fertilisers to promote growth of plants. Overuse or misuse of fertilisers can result in nitrate ions being leached from the soil into rivers and lakes. Phosphates contain the very soluble PO_4^{3-} ion. They are used in fertilisers and also in detergents to increase the cleaning action. Washing is a physical process and the phosphates are chemically unchanged when they are disposed of through the sewage system. Most of the phosphates are biodegradable; they decompose by the action of living organisms on them, but some end up in rivers and lakes.

The presence of nitrates and phosphates in water encourages the growth of tiny green water plants called algae. The algae cover the surface of the water, blocking the light from reaching the plants in the

The River Lagan flows over 70 km from the Mourne Mountains in County Down to Stranmillis Weir in Belfast. At the weir oxygen is bubbled into the water to increase the mass of dissolved oxygen in the water available to support aquatic life.

water. Without light the plants die. The dead plants are decomposed by bacteria which use oxygen. This decreases the mass of dissolved oxygen available for the fish. Soon all living organisms in the water die from oxygen starvation. This premature aging of a water source is known as **eutrophication**.

Eutrophication

* nitrates and phosphates enter the water system
* encourage growth of algae
* algae cover water surface blocking light
* plants die due to lack of light
* dead organic matter is decomposed by bacteria which use oxygen
* reduces the dissolved oxygen available for fish which eventually die of oxygen starvation.

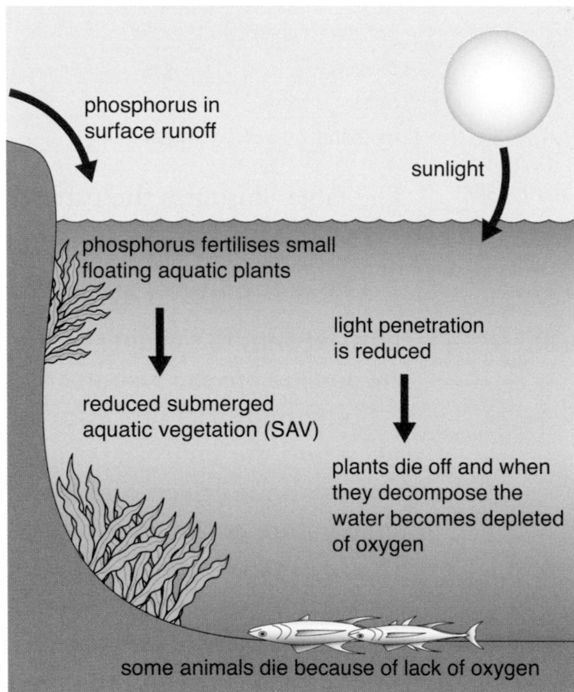

Figure 7

Measuring solubility

Solubility is:
The maximum mass of a solute that will dissolve in 100 g of a solvent at a given temperature.

Solubility of a solid is affected by a number of conditions. Solids become more soluble as the temperature increases. Also a large volume of water can dissolve more solid than a small volume of water. Therefore a standard measurement of solubility is set. When chemists speak of the solubility of a substance in water they are speaking of a standard volume of water and are quoting a specific temperature.

The solubility of a substance is defined as:

The maximum mass of a solute that will dissolve in 100 g of a solvent at a given temperature.

7.2 g of sodium chloride will dissolve in and saturate 20 cm^3 of water at 25 °C.

To find the solubility of sodium chloride, calculate how much will dissolve in 100 g of water at the temperature quoted. (Remember: 1 cm^3 H_2O = 1 g)

* 7.2 g dissolves in 20 cm^3 (or 20 g)
* How many grams (? g) dissolves in 20 × 5 = 100 g?
* 7.2 × 5 = 36 g

Therefore the solubility of sodium chloride in water at 25 °C is 36 g/100 g of water.

Constructing a solubility curve

A solubility curve is a graph which illustrates the solubility of a substance in a solvent over a range of different temperatures. The graphs below show several solubility curves.

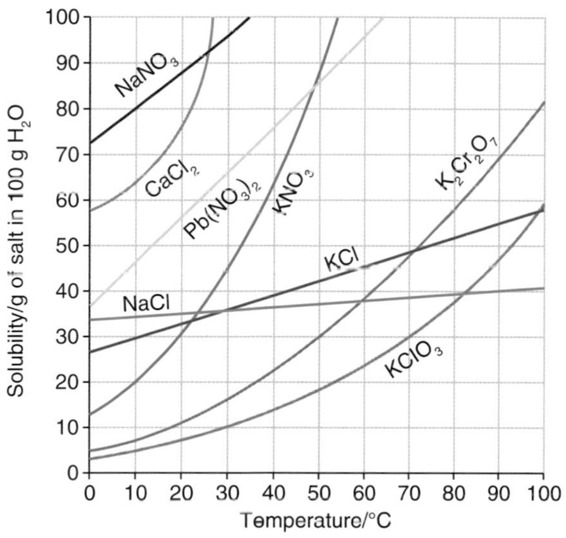

Figure 8 The solubility curves of several different solids in water illustrating the solubility of a solid increases as the temperature increases

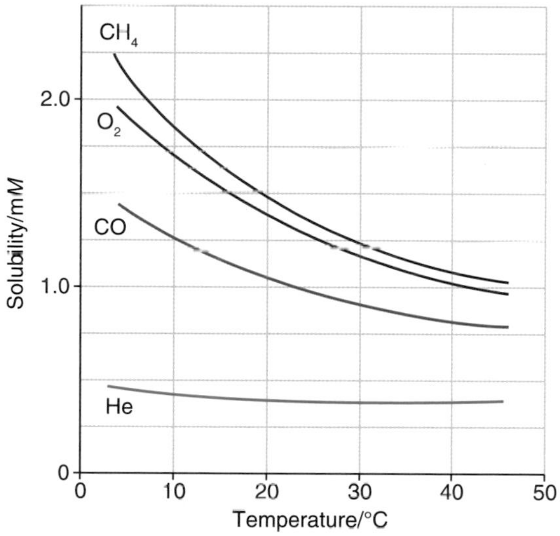

Figure 9 The solubility curves for several gases in water illustrating the solubility of a gas in water decreases as the temperature increases

It seems easy to work out the solubility of a solid by adding it to a measured volume of water at a specific temperature until the solution is saturated. In practice, it is not quite so easy as it is difficult to ensure the water stays at a very steady temperature and it can be difficult to accurately observe the actual point of saturation. Instead the following method is used.

An accurately measured mass of solid is dissolved in a known volume of water by heating the water. The solution is allowed to cool. As the water cools it is able to hold less of the solute and the excess solute begins to crystallise. The temperature of the solution is recorded as soon as the first crystals are observed.

Potassium chlorate works well as the solute in this experiment as the crystals reflect light and sparkle as they appear.

1. Accurately weigh 4.0 g of potassium chlorate and place it into a boiling tube.
2. Add 10 cm^3 of water from a pipette.

3. Set the boiling tube into a clamp and retort stand as shown in the diagram.

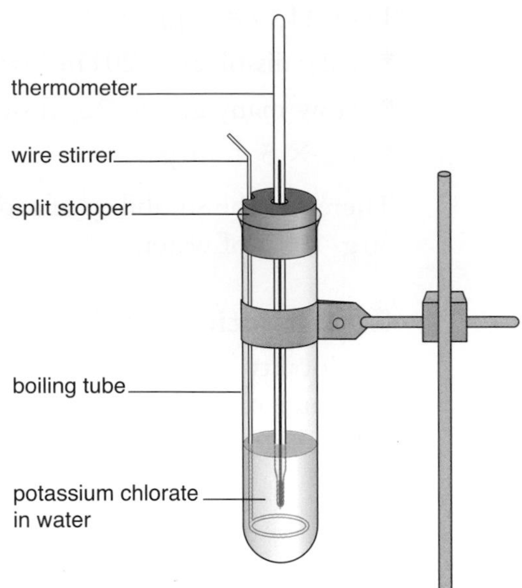

Figure 10

4. Place a thermometer and a wire stirrer into the boiling tube.
5. Lower into a water bath and heat gently until the salt has dissolved.

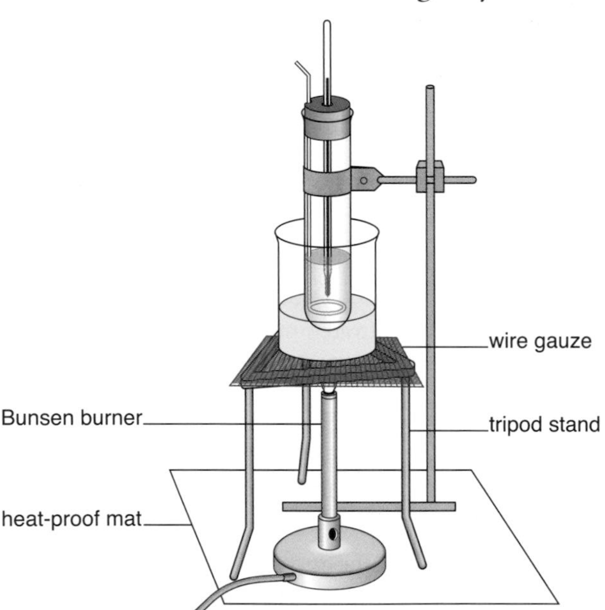

Figure 11

6. Remove from the water bath and allow to cool.
7. Record the temperature at the point when the first crystals appear.
8. Add 2.5 cm^3 of water to the boiling tube using a pipette.
9. Repeat steps **5–8** until the boiling tube holds 20 cm^3 of water.
10. Calculate the solubility of the potassium chlorate at each recorded temperature using the formula

$$\text{solubility (g/100 g } H_2O) = \frac{\text{mass of solid} \times 100}{\text{mass of water}}$$

1 cm^3 of H_2O = 1 g

Reading solubility curves

The solubility curve of potassium chlorate is shown below.

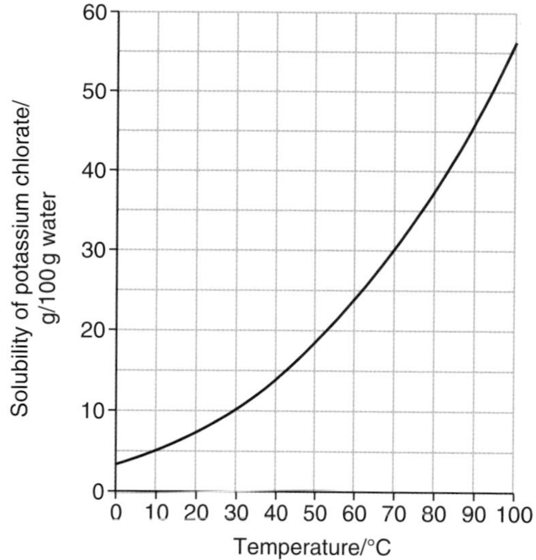

Figure 12 Solubility curve of potassium chlorate

1. From the graph calculate the solubility of potassium chlorate in 50 g H_2O at 30 °C.

The title on the *y*-axis of the graph clearly shows that the solubility curve displays the solubility in g/100 g H_2O.

Solubility in g/**100 g** H_2O at 30 °C = 10

Therefore solubility in g/**50 g** H_2O = 10/2 = 5.0 g

2. From the graph calculate how much salt will crystallise out of 25 cm^3 of a saturated solution when it is cooled from 90 °C to 70 °C.

Solubility in g/**100 g** H_2O at 90 °C = 46

Solubility in g/**100 g** H_2O at 70 °C = 30

Mass of crystals formed on cooling **100 g** of solution
= 46 − 30 = 16 g

Mass of crystals formed on cooling **25 cm^3** of solution
= 16 = 4.0 g

3. From the graph calculate how much salt will crystallise out of 100 cm^3 of a solution containing 15 g of potassium chlorate at 60 °C as it is cooled to room temperature (20 °C).

The first thing to remember here is that the solution at 60 °C is not saturated.

Mass in g/100 g H_2O at 60 °C = 15

Solubility in g/100 g H_2O at 20 °C = 7.5

Mass of crystals formed on cooling 100 g of solution
= 15 − 7.5 = 7.5 g

▶ Exam questions

1 The graph shows solubility curves for three substances, KBr, NH_4Cl and NaCl.

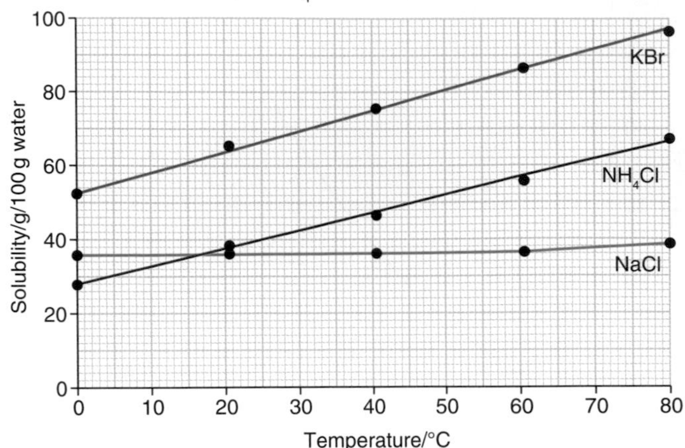

a) Which substance has the lowest solubility at 10 °C? *(1 mark)*

b) What is the solubility of NH_4Cl at 65 °C? *(1 mark)*

c) If a saturated solution of NH_4Cl in 100 g water at 65 °C is cooled to 25 °C, how many grams of solid will be precipitated? *(1 mark)*

d) Which of the saturated solutions shown would **least readily** form crystals when cooled from 60 °C? *(1 mark)*

2 a) The diagram below shows the apparatus used in the laboratory to find the solubility of potassium chlorate.

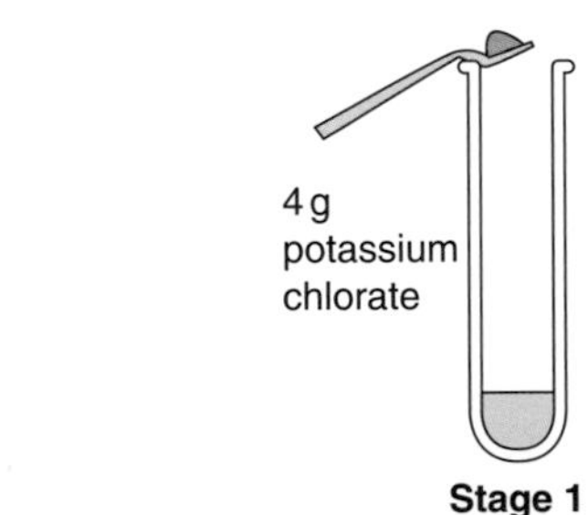

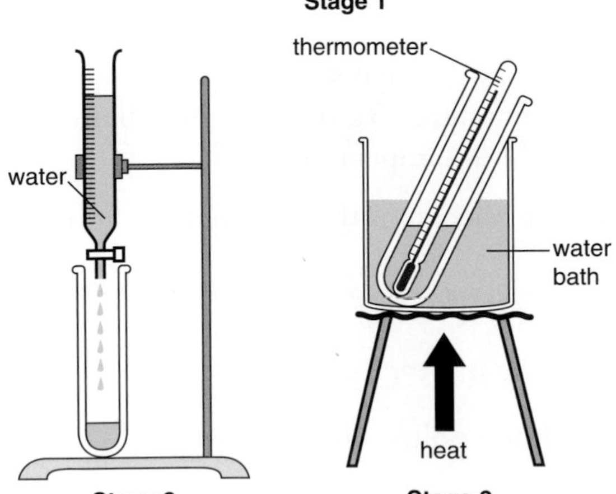

Stage 1: Four grams of potassium chlorate were placed in a boiling tube.

Stage 2: 10 cm^3 of water was added.

Stage 3: The boiling tube was placed in a beaker of hot water and heated until all the potassium chlorate had dissolved.

Four grams of potassium chlorate were weighed and placed in a boiling tube to which 10 cm^3 of water was added as shown in the diagram. The tube was immersed in a beaker of hot water and heated until all the potassium chlorate had dissolved.

Describe how you would continue this experiment, to obtain a series of measurements to plot a solubility curve for potassium chlorate. *(5 marks)*

b) 10 cm^3 (= 10 g) of water were placed in a boiling tube containing a thermometer. 4.0 g of solid potassium chloride were added. The boiling tube was heated in a water bath until the solid dissolved completely. When cooled slowly, crystals appeared in the solution at 40 °C.

i) Calculate the solubility of potassium chloride at 40 °C. *(1 mark)*

ii) Explain what is meant by the term solubility. *(4 marks)*

c) Some substances dissolve very well in water and are said to have a high solubility. Define the term **solubility**. *(4 marks)*

d) The solubility curves for three potassium salts are shown on the graph on the following page. Study the solubility curves and answer the following questions.

i) Which potassium salt is the least soluble at 40 °C? *(1 mark)*

ii) What is the minimum mass of water needed to dissolve 180 g of potassium bromide at 80 °C? *(2 marks)*

iii) When 1 kg of water saturated with potassium chloride is cooled from 80 °C to 50 °C, what mass of solid crystallises out of the solution? *(4 marks)*

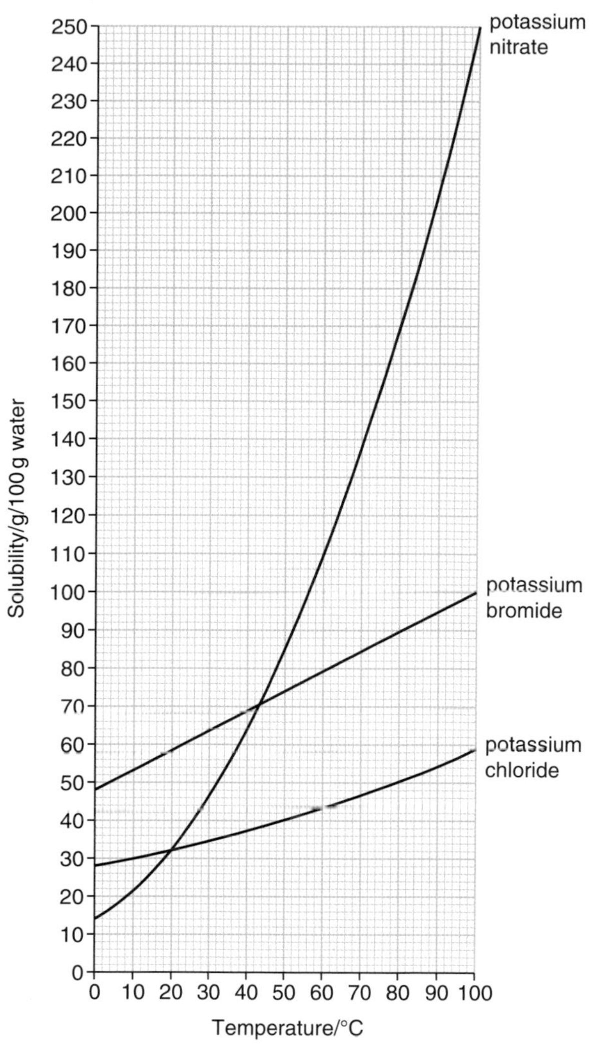

3 When a fish is caught in a river and put into a jar of water, it survives for a long time if the jar is kept cool. However, if the water in the jar is allowed to warm up, the fish soon dies. Explain why this happens. **Quality of written communication will be assessed in this question.** *(5 marks)*

4 a) Sugar is soluble in water. It has a high **solubility**.

i) What is meant by the term **solubility**? *(4 marks)*

ii) How does the solubility of sugar vary as the temperature of the water increases? *(1 mark)*

b) Potassium chloride and potassium nitrate are both soluble in water. The solubilities of the two salts at specific temperatures are given in the following table.

Temperature/°C	0	10	20	30	40	50	60
Solubility of potassium chloride/ g/100 g water	13	21	32	46	63	83	106
Solubility of potassium nitrate/ g/100 g water	28	30.5	33	36	39	42	45

The solubility curve for potassium nitrate has been plotted on the graph below.

i) Using this graph, find the solubility of potassium nitrate at 45 °C. *(1 mark)*

ii) Using your graph, find the temperature at which 19 g of potassium nitrate saturates 50 g of water. *(2 marks)*

iii) Draw a copy of the graph and plot the solubility curve for potassium chloride. *(3 marks)*

iv) At what temperature do the two salts have the same solubility? *(1 mark)*

v) What mass of potassium chloride will crystallise from a saturated solution containing 1000 g of water, if the solution is cooled from 58 °C to 24 °C? *(4 marks)*

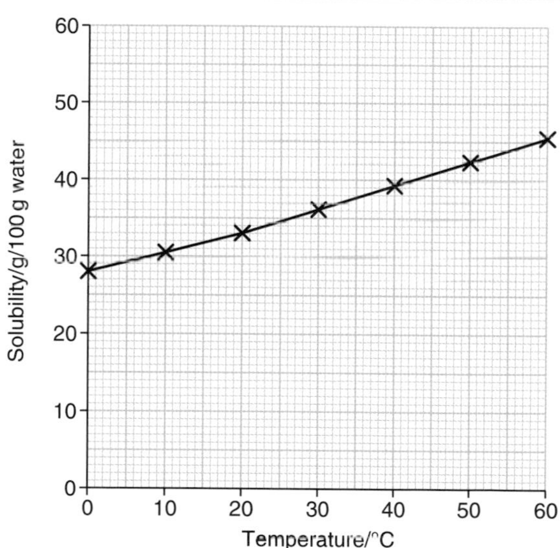

5 Some substances dissolve very well in water and are said to have high solubility.

a) Explain what is meant by the term solubility. *(4 marks)*

b) To determine the solubility of potassium chloride in water, 20 g of potassium chloride were placed in a beaker.
40 cm^3 of water were added to the beaker and warmed until all the potassium chloride had dissolved.

The beaker was then allowed to cool. The temperature at which crystals first appeared was recorded.

The experiment was repeated five more times adding an extra 5 cm^3 of water each time.

The results obtained are shown in the table below

Mass of potassium chloride/g	Volume of water/cm^3	Temperature at which crystals first appear/°C	Solubility/ g/100 g water
20	40	80	50.0
20	45	59	44.4
20	50	41	
20	55	27	36.4
20	60	15	33.3
20	65	5	30.8

i) Calculate the solubility of potassium chloride at 41 °C. *(1 mark)*

ii) Use the results table to plot a solubility curve for potassium chloride. *(4 marks)*

iii) How does the solubility of potassium chloride vary with increasing temperature? *(1 mark)*

iv) Using your graph, determine the solubility of potassium chloride at 10 °C. *(1 mark)*

v) If a saturated solution of potassium chloride containing 50 g of water is cooled from 80 °C to 5 °C, what mass of potassium chloride will crystallise out of solution? *(3 marks)*

c) The solution of potassium chloride was tested for the presence of chloride ions.

Name a suitable reagent that could be used to test for the presence of chloride ions and state the observations for a positive test. *(3 marks)*

d) Many substances, such as sodium hydroxide and anhydrous calcium chloride, interact with moist air.

i) Describe the observations made when some pellets of sodium hydroxide are left on a watch glass in a laboratory for several days. *(3 marks)*

ii) Explain what you understand by the term anhydrous. *(2 marks)*

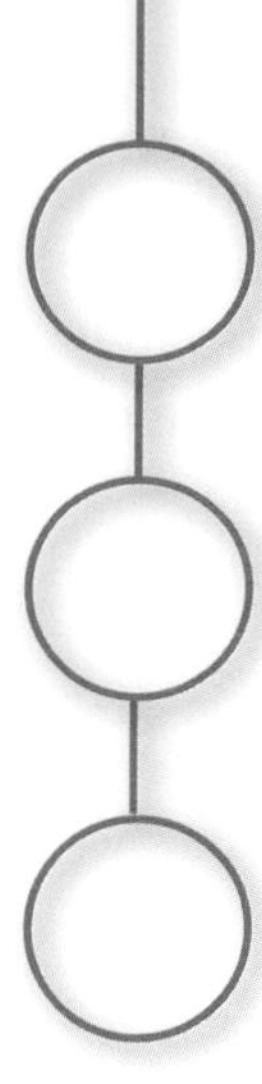

Quantitative Chemistry 1

▶ Relative atomic mass

Chemists are interested in every aspect of a chemical reaction. Their interest extends to knowing how the products are formed from the reactants, how fast or slow the reaction happens (the rate of the reaction, Chapter 13, page 164), the ratio in which the reactants react together and the ratio of reactants to products. Chemists need to know the mass of each reactant that combines to form a certain mass of product or the mass or volume of product which can potentially be formed from a certain amount (volume or mass) of reactants. In short, chemists like to know 'how much?'.

The starting point for these calculations is finding a way to either count atoms or weigh atoms. However, atoms are infinitesimally small, smaller than anything you can imagine. These pictures of groups of atoms (Figure 1) are three-dimensional computer generated pictures of areas of electrical charge. Atoms cannot be photographed using light in the normal way. Each atom of hydrogen, which is the smallest atom known, has a mass of 1.007825×10^{-27} kg; in other words 0.000000000000000000000000001007825 kg. 5 million atoms of hydrogen can fit in a line the diameter of this full stop. Numbers so small and so large can be difficult to deal with.

Figure 1 Atoms

Chemists have devised a system which does not deal in actual masses of atoms but relative masses, the mass of one atom relative to or compared to another. Initially, hydrogen was assigned a mass of 1 as it is the smallest atom and the masses of other atoms were compared to it. For example, an atom of oxygen was 16 times heavier than hydrogen therefore oxygen was said to have a relative atomic mass of 16. Relative atomic masses do not have units.

As more was learned about the nature of atoms and the existence of isotopes it was decided that hydrogen was not a suitable standard for comparison. (See isotopes, Chapter 1, page 7.) Today, chemists use the carbon-12 (^{12}C) isotope of the element carbon as the standard to which the mass of all of the other known elements are compared.

The relative isotopic mass is the easier of the two definitions to understand. Simply, the mass of one atom of an element is compared to the mass of one atom of carbon-12.

Relative atomic mass The weighted mean mass of a mole of the element compared to 1/12 of a mole of carbon-12

Relative isotopic mass The mass of an atom/isotope of an element compared to 1/12 of a carbon-12 atom

However, since most elements exist as isotopes, there is a slight difference in the atoms of the element. All of the atoms have the same number of protons but different numbers of neutrons. Chemists rarely use elements in a single isotopic form so an average mass is calculated.

More mathematically correct, a weighted mean mass is calculated. Chlorine is a good example of this.

Chlorine exists as two different isotopes.

Isotope one: ^{35}Cl, relative isotopic mass 35

Isotope two: ^{37}Cl, relative isotopic mass 37

The average mass of one ^{35}Cl and one ^{37}Cl is $\frac{35 + 37}{2} = 36$

However, this does not take into consideration the fact that ^{35}Cl is a more common isotope than ^{37}Cl. In a naturally occurring sample of chlorine there will be about 3/4 ^{35}Cl and 1/4 ^{37}Cl.

In every 100 atoms of chlorine, 75 are ^{35}Cl and 25 are ^{37}Cl

The weighted mean is therefore $\frac{(75 \times 35) + (25 \times 37)}{100} = 35.5$

The relative atomic mass of chlorine is 35.5.

Using relative atomic mass to calculate relative formula mass (RFM)

The relative formula mass (RFM) is sometimes called relative molecular mass (RMM) if the substance is a molecule. For example the relative molecular mass of carbon dioxide, $CO_2 = 12 + 16 + 16 = 44$.

The relative atomic mass of an element is shown in the Periodic Table. In the Periodic Table in Appendix 1 of this book, the relative atomic mass of the element is the number written above each symbol. Adding the relative atomic masses in the correct way will produce the relative formula masses. The relative formula masses of several compounds are worked out in the table below.

Name of element or compound	Formula	Relative formula mass
oxygen gas	O_2	16 + 16 = 32
potassium chloride	KCl	39 + 35.5 = 74.5
sodium oxide	Na_2O	(23 × 2) + 16 = 62
calcium fluoride	CaF_2	40 + (19 × 2) = 78
aluminium oxide	Al_2O_3	(27 × 2) + (16 × 3) = 54 + 48 = 102
calcium carbonate	$CaCO_3$	40 + 12 + (16 × 3) = 52 + 48 = 100
copper hydroxide	$Cu(OH)_2$	64 + (2 × (16 + 1)) = 64 + (2 × 17) = 98
sodium sulfate	Na_2SO_4	(23 × 2) + 32 + (16 × 4) = 46 + 32 + 64 = 142
aluminium sulfate	$Al_2(SO_4)_3$	(27 × 2) + (3 × (32 + (16 × 4))) = 54 + (3 × (32 + 64)) = 54 + (3 × 96) = 342

Questions

Now try these for yourself.

1 Calculate the relative formula mass (RFM) of the following elements and compounds.

a) fluorine gas F_2

b) sodium chloride NaCl

c) lithium oxide Li_2O

d) magnesium bromide $MgBr_2$

e) iron(III) oxide Fe_2O_3

f) copper(II) carbonate $CuCO_3$

g) aluminium hydroxide $Al(OH)_3$

h) potassium carbonate K_2CO_3

i) aluminium carbonate $Al_2(CO_3)_3$

j) ethanoic acid CH_3COOH

Percentage of an element in a compound

The percentage of an element in a compound is calculated as follows:

$$\%\text{ of an element in a compound} = \frac{\text{mass of element in one mole of the compound}}{\text{mass of one mole of the compound}} \times 100$$

Calculate the percentage by mass of nitrogen in ammonia (NH_3).

$$\%\text{ of N in } NH_3 = \frac{14}{17} \times 100 = 82.4\%$$

Questions

2 Try these examples.

a) Calculate the percentage of calcium in calcium carbonate, $CaCO_3$.

b) Iron forms two common oxides, FeO and Fe_2O_3. Which oxide contains the greater percentage of iron?

c) Ammonium nitrate, NH_4NO_3, is used as a fertiliser due to the high usable nitrogen content. Calculate the percentage of nitrogen in ammonium nitrate. (Hint: Remember the element N appears in both the ions in this salt. **N**H_4**N**O_3.)

▶ The mole concept

There is an unusual connection between the relative formula mass of a substance in grams and the number of particles of that substance. When the number of grams equal to the relative formula mass of any substance is weighed out, it always contains the same number of particles, no matter what the substance.

100 g of calcium carbonate ($CaCO_3$ RFM = 100) contains the same number of particles as 32 g of oxygen (O_2 RFM/RMM = 32)

The relative formula mass of a substance in grams is known as a **mole** of the substance.

Students of chemistry sometimes treat the concept of the mole as something quite mysterious. It is really not so.

There are always **2** socks in a **pair**.

There are always **12** eggs in a **dozen**.

There are always **500** sheets of paper in a **ream**.

There are always $\mathbf{6.02 \times 10^{23}}$ particles in a **mole** of a substance.

Pair, dozen, ream and mole are only some of the words in the English language which describe specific numbers; score meaning 20 and gross meaning 144 are two other examples. When you need a pair of anything you count out two of them, and when you need a dozen of anything you count out 12 of them. It is not quite so easy, however, to count out 500 sheets of paper or 6.02×10^{23} particles of a substance.

Chemists, like paper manufacturers, resort to weighing out the substance.

What mass of sodium chloride would you weigh out to have 1 mole of sodium chloride?

The relative formula mass of a substance in grams is known as a **mole** of the substance. To obtain a mole of sodium chloride, simply work out the relative formula mass and weigh out that number of grams of sodium chloride.

The RFM of NaCl = 58.5, therefore 1 mole of NaCl = 58.5 g

Questions

3 How many grams of NaCl in 0.5 moles?

4 How many grams of NaCl in 2.31 moles?

5 What is the mass of 1.68 moles of NaCl?

6 How many moles of NaCl in 117 g of NaCl?

7 How many moles of NaCl in 0.125 g of NaCl?

Question 7 may have proved a little more tricky than Questions 3–6. The following formula shows the simple relationship between the mass in g, the relative formula mass (RFM) and the number of moles:

$$\text{Number of moles} = \frac{\text{mass (g)}}{\text{RFM}}$$

Use the mathematical formula above to answer Question 7.

$$\begin{aligned}\text{Number of moles} &= \frac{\text{mass (g)}}{\text{RFM}}\\ &= \frac{0.125}{58.5}\\ &= 2.136 \times 10^{-3}\text{ moles}\end{aligned}$$

This mathematical relationship can be used to calculate the mass or the RFM also.

The answers are shown in two different ways. Some students prefer to change the subject of the formula or to learn three different mathematical formulae or indeed to use the triangle method. Some students prefer to learn one mathematical formula and to immediately substitute the values given in the question and then cross multiply. Choose the way which suits you best, and practise lots of questions. Either way you will arrive at the answer.

Example 1

Calculate the mass of 4.25 moles of carbon dioxide, CO_2, RFM = 44.

$$\text{Number of moles} = \frac{\text{mass (g)}}{\text{RFM}} \quad \text{or} \quad \text{mass} = \text{number of moles} \times \text{RFM}$$

$$4.25 = \frac{\text{mass}}{44} \qquad\qquad = 4.25 \times 44$$

$$4.25 \times 44 = 187 \qquad\qquad = 187\text{ g}$$

$$= 187\text{ g}$$

Example 2

2 moles of a substance have a mass of 64 g. What is the relative formula mass of the substance?

$$\text{Number of moles} = \frac{\text{mass (g)}}{\text{RFM}} \quad \text{or} \quad \text{RFM} = \frac{\text{mass (g)}}{\text{number of moles}}$$

$$2 = \frac{64}{\text{RFM}} \qquad\qquad = \frac{64}{2}$$

$$\text{RFM} = \frac{64}{2} \qquad\qquad \text{RFM} = 32$$

$$\text{RFM} = 32$$

▶ The quantitative interpretation of equations

'How Much?' part one

Using this mathematical relationship with a balanced chemical equation is a powerful tool for the chemist. (Balanced chemical equations are explained in Chapter 4.) It enables the chemist to calculate the mass of product produced from a known mass of reactants or the mass of reactants needed to produce a required amount of product.

Calcium carbonate reacts with hydrochloric acid to form calcium chloride, water and carbon dioxide according to the following balanced equation.

$$CaCO_3 + 2HCl \rightarrow CaCl_2 + H_2O + CO_2$$

In Chapter 4, while learning how to balance chemical equations, you concentrated on the number of atoms of each element present. You can now read this balanced equation in terms of moles of each substance.

1 mole of calcium carbonate reacts with 2 moles of hydrochloric acid to produce 1 mole of each of the products.

Nitrogen and hydrogen react together to form ammonia according to the following balanced equation.

$$N_2 + 3H_2 \rightarrow 2NH_3$$

In terms of moles this equation reads: 1 mole of nitrogen reacts with 3 moles of hydrogen to produce 2 moles of ammonia.

Therefore, 1 mole of $CaCl_2$ is formed when 1 mole of $CaCO_3$ is completely reacted with excess HCl, and 2 moles of ammonia are formed when 3 moles of hydrogen completely react with nitrogen. In practice, in industry much larger numbers of moles are used and in the laboratory much smaller numbers of moles are used.

Example 1

Calcium carbonate reacts with hydrochloric acid to form calcium chloride, water and carbon dioxide according to the following balanced equation.

$$CaCO_3 + 2HCl \rightarrow CaCl_2 + H_2O + CO_2$$

Keeping the information for each of the chemicals in the columns helps you keep track of which chemical you are working on. It is useful to work out the number of moles of all of the substances in the equation as often the examiner will ask about another substance in the reaction.

a) Calculate the mass of calcium chloride produced when 25 g of calcium carbonate completely react with excess hydrochloric acid.

Copy out the balanced chemical equation	$CaCO_3$ +	2HCl →	$CaCl_2$ +	H_2O +	CO_2
Write in the ratio	1	2	1	1	1
Write in the information given in the question	25 g		?		
Calculate the number of moles	25/100 = 0.25 moles				
Use the molar ratio to work out the number of moles for all the substances in the equation	0.25 moles	0.5 moles	0.25 moles	0.25 moles	0.25 moles

Relative formula mass of calcium chloride

$CaCl_2 = 40 + 35.5 + 35.5$
$= 111$

Answer the question

Mass = no. of moles × RFM
= 0.25 × 111
= 27.75 g

b) Calculate the mass of hydrochloric acid required to completely react with 25 g of calcium carbonate.
The preparation for this question is already complete. Look back at the working out completed for part a) of the question.

Copy out the balanced chemical equation	$CaCO_3$ +	2HCl →	$CaCl_2$ +	H_2O +	CO_2
Write in the ratio	1	2	1	1	1
Write in the information given in the question	25 g		?		
Calculate the number of moles	25/100 = 0.25 moles				
Use the molar ratio to work out the number of moles for all the substances in the equation	0.25 moles	0.5 moles	0.25 moles	0.25 moles	0.25 moles

Beware! The relative formula mass is the mass of **one** mole of a substance. Some students are apt to calculate twice the RFM because of the number 2 in the balanced chemical equation.

RFM of HCl = 1 + 35.5
= 36.5

$$\text{Number of moles} = \frac{\text{mass (g)}}{\text{RFM}} \quad \text{or} \quad \text{mass} = \text{number of moles} \times \text{RFM}$$

$$0.5 = \frac{\text{mass}}{36.5} \qquad \text{mass} = 0.5 \times 36.5$$

$$\text{mass} = 0.5 \times 36.5 \qquad \text{mass} = 18.25\text{ g}$$

$$\text{mass} = 18.25\text{ g}$$

Example 2

Nitrogen and hydrogen react together to form ammonia according to the following balanced equation.

$$N_2 + 3H_2 \rightarrow 2NH_3$$

a) Calculate the mass of nitrogen needed to completely react with 150 g of hydrogen.

b) What is the mass of ammonia formed when 150 g of hydrogen are completely reacted with nitrogen?

Answer:

Copy out the balanced chemical equation	N_2 +	$3H_2$ →	$2NH_3$
Write in the ratio	1	3	2
Write in the information given in the question		150 g	
Calculate the number of moles		150/2 = 75 moles	
Use the molar ratio to work out the number of moles for all the substances in the equation	25 moles	75 moles	50 moles

Answer the question

a) mass = $\frac{\text{no. of}}{\text{moles}}$ × RFM

mass = 25 × 28

mass = 700 g

b) mass = $\frac{\text{no. of}}{\text{moles}}$ × RFM

mass = 50 × 17

mass = 850 g

Carrying out the calculations in a specific column helps you to remember which RFM to use. It keeps the information you have about the individual chemicals organised.

The questions can be completed in exactly the same way as the worked examples. However, sometimes the examiner will set the question in a real life situation or give an example of a common chemical reaction as in Question 8. Examiners try to find balanced chemical equations where the ratio of moles is not always 1:1 as in all of these examples. Sometimes examiners give other information which is not needed for the calculation but that they may ask about later, as in the state symbols in the balanced equation for Question 9. Remember that there are millions of chemical reactions and the examiners will use a different one each year. It does not matter what the reaction is working out, 'How Much?' is always the same. Sometimes the examples used are not familiar chemicals to you and the names can sound a little strange as in Question 10 but the calculation is the same. **Once you can work out one you can do them all!**

Questions

Now try these three questions.

8 Cells in our bodies use the breakdown of glucose as a major source of energy. High energy drinks contain glucose to give an almost instant release of energy into the bloodstream. Glucose burns in an excess of oxygen to form carbon dioxide and water.

$$C_6H_{12}O_6 + 6O_2 \rightarrow 6CO_2 + 6H_2O$$

Calculate the mass of glucose required to produce 432 g of water.

9 2.74 g of a sample of solid oxide of lead, Pb_3O_4, decomposes when heated according to the equation below.

$$2Pb_3O_{4(s)} \rightarrow 6PbO_{(s)} + O_{2(g)}$$

Calculate the mass of PbO which would be formed on heating 2.74 g of Pb_3O_4 until no more oxygen was released.

10 When anhydrous borax is heated it decomposes according to the equation:

anhydrous borax → sodium metaborate + boric oxide

$$Na_2B_4O_7 \rightarrow 2NaBO_2 + B_2O_3$$

Calculate the mass of sodium metaborate which is produced when 5.05 g of anhydrous borax are heated.

The scale of a chemical reaction

Figure 2 Industrial and laboratory scale preparation

The pictures above illustrate two different scales of chemical preparation. In industry, the masses of solids used are generally measured in tonnes or kilograms. In the laboratory, the masses of solids are generally measured in grams. Calculating 'How Much?' is exactly the same.

Remember:

$$\text{number of moles} = \frac{\text{mass (g)}}{\text{relative molecular mass}}$$

Conversion of units	
1 kg	1000 g
1 tonne	1000 kg
1 tonne	1 000 000 g

Example

Iron is manufactured in the blast furnace by the reduction of iron ore. The main reduction reaction is illustrated by the balanced chemical equation below.

$$Fe_2O_3 + 3CO \rightarrow 2Fe + 3CO_2$$

a) Calculate the relative formula mass of the iron ore, Fe_2O_3.

b) How many moles of iron are present in 5.3 tonnes of iron?

c) Calculate the mass of iron ore, Fe_2O_3, required to produce 5.3 tonnes of iron.

Answer:

a) RFM $Fe_2O_3 = (56 \times 2) + (16 \times 3) = 160$

b) $\text{number of moles} = \frac{\text{mass (g)}}{\text{relative molecular mass}}$

$= \frac{5\,300\,000\text{ g}}{56}$

$= 94642.857$

c)

Fe_2O_3 +	3CO →	2Fe +	$3CO_2$
1	3	2	3
? moles 94 642.857/2 = 47 321.428 moles		94 642.857 moles	

moles = mass/RFM

mass = $47\,321.428 \times 160 = 7\,571\,428$ g

It is good practice to give the answer in the same units as appear in the question:

7.57 tonnes of iron ore

Theoretical yield, actual yield and percentage yield

In practice, the 7.57 tonnes of iron ore used in the previous example will produce a little less than 5.3 tonnes of iron. The 5.3 tonnes of iron is known as the theoretical yield.

The **theoretical** yield is the **maximum** yield which can be produced based on a calculation using a balanced chemical equation for the reaction.

The mass of the product (or volume of the product) measured at the end of the reaction is known as the **actual yield**.

Chemists routinely work out the **percentage yield** of a product as a measure of how efficient a chemical process is.

$$\text{percentage yield} = \frac{\text{actual yield}}{\text{theoretical yield}} \times 100$$

Example

Sodium sulfate, Na_2SO_4, can be produced in the laboratory in two different ways. The information on the left gives a balanced chemical equation for each of the reactions producing sodium sulfate, and the actual yield of sodium sulfate produced from 50.0 g of sodium hydroxide or sodium oxide.

Reaction 1	Reaction 2
sodium hydroxide + sulfuric acid → sodium sulfate + water	sodium oxide + sulfuric acid → sodium sulfate + water
$2NaOH + H_2SO_4 \rightarrow Na_2SO_4 + 2H_2O$	$Na_2O + H_2SO_4 \rightarrow Na_2SO_4 + H_2O$
Mass of NaOH = 50.0 g	Mass of Na_2O = 50.0 g
Sulfuric acid in excess	Sulfuric acid in excess
Actual yield of Na_2SO_4 = 64.2 g	Actual yield of Na_2SO_4 = 78.1 g

a) Calculate the theoretical yield of sodium sulfate produced from 50 g of sodium hydroxide. (Hint: this is the same calculation as, 'Calculate the mass of sodium sulfate produced from 50.0 g of sodium hydroxide'.)

b) Calculate the theoretical yield of sodium sulfate produced from 50.0 g of sodium oxide.

c) Calculate the percentage yield of sodium sulfate produced in reaction 1.

d) Calculate the percentage yield of sodium sulfate produced in reaction 2.

e) Using your answers to part c) and d), consider which reaction is the more efficient.

Answer:

a) $2NaOH + H_2SO_4 \rightarrow Na_2SO_4 + 2H_2O$

2NaOH +	H_2SO_4 →	Na_2SO_4 +	$2H_2O$
2	1	1	2
50 g		? g	
moles = $\frac{\text{mass}}{\text{RMM}}$ = 50/40			
1.25 moles	0.625 moles	0.625 moles	1.25 moles
		mass = moles × RMM = 0.625 × 142 = **88.8 g**	

b) $Na_2O + H_2SO_4 \longrightarrow Na_2SO_4 + H_2O$

Na_2O +	H_2SO_4 →	Na_2SO_4 +	H_2O
1	1	1	1
50 g		? g	
moles = $\frac{\text{mass}}{\text{RMM}}$ = 50/62			
= 0.806 moles	0.806 moles	0.806 moles	0.806 moles
		mass = moles × RMM = 0.806 × 142 = **114.5 g**	

c) reaction 1

$$\text{percentage yield} = \frac{\text{actual yield}}{\text{theoretical yield}} \times 100$$
$$= \frac{64.2}{88.8} \times 100$$
$$= 72.3\%$$

d) reaction 2

$$\text{percentage yield} = \frac{\text{actual yield}}{\text{theoretical yield}} \times 100$$
$$= \frac{78.1}{114.5} \times 100$$
$$= 68.2\%$$

e) Reaction 1 is the more efficient as less of the product is lost.

The reasons why the yield from a chemical reaction is less than the actual yield fall into two categories: chemical and physical.

Chemical

In some chemical processes several different chemical reactions may happen, not just the one the chemist wishes to happen. These reactions are called competing reactions or side reactions. In the reaction used as an example above the sodium oxide and sulfuric acid will also form sodium hydrogen sulfate rather than the sodium sulfate that the chemist wants to form. At GCSE, you are not expected to know individual competing reactions. You just need to be aware that they exist.

Physical

When a product is formed it has to be removed from the reaction mixture and purified. The separation may entail an evaporation, a crystallisation or a filtration process. Inevitably, small amounts of the substance are left on the individual pieces of apparatus. The greater the number of separation processes the greater the chance of loss of the product.

▶ Empirical and molecular formulae

The empirical formula of a compound is the simplest formula for a compound. An empirical formula states the elements present and their ratio.

NaCl, H_2O and HCl are examples of **empirical formulae**. For NaCl, this means the compound sodium chloride contains one sodium ion for every one chloride ion or 1 mole of sodium ions for every 1 mole of chloride ions.

C_6H_6 is the formula for an organic liquid called benzene. The empirical formula for this compound is CH. C_6H_6 is known as the **molecular formula**. This formula gives more information. The ratio of the elements can be inferred and the actual number of atoms in the molecule is given.

State whether the following formulae are empirical or molecular formulae. For those compounds for which the molecular formula is stated give the empirical formula.

Name of compound	Formula of compound
a) potassium iodide	KI
b) ethane	C_2H_6
c) copper(II) carbonate	$CuCO_3$
d) aluminium chloride	Al_2Cl_6
e) glucose	$C_6H_{12}O_6$
f) sodium oxide	Na_2O

a), c) and f) in the table are empirical formulae. They state the simplest ratio of the elements present. b), d) and e) are molecular formulae. The ratio of the elements present can be calculated from the actual number of atoms in the molecule.

The empirical formulae of b), d) and e) are:

b) ethane, CH_3

d) aluminium chloride, $AlCl_3$

e) glucose, CH_2O

Hint: one way to find the smallest whole number ratio is to divide all of the numbers by the smallest number. For example, faced with a ratio of moles:

a) 0.863 : 1.726

Divide both by 0.863

$$\frac{0.863}{0.863} : \frac{1.726}{0.863}$$

1 : 2

This type of ratio is common.

b) 0.254 : 0.381

Divide both by 0.254

1 : 1.5

The smallest **whole number ratio** is therefore

2 : 3

Using experimental data to work out the formula of a compound

Calculating empirical formulae

The empirical formula of a compound can be calculated from the mass or percentage of the individual elements present.

Example 1

An oxide of aluminium contains 1.35 g of aluminium and 1.2 g of oxygen. Calculate the empirical formula.

Elements present	**Al**	**O**
mass of element present	1.35 g	1.2 g
number of moles $= \dfrac{\text{mass (g)}}{\text{relative atomic mass}}$	1.35/27 = 0.05	1.2/16 = 0.075
smallest whole number ratio	2	3
empirical formula	Al_2O_3	

Example 2

A 2.5 g sample of iron is burned completely in oxygen to form 3.2 g of the oxide. Calculate the empirical formula of the oxide.

Elements present	**Fe**	**O**
mass of element present	2.5 g	3.2 − 2.5 = 0.7 g
number of moles = $\frac{\text{mass (g)}}{\text{relative atomic mass}}$	2.5/56 = 0.044	0.7/16 = 0.044
smallest whole number ratio	1	1
empirical formula	FeO	

Hint: when the information given about the element in the compound is given in the form of a percentage the calculation is essentially the same. One way to begin is to assume there are 100 g of the compound. For example, in Question 13 this would mean the first oxide of copper contained 89 g of copper and 11 g of oxygen. The final ratio will work out the same even if you assume that there are only 2 g of the compound to start with.

Questions

11 An oxide of iron contains 2.24 g of iron and 0.96 g of oxygen. Calculate the molecular formula of this oxide of iron.

12 Copper and sulfur and oxygen form a compound which contains 1.7 g of copper, 0.85 g of sulfur and 1.7 g of oxygen. Calculate the empirical formula of this compound. Name the compound.

13 Copper forms two oxides. One is red in colour and does not dissolve in water. A sample of this oxide contains 89% copper and 11% oxygen. The other oxide is black and is also insoluble in water. It contains 80% copper and 20% oxygen. What are the empirical formulae of the two oxides of copper?

Working out the molecular formula

Carbon reacts with hydrogen gas to form a range of hydrocarbons. The mass of carbon and hydrogen in each compound is given in the table below. The mass of 1 mole of the compound is also given. Calculate the empirical formula and use the mass of 1 mole to state the molecular formula of each compound.

Hydrocarbon	Mass of element present (g)		Mass of 1 mole (g)
	carbon	hydrogen	
A	9	2.25	30
B	3	0.5	28
C	6	1	42
D	9	2	44

Using the method set out on page 117, the empirical formula of hydrocarbon A is CH_3. To work out the molecular formula calculate the mass of 1 mole of this group of elements.

Mass of 1 mole $CH_3 = 12 + (3 \times 1) = 15$ g

The actual mass of the compound is twice this value. Therefore, the molecular formula is C_2H_6.

Complete the exercise for the hydrocarbons B, C and D. If you have studied Chapter 15, Organic Chemistry 1, name the hydrocarbons when you have worked out the empirical formulae.

Anhydrous: does not contain water of crystallisation.

Hydrated: contains water of crystallisation.

Water of crystallisation is water which is chemically combined into the crystalline structure of the salt.

▶ Working out the formula of a compound containing water of crystallisation

The formula of hydrated salts can be calculated in a similar way.

A hydrated salt is one which contains water of crystallisation. Water of crystallisation is water which is chemically combined into the crystalline structure of the salt. A salt which has lost the water of crystallisation is said to be anhydrous. Copper(II) sulfate crystals which contain water of crystallisation are blue. Anhydrous copper(II) sulfate exists as a white powder. (See test for water, Chapter 7.)

Figure 3 Driving off the water of crystallisation from blue hydrated copper(II) sulfate crystals to form a white powder of anhydrous copper(II) sulfate

The formula of a hydrated salt is written in this form.

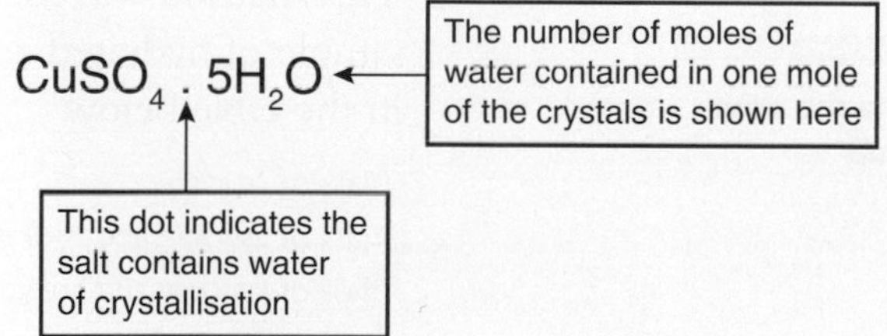

The formula of compounds containing an unknown number of moles of water of crystallisation, like hydrated iron(II) oxide or rust, is written like this.

$Fe_2O_3.xH_2O$

A sample of hydrated copper sulfate (6.25 g) was placed in a crucible and heated until all the water was driven off. When the crucible was cooled the remaining salt had a mass of 4.05 g. What is the formula and the mass of one mole of the hydrated salt?

Compounds present	$CuSO_4$	H_2O
mass of compound present	4.05 g	6.25 − 4.05 = 2.20 g
moles = mass/RAM	4.05/160 = 0.025	2.20/18 = 0.122
smallest whole number ratio	1	5
empirical formula	$CuSO_4.5H_2O$	

Mass of one mole of $CuSO_4.5H_2O$:

$$64 + 32 + (4 \times 16) + (5 \times 18) = 250\,g$$

(Mass of one mole of H_2O: $1 + 1 + 16 = 18$)

Compare the method used here with the examples on pages 117 and 118. They are very similar. **Once you can do one calculation of this type you can do them all!**

Examination questions can give more detail about the measurements made. These details become clear when you have carried out the experiment to find out the mass of water in a hydrated compound.

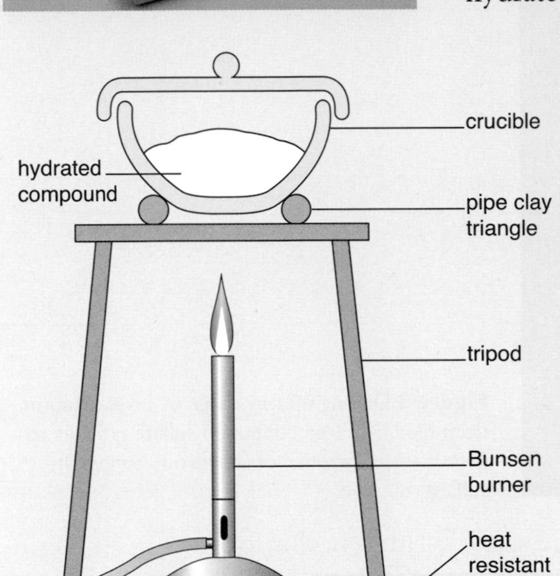

Figure 4 Apparatus used to find the mass of water in a hydrated compound

Finding the mass of water in a hydrated compound

* weigh and record the mass of a crucible
* add around 25 g of hydrated compound and weigh and record accurately the mass of crucible and hydrated compound
* heat the compound using a Bunsen burner to drive off the water
* allow the crucible to cool, then weigh and record the mass of the crucible and compound accurately
* repeat the heating, cooling and weighing process until there is no change in the mass of the crucible and the contents. This ensures that the compound in the crucible is now completely anhydrous.

This method was used to find the mass of water in a sample of hydrated cobalt chloride. The results are shown in the table below.

Mass of crucible		10.52 g
Mass of crucible and hydrated salt		35.90 g
Mass of crucible and anhydrous salt	1st weighing	26.78 g
	2nd weighing	23.52 g
	3rd weighing	23.52 g

1 Using the results in the table work out the mass of
a) anhydrous cobalt chloride b) water.

2 What is the formula of this sample of hydrated cobalt chloride, $CoCl_2.xH_2O$.

Answer

1 a) mass of anhydrous cobalt chloride = mass of salt without water
= mass of crucible and anhydrous salt − mass of crucible
= 23.52 g − 10.52 g = 13.00 g

b) mass of water = mass of crucible and hydrated salt − mass of crucible and anhydrous salt = 35.90 g − 23.52 g = 12.38 g

2 $CoCl_2.6H_2O$. The method of calculation is similar to the calculation on page 119.

Questions

Use the method on page 106 of this chapter to calculate the percentage of water in the following hydrated compounds.

14 Hydrated copper chloride, $CuCl_2.2H_2O$

15 Hydrated copper sulfate, $CuSO_4.5H_2O$

16 Hydrated magnesium sulfate, $MgSO_4.7H_2O$

17 A sample of hydrated aluminium nitrate, $Al(NO_3)_3.xH_2O$, was heated to constant mass in an oven. Using the results recorded below calculate the value of x in the formula $Al(NO_3)_3.xH_2O$ and write the formula for hydrated aluminium nitrate.

mass of crucible = 64.13 g

mass of crucible + hydrated salt = 71.63 g

mass of crucible + contents after heating to constant mass = 68.39 g

Exam questions

1 This question is about how much iron(II) oxide would be needed to produce a certain amount of iron(II) sulfate.

$$FeO + H_2SO_4 \rightarrow FeSO_4 + H_2O$$

a) The relative formula mass of FeO is 72. What is the relative formula mass of $FeSO_4$? (Relative atomic masses: Fe = 56, S = 32, O = 16) *(1 mark)*

b) Use your answer to part **a)** to calculate the number of moles in 7.6 g of $FeSO_4$. *(1 mark)*

c) Use the information in part **a)** and the equation:

$$FeO + H_2SO_4 \rightarrow FeSO_4 + H_2O$$

to calculate the mass of FeO needed to produce 7.6 g of $FeSO_4$. *(2 marks)*

d) If 1 mole of iron(II) oxide is reacted with a solution containing 2 moles of sulfuric acid, what is the maximum number of moles of iron(II) sulfate that can be produced? *(1 mark)*

2 Magnesium nitrate decomposes on heating according to the equation:

$$2Mg(NO_3)_2 \rightarrow 2MgO + 4NO_2 + O_2$$

a) What is the relative formula mass of MgO? (Relative atomic masses: Mg = 24, O = 16) *(1 mark)*

b) What is the relative formula mass of $Mg(NO_3)_2$? (Relative atomic masses: Mg = 24, N = 14, O = 16) *(1 mark)*

c) Use your answer to part **a)** to calculate the number of moles in 5.0 g of magnesium oxide. *(1 mark)*

d) Use your answer to part **c)** and the equation below to calculate the mass of magnesium nitrate required to produce 5.0 g of magnesium oxide. *(2 marks)*

$$2Mg(NO_3)_2 \rightarrow 2MgO + 4NO_2 + O_2$$

3 Oxides and hydroxides of metals are solids at room temperature and pressure. Many oxides of non-metals are gases.

a) 2.74 g of a sample of solid oxide of lead, Pb_3O_4, decomposes when heated according to the equation below.

$$2Pb_3O_{4(s)} \rightarrow 6PbO_{(s)} + O_{2(g)}$$

The decomposition is carried out in a fume cupboard using the apparatus shown below.

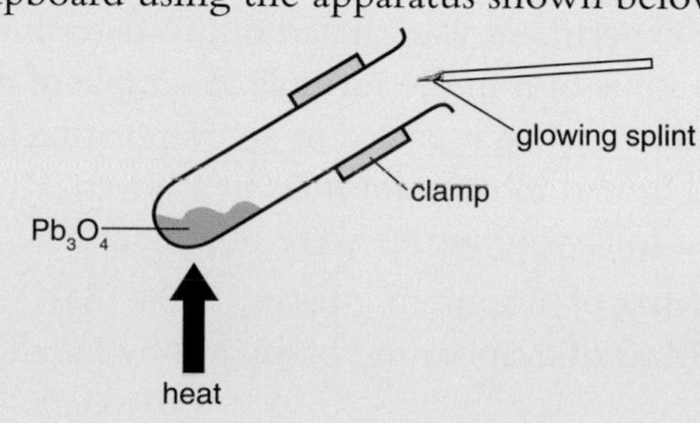

i) What would happen to the glowing splint? *(1 mark)*

ii) Calculate the mass of PbO which would be formed on heating 2.74 g of Pb_3O_4 to constant mass. (Relative atomic masses: O = 16, Pb = 207) *(5 marks)*

4 Hydrocarbons are compounds containing only the elements carbon and hydrogen.
Analysis of a hydrocarbon showed that 1.44 g of carbon were combined with 0.36 g of hydrogen.

a) Calculate the number of moles of carbon atoms present in the hydrocarbon. *(1 mark)*

b) Calculate the number of moles of hydrogen atoms present in the hydrocarbon. *(1 mark)*

c) Using your answers to **a)** and **b)**, work out the empirical formula of the hydrocarbon. *(2 marks)*

d) Given the formula mass of the hydrocarbon is 30, work out the molecular formula of the hydrocarbon. *(2 marks)*

e) Name the hydrocarbon. *(1 mark)*

f) Name the homologous series to which the hydrocarbon belongs. *(1 mark)*

5 Cells in our bodies use the breakdown of glucose as a major source of energy. High energy drinks contain glucose to give an almost instant release of energy into the bloodstream. Glucose burns in an excess of oxygen to form carbon dioxide and water.

$$C_6H_{12}O_6 + 6O_2 \rightarrow 6CO_2 + 6H_2O$$

Calculate the mass of glucose required to produce 1.08 kg of water. *(5 marks)*

6 The formula of aluminium nitrate may be written as

$Al(NO_3)_3.nH_2O$

It is used in antiperspirants and in tanning leather.
An experiment was carried out to determine the value of n in the formula. A sample of the hydrated salt was placed in an evaporating basin and heated to constant mass in an oven.
The following results were obtained:

Mass of evaporating basin = 54.13 g
Mass of evaporating basin and hydrated salt = 61.63 g
Mass of evaporating basin and contents after heating to constant mass = 58.39 g

Use the results above to calculate the value of n in the formula $Al(NO_3)_3.nH_2O$. *(7 marks)*

7 a) When borax crystals are left in air they lose some of their water of crystallisation.
To find the value of x in a sample of hydrated borax $Na_2B_4O_7.xH_2O$, which has been left in air for a month, the sample was heated to constant mass. 7.28 g of hydrated borax produced 4.04 g of anhydrous borax.
(Relative atomic masses: H = 1, B = 11, O = 16, Na = 23)

i) What is meant by 'heated to constant mass'? *(1 mark)*

ii) Calculate the mass of water lost. *(1 mark)*

iii) Calculate the number of moles of water lost. *(2 marks)*

iv) Calculate the number of moles of anhydrous borax. *(1 mark)*

v) Using your answers to **iii)** and **iv)** determine the value of x in $Na_2B_4O_7.xH_2O$. *(2 marks)*

b) When anhydrous borax is heated it decomposes according to the equation:

anhydrous borax → sodium metaborate + boric oxide

$$Na_2B_4O_7 \rightarrow 2NaBO_2 + B_2O_3$$

Calculate the mass of sodium metaborate which is produced when 5.05 g of anhydrous borax is heated. (Relative atomic masses: B = 11, O = 16, Na = 23) *(5 marks)*

8 a) Ozone is used in very small amounts in underground railway stations to remove compounds which cause stations to be stuffy. One of the compounds which is formed is formaldehyde, CH_2O. Calculate the percentage by mass of carbon in CH_2O. *(3 marks)*

b) 1.92 g of sulfur dioxide, SO_2, reacts completely with ozone to form 2.40 g of sulfur trioxide, SO_3.

i) Calculate the number of moles of sulfur dioxide used. *(2 marks)*

ii) Calculate the mass of ozone which reacts. *(2 marks)*

iii) Calculate the number of moles of ozone which reacts. *(2 marks)*

iv) Calculate the number of moles of sulfur trioxide formed. *(2 marks)*

v) Using your answers to **i), ii)** and **iv)** or otherwise, balance the symbol equation for the reaction. *(1 mark)*

$SO_2 + O_3 \rightarrow SO_3$

9 Many calcium containing compounds such as limestone (calcium carbonate) and gypsum (hydrated calcium sulfate) occur naturally.

Plaster of Paris is formed by heating gypsum to just above 100 °C:

$$\underset{\text{gypsum}}{CaSO_4.H_2O} \rightarrow \underset{\text{plaster of Paris}}{CaSO_4.\tfrac{1}{2}H_2O} + 1\tfrac{1}{2}H_2O$$

Calculate the percentage of water present in gypsum. *(3 marks)*

Oxidation and Reduction

Two types of chemical reaction appear repeatedly throughout your study of GCSE Chemistry: **oxidation** reactions and **reduction** reactions. In some instances they happen simultaneously. A chemical reaction in which oxidation occurs at the same time as reduction is known as a **redox** reaction.

Combustion of fuels, rotting of fruit or vegetables and corrosion are examples of oxidation reactions.

For example when charcoal (which is almost pure carbon) is burned in oxygen, carbon dioxide is produced.

charcoal + oxygen → carbon dioxide

$$C + O_2 \rightarrow CO_2$$

The carbon is said to be oxidised as it has gained oxygen.

Gain of oxygen is oxidation.

Magnesium will burn in the carbon dioxide produced in this reaction and the carbon is reformed.

magnesium + carbon dioxide → magnesium oxide + carbon

$$2Mg + \underbrace{CO_2 \rightarrow 2MgO + C}_{\text{The carbon dioxide has lost oxygen to form carbon}}$$

This is opposite to the combustion reaction. The carbon dioxide is said to be reduced. (Note: the carbon dioxide is reduced not carbon.)

Loss of oxygen is reduction.

Oxidation	Reduction
gain of oxygen	loss of oxygen

There are two other ways to define oxidation and reduction, first in terms of the loss or gain of hydrogen and second in terms of the loss or gain of electrons.

Defining oxidation and reduction in terms of loss or gain of hydrogen

Chlorine reacts with hydrogen to form hydrogen chloride according to the equations below.

chlorine + hydrogen → hydrogen chloride

$$\underbrace{Cl_2 + H_2 \rightarrow 2HCl}_{\text{Chlorine is said to be reduced as it has gained hydrogen}}$$

Gain of hydrogen is reduction.

Oxidation	Reduction
gain of oxygen	loss of oxygen
loss of hydrogen	gain of hydrogen

When methanol, an organic liquid, is passed over a heated catalyst, methanal (an important liquid used in the production of vaccines) and hydrogen are produced according to the following equations.

$$\text{methanol} \rightarrow \text{methanal} + \text{hydrogen}$$
$$\underbrace{CH_3OH \rightarrow CH_2O}_{} + H_2$$

Methanol is said to be oxidised as it has lost hydrogen

Loss of hydrogen is oxidation.

Defining oxidation and reduction in terms of loss or gain of electrons

When magnesium metal burns with the characteristic white light in a supply of oxygen, white powdery magnesium oxide is formed. This is an oxidation reaction because the magnesium has gained oxygen.

$$\text{magnesium} + \text{oxygen} \rightarrow \text{magnesium oxide}$$
$$\underbrace{2Mg + O_2 \rightarrow 2MgO}_{}$$

Consider only what happens to the magnesium atom as it forms the compound.

$$Mg - 2e^- \rightarrow Mg^{2+}$$

The magnesium atom has lost two electrons to form a magnesium ion. Therefore, the loss of electrons can be defined as an oxidation.

Loss of electrons is oxidation.

During the extraction of iron from its ore in the blast furnace, the following reaction occurs.

$$\text{iron(III) oxide} + \text{carbon monoxide} \rightarrow \text{iron} + \text{carbon dioxide}$$
$$\underbrace{Fe_2O_3 + 3CO \rightarrow 2Fe}_{} + 3CO_2$$

The iron oxide is reduced as it has lost oxygen. (Note: the iron oxide is reduced not the iron.)

Consider only the iron(III) ion in the ore and what happens to it during the process of reduction.

$$Fe^{3+} + 3e^- \rightarrow Fe$$

Oxidation	Reduction
gain of oxygen	loss of oxygen
loss of hydrogen	gain of hydrogen
loss of electrons	gain of electrons

The iron(III) ion has gained three electrons to become an iron atom. Therefore the gain of electrons can be defined as a reduction.

Gain of electrons is reduction.

Figure 1 Oxidation and reduction
LEO – Loss of Electrons is Oxidation
GER – Gain of Electrons is Reduction

Examples

Classify the following reactions as oxidation or reduction reactions and explain why the reaction is classified in this way.

1. $2Ca + O_2 \rightarrow 2CaO$
2. $2HI \rightarrow H_2 + I_2$
3. $2Na + H_2 \rightarrow 2NaH$
4. $Cu^{2+} + 2e^- \rightarrow Cu$
5. $2Br^- - 2e^- \rightarrow Br_2$
6. $Zn - 2e^- \rightarrow Zn^{2+}$
7. $N_2 + 3H_2 \rightarrow 2NH_3$

Reaction 1 is an oxidation reaction as the calcium has gained oxygen. Gain of oxygen is defined as oxidation.

Reaction 2 is an oxidation reaction as the hydrogen iodide has lost hydrogen. (Note: the hydrogen iodide has lost hydrogen not the iodine.) Loss of hydrogen is defined as oxidation.

Reaction 3 is a reduction reaction as the sodium has gained hydrogen. Gain of hydrogen is defined as reduction.

Reaction 4 is a reduction reaction as the copper ion has gained electrons. (Note: the copper ion has gained electrons not just copper.) Gain of electrons is defined as reduction (GER).

Reaction 5 is an oxidation as the bromide ion has lost electrons. (Note: the bromide ion has lost electrons not just the bromide or bromine.) Loss of electrons is defined as oxidation (LEO).

Reaction 6 is an oxidation as the zinc atoms have lost electrons. (Note: the zinc atoms have lost electrons not just the zinc.) Loss of electrons is defined as oxidation (LEO).

Reaction 7 is a reduction as hydrogen has been added to the nitrogen. Gain of hydrogen is defined as reduction.

Redox reactions

State whether the following reaction is an oxidation or a reduction and explain why the reaction is classified in this way.

hydrogen + oxygen → water

$$2H_2 + O_2 \rightarrow 2H_2O$$

Careful examination of the equation will lead you to state that both oxidation and reduction are occuring simultaneously. This type of reaction is called a **redox** reaction.

hydrogen is oxidised as it is gaining oxygen

$$2H_2 + O_2 \rightarrow 2H_2O$$

oxygen is reduced as it is gaining hydrogen

In Chapter 11 the displacement reactions studied as part of the reactivity series are redox reactions. Copper will displace silver from an aqueous solution of silver nitrate to produce silver and copper(II) nitrate solution.

silver ions are reduced as they are gaining electrons to become silver atoms

$$AgNO_3 + Cu \rightarrow CuNO_3 + Ag$$

copper atoms are oxidised as they are losing electrons to become copper ions

When reduction and oxidation occur simultaneously the reaction is said to be a redox reaction.

Example

Explain why the displacement reaction between zinc and copper(II) sulfate solution (illustrated by the balanced chemical equation below) is considered to be a redox reaction.

$$Zn_{(s)} + CuSO_{4(aq)} \rightarrow ZnSO_{4(aq)} + Cu_{(s)}$$

Answer

The zinc atoms are oxidised as the zinc atom is losing two electrons to form the zinc ion. Loss of electrons is defined as oxidation. The copper ions are reduced as they are gaining two electrons to form copper atoms. Gain of electrons is defined as reduction. When reduction and oxidation occur simultaneously the reaction is said to be a redox reaction.

The answer can be worded slightly differently using half equations, showing the movement of the electrons.

$Zn - 2e^- \rightarrow Zn^{2+}$ Loss of electrons is defined as oxidation.

$Cu^{2+} + 2e^- \rightarrow Cu$ Gain of electrons is defined as reduction.

When reduction and oxidation occur simultaneously the reaction is said to be a redox reaction.

Exam questions

1 a) Many laboratory reactions involve oxidation.

i) Explain why the burning of sulfur in air is an oxidation reaction. *(2 marks)*

ii) The burning of magnesium in air can be represented by the half equation:

$$Mg \rightarrow Mg^{2+} + 2e^-$$

Explain in terms of electrons why this is an oxidation reaction. *(2 marks)*

b) The extraction of iron from its ore, haematite, in the blast furnace can be described as a redox reaction. What is meant by the term **redox**? *(2 marks)*

2 a) When an object rusts, an oxidation reaction occurs. What is meant by the term **oxidation**? *(1 mark)*

b) Each of the following reactions can be classified as an oxidation or reduction reaction.

Reaction 1: $CH_4 + 2O_2 \rightarrow CO_2 + 2H_2O$
Reaction 2: $CuO + Mg \rightarrow Cu + MgO$
Reaction 3: $N_2 + 3H_2 \rightarrow 2NH_3$

i) Write the formula of the substance being oxidised in reaction 1. *(1 mark)*

ii) In reaction 2, which substance is reduced? *(1 mark)*

iii) Explain why nitrogen is reduced in reaction 3. *(2 marks)*

iv) Write a balanced ionic equation for reaction 2. *(2 marks)*

3 Magnesium reacts with copper(II) sulfate solution according to the equation

$$Mg + CuSO_4 \rightarrow MgSO_4 + Cu$$

The reaction may be described as a redox reaction.

Explain in terms of electrons why this reaction may be described as a redox reaction. You may use ionic equations to help answer this question. *(7 marks)*

Materials and Electrolysis

▶ Natural and synthetic materials

Scientists use the term 'material' to describe the different types of matter that are used to make things. For example, glass or plastic can be used to make bottles, copper is used to make pipes, while paper is used in the production of bags. In everyday life, there are a wide range of materials available and these materials are used for many different purposes.

Because there is a continuous demand for new materials with specialised properties, it is important for scientists to design new products to meet these needs. An example of this is the special ceramic coatings which have been designed for the outside of space shuttles to protect them from burning up on re-entry into the Earth's atmosphere.

Another example is Kevlar, probably the most important man-made fibre ever developed. It is five times stronger than steel, is much lighter and does not corrode. Kevlar is used to make bulletproof vests and anchor lines for ships. Some of the gels shown in Figure 1 have many important potential uses. SEAgel is the first lighter-than-air solid and is produced from agar; it could be used as a thermal insulator. Supergel is a water-based hydrogel capable of absorbing up to half its own weight in oil and could be used to clean up oil spillages.

Materials are classified as **natural** or **synthetic**. Wood, cotton, silk and wool are all **natural materials** but glass and plastic are synthetic or made by humans. Manufactured materials are obtained from air, sea, living things and crude oil. A few examples are plastics from crude oil, chlorine from seawater, cotton from cotton plants and iron from haematite ore which is dug out of the ground.

Figure 1 a) The nose cone of a shuttle is made of a 'reusable' carbon composite, b) SEAgel, c) Supergel

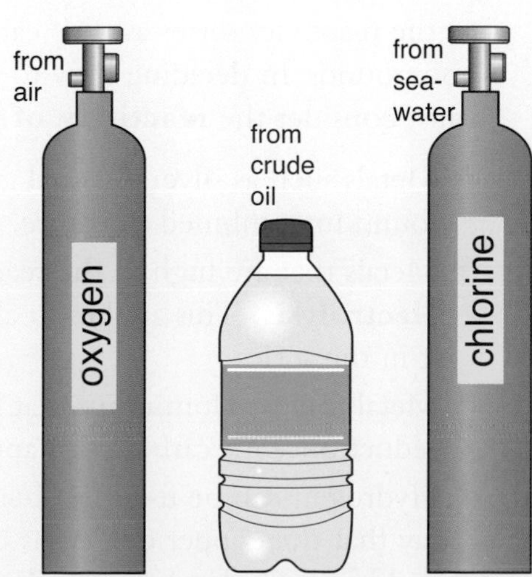

Figure 2 Manufactured materials

Questions

1 What raw material does linen come from?

2 Today, many clothes are made from PVC. What raw material is PVC obtained from?

3 **a)** Give two advantages of making windows out of glass.

b) Suggest two disadvantages of using glass as a container for liquids.

4 Copy and complete the following table. The first one is done for you.

Manufactured material	Raw material obtained from
iron	rocks
	rocks
PVC	
hydrogen	
alcohol	

5 Suggest two reasons why plastic bags have replaced paper bags in supermarkets.

Table 1 lists some other important manufactured materials made from different raw materials.

Raw material	Some useful manufactured materials obtained from the raw material
Rocks	Metals: aluminium from bauxite, copper from copper pyrites
	Glass from sand, limestone and sodium carbonate
	Ceramics from sand and clay
	Lime from limestone
Crude oil	Fuels: petrol and diesel
	Plastics: PVC and polypropene
	Detergents
Air	Nitrogen: ammonia, nitric acid and fertilisers
	Oxygen for breathing equipment
Seawater	Salt, iodine, hydrogen and sodium hydroxide
Plants	Fuels from biomass materials
	Cotton
	Medicines

Table 1 Some important manufactured materials

▶ Obtaining metals from their ores

Metals such as silver and gold occur '**native**' as the free metal. They are very unreactive metals and do not combine with oxygen, water or other substances in the atmosphere. However, most metals are reactive and are found as compounds in ores in the rocks. The metal compounds in the ores usually occur as oxides, carbonates and sulfides. To understand how metals are extracted from their ores it is necessary to consider the **reactivity series** (see page 140):

K Na Ca Mg Al **(C)** Zn Fe **(H)** Cu Ag Au
most reactive **least reactive**

Although carbon and hydrogen are non-metals they may be added to the reactivity series as they can displace some metals from their compounds. In deciding how to extract metals from their ores we must consider the **reactivity of the metal**.

* Metals such as silver, Ag, and gold, Au, with the lowest reactivity are found uncombined in nature.
* Metals that are high in the reactivity series are extracted by **electrolysis**. This applies to aluminium, Al, and those metals above it in the series.
* Metals below aluminium that have lower reactivity are extracted by reduction with carbon; this applies to iron and zinc.
* Hydrogen can be used to obtain copper from copper(II) oxide. We say that the copper oxide has been **reduced as it loses oxygen** and hydrogen has been **oxidised as it gains oxygen**.
* The extraction of metals from their ores are all **redox reactions**.

Electrolysis

In this section we will look at how electrolysis is used to obtain a reactive metal like aluminium from aluminium oxide. Before doing this it is important to study the theory of electrolysis.

Some definitions:

Electrolysis is the decomposition of a liquid electrolyte using a direct current of electricity.

An **electrolyte** is an ionic compound that is molten or dissolved in water and conducts electricity. Figure 3 shows the apparatus which is used to test if a liquid conducts electricity. Two graphite rods are connected to the terminals of a battery or power pack and placed in the liquid to be tested. A bulb is also placed in the circuit and if the bulb lights up then the liquid is a conductor of electricity.

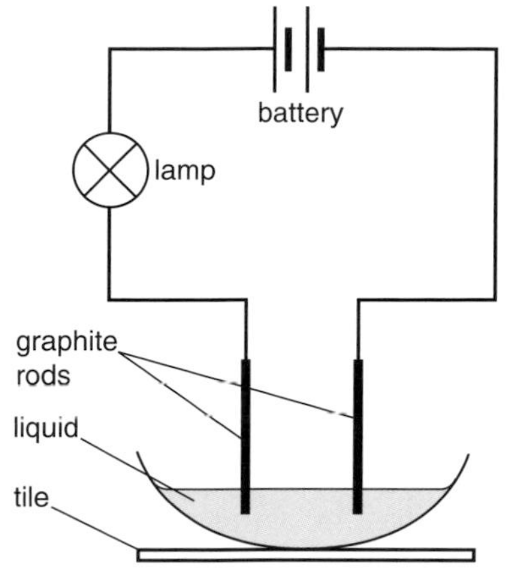

Figure 3 Electrical circuit used to test if a liquid conducts electricity

Electrodes are the graphite rods that are used as they conduct electricity and are unreactive (see Figure 3). Another unreactive or inert electrode material is platinum.

The electrode that is connected to the negative terminal of the battery is called the **cathode** and it is the **negative electrode** (−). The electrode that is connected to the positive terminal of the battery is called the **anode** and it is the **positive electrode** (+).

Conduction in an electrolyte

All electrolytes conduct electricity as they have free ions that can move and carry the charge as shown in Figure 4.

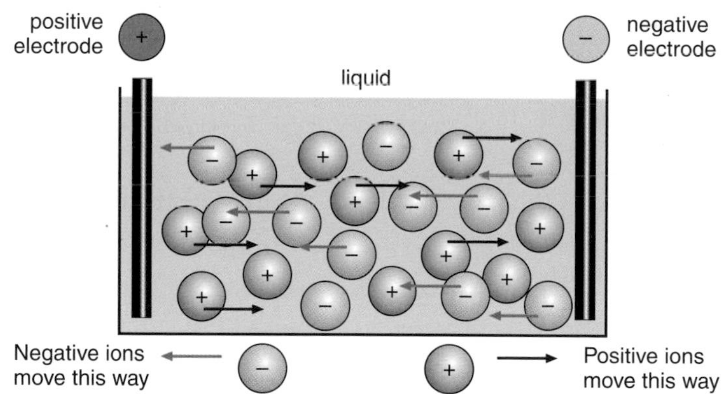

Figure 4 How ions move in a liquid ionic compound

In Figure 4 we see that the positive and negative ions are free to move. The positive ions move to the negative cathode and are called **cations** while the negative ions are attracted to the positive anode and are called **anions**.

At the cathode (−), positive ions gain electrons to form atoms or molecules, for example:

$$Na^+ + e^- \rightarrow Na$$

or

$$2H^+ + 2e^- \rightarrow H_2$$

At the anode (+), the negative ions lose electrons to become atoms/molecules, for example:

$$2Cl^- - 2e^- \rightarrow Cl_2$$

Chemists usually write this type of equation in the form:

$$2Cl^- \rightarrow Cl_2 + 2e^-$$

Electrolysis of molten salts

For this type of electrolysis we need to know what happens to molten electrolytes when they undergo electrolysis. Molten lead bromide and molten lithium chloride will be studied. The reactions are carried out in a fume cupboard as harmful or toxic vapours may be given off during the reactions.

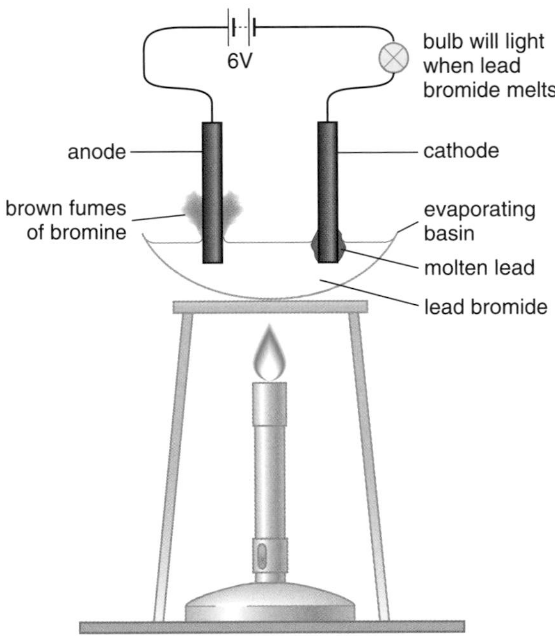

Figure 5 Electrolysis of molten lead bromide

Electrolysis of molten lead bromide, $PbBr_2$

Figure 5 shows the apparatus that is required for the electrolysis of a molten lead bromide. The same apparatus is used for all electrolysis reactions using molten salts.

When the lead bromide is heated, it melts and the bulb lights up as the lead ions, Pb^{2+}, and bromide ions, Br^-, are now free to move and carry the charge. As the electrolysis proceeds red-brown pungent vapours of bromine are given off **at the anode**. The ionic half equation for the reaction that is taking place is:

$$2Br^- - 2e^- \rightarrow Br_2$$

or more correctly:

$$2Br^- \rightarrow Br_2 + 2e^-$$

At the cathode: a silver grey liquid is formed, which, on cooling, gives a silver grey bead of metallic lead.

The ionic half equation for this reaction is:

$$Pb^{2+} + 2e^- \rightarrow Pb$$

Electrolysis of molten lithium chloride, LiCl

The apparatus is exactly the same as that for lead bromide in Figure 5 except that lithium chloride is used in the evaporating basin.

At the anode: a yellow-green chlorine gas is given off which has a pungent smell.

The ionic half equation is: $2Cl^- \rightarrow Cl_2 + 2e^-$

At the cathode: a silver grey liquid is formed, which, on cooling, gives a silver grey bead of lithium.

The ionic half equation is: $Li^+ + e^- \rightarrow Li$

Predicting the products of electrolysis of a molten electrolyte

It is not difficult to predict the products formed during the electrolysis of molten electrolytes as the only substance present is the molten electrolyte. This means that when inert electrodes are used there are only two possible products. The metal ion is discharged as the metal at the cathode and the non-metal anion is discharged at the anode.

Table 2 gives some examples of the products produced during the electrolysis of a number of molten salts.

Molten electrolyte	Cathode product	Anode product
magnesium chloride	magnesium	chlorine
aluminium oxide	aluminium	oxygen
potassium bromide	potassium	bromine
calcium chloride	calcium	chlorine

Table 2 Products of the electrolysis of molten salts

Questions

6 Explain the meaning of the following terms:
  a) electrolyte **b)** electrolysis **c)** electrode **d)** anode
  e) cathode **f)** anion **g)** cation.

7 Predict the products of electrolysis of the molten salts:
  a) lead bromide **b)** potassium chloride **c)** lithium iodide.

8 Write balanced ionic equations to show what happens at the electrodes for the electrolysis of molten:
  a) lithium chloride **b)** lead bromide **c)** magnesium chloride.

Electrolysis in industry

The industrial extraction of aluminium from alumina using electrolysis

We will see how a reactive metal like aluminium is obtained from its ore, bauxite, using electrolysis. The first stage in the production of aluminium is the purification of the bauxite, to give pure **aluminium oxide (also called alumina)**. Bauxite is hydrated aluminium oxide and contains impurities such as silica and iron(III) oxide. The purification of the crushed bauxite involves several processes to remove the impurities.

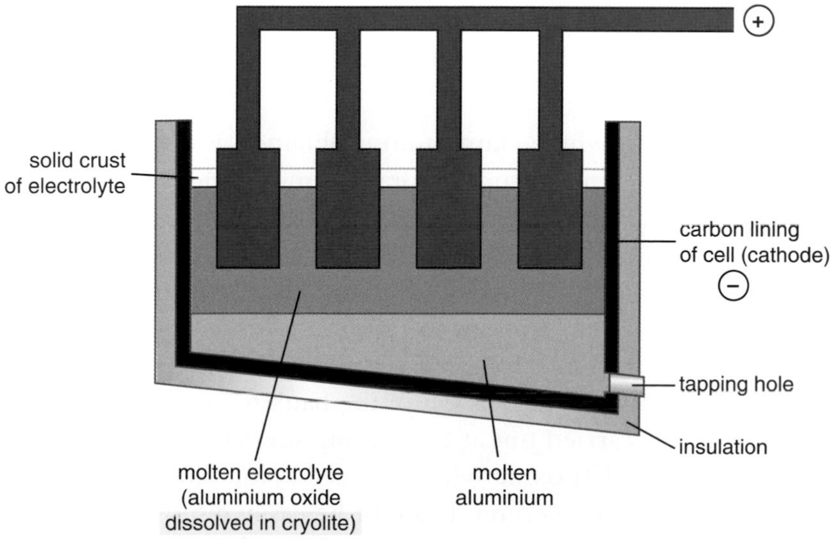

After purification, the aluminium oxide is dissolved in molten cryolite. This reduces its melting point and increases its conductivity.

Electrolysis is carried out as shown in Figure 6.

Figure 6 The electrolytic cell for the production of aluminium

To melt the aluminium oxide would require a temperature of 2050 °C and such an operating temperature is just too high to make the process viable. Using molten cryolite to dissolve the aluminium oxide allows a realistic operating temperature of around 950 °C. In addition to this a solid crust of aluminium oxide forms on the surface of the electrolyte and this stops heat loss and helps to reduce the energy costs.

As the electrical costs for this industrial electrolysis process are enormous, it means that the aluminium plant must be sited where electrical energy is cheap. This is why **aluminium extraction** plants are sited where hydroelectric power is available.

The largest producers of aluminium metal are Russia, China, the United States and Canada, countries which have abundant hydroelectric power.

Reactions at the anode and cathode

Cathode (−)

Positive aluminium ions are attracted to the negative cathode and are reduced to aluminium. The molten aluminium then sinks to the bottom of the cell where it is tapped off.

The ionic half equation is: $Al^{3+} + 3e^- \rightarrow Al$

Anode (+)

Negative oxide ions are attracted to the positive anode and oxygen gas is given off.

The ionic half equation is: $2O^{2-} \rightarrow O_2 + 4e^-$

The carbon anodes react with the oxygen produced due to the very high temperature. As a result of this, the anodes are gradually burnt away and must be replaced periodically.

$$C + O_2 \rightarrow CO_2$$

The molten aluminium is deposited at the cathode and sinks to the bottom of the tank where it is tapped off from the cell.

Bauxite, the ore from which aluminium is obtained, is often found near the surface in countries such as Brazil, Jamaica and Australia. This means that it can be extracted by open cast mining where a surface layer of about 60 metres in depth is excavated. Open cast mining scars the countryside and is unsightly. However, many mining companies are taking steps to restore the landscape after all the bauxite is extracted and the mine is no longer in use.

In many instances the purification of the bauxite into pure aluminium oxide is carried out at the mining site. One impurity in the bauxite is iron(III) oxide which is a red colour and this leads to waste called red mud. Red mud cannot be easily disposed of. In most countries where red mud is produced, it is pumped into red mud ponds. Red mud presents a problem as it is unsightly and takes up a large area of land. Red mud cannot be pumped into the sea as it would harm the living organisms.

After the aluminium oxide has been purified it is transported to the aluminium extraction plant (sometimes called a smelter) and here the aluminium is produced using electrolysis. As the extraction requires large amounts of energy, the extraction plants are generally located close to hydroelectric power stations where they benefit from the relatively cheap electricity. British Alcan's aluminium plant in Scotland is powered by the company's own hydroelectric plant, which also provides power for the nearby town of Fort William. The areas that are suited to hydroelectric power stations are often areas of outstanding natural beauty and this leads to many objections from conservationists to the siting of aluminium extraction plants and the pollution problems it will cause.

Another problem that may emerge in siting an extraction plant in a remote area of outstanding natural beauty is finding a suitable workforce to manage and run the production plant. One solution is to bring a suitably skilled workforce into the area and build housing to accommodate them; alternatively it may be more cost effective to construct an aluminium plant in an area of greater population, where there is a skilled workforce and good transport links, but pay a higher price for electricity from an oil or gas fired power station.

Air and water pollution from aluminium plants can be a problem. The gases from the plant are scrubbed with water and then passed into the atmosphere through tall chimneys. The water from the scrubbing process contains fluoride ions from the electrolyte and this is discharged into rivers. There are concerns that fluoride ions are harmful to grass and cattle and chemists now must carefully control the amount of fluoride entering the water.

The main factors that influence the siting of an aluminium extraction plant are:

a) Large amounts of electricity are required to obtain aluminium from aluminium oxide by electrolysis. This means that the plant must be sited near a cheap source of electricity, for example, many plants are close to hydroelectric power stations.
b) The raw materials, bauxite, cryolite and carbon, need to be available and transported easily. Thus good transportation through roads, railways and ports is necessary. Similarly, there needs to be good transportation to deliver the finished product, aluminium.
c) A good water supply is required during the production of aluminium for washing, dissolving, cooling and for steam generation.
d) Suitable capacity and facilities to deal with waste disposal.
e) Suitable workforce with the skills and knowledge necessary to meet competitive productivity targets.

Figure 7 Aluminium cans being recycled

Recycling of aluminium

The production of aluminium by the electrolysis of molten aluminium oxide requires large quantities of energy, bauxite and cryolite. Recycling aluminium requires **only 5% of the energy** and produces **only 5% of the carbon dioxide emissions** compared with the actual production of aluminium from bauxite ore. Additionally, it reduces the amount of waste going to landfill sites.

Aluminium is the most cost effective material to recycle. Recycling 1 kilogram of aluminium saves up to 6 kilograms of bauxite and 14 kWh of electricity while a recycled aluminium can saves enough energy to run a television for 3 hours. Like the recycling of most metals, aluminium can be used over and over again as the processes involved in its recycling do not damage its structure. It is surprising and disappointing that only around 26% of aluminium cans are recycled.

Questions

9 Aluminium metal is extracted from pure aluminium oxide by electrolysis. Describe the production of aluminium metal from pure aluminium oxide in an electrolytic cell. Your answer should include:

a) why electrolysis is used

b) why extraction plants are often built close to hydroelectric power stations

c) why cryolite is used in the extraction

d) what the electrodes are made from

e) why the anodes are replaced from time to time

f) ionic equations to show what happens at the electrodes

g) how the aluminium is removed from the cell.

10 Discuss the factors that must be considered when siting an aluminium extraction plant.

11 Give three reasons why it is important to recycle aluminium.

▶ Nanotechnology

Nanotechnology is a relatively new science and belongs to the 21st century. It is the study of atoms and molecules. The term nanometre (nm) means 10^{-9} metres or 0.000 000 001 metres. This is 1000 million times smaller than a metre or 10 million times smaller than a centimetre. Nanotechnology refers to particles that are 1 to 100 nm in size. This is approximately the size of a few hundred atoms or molecules. Present day scientists have the ability to control atoms at this dimension. Nanomaterials cover a wide range of materials which include metals, plastics, carbon and a number of polymers.

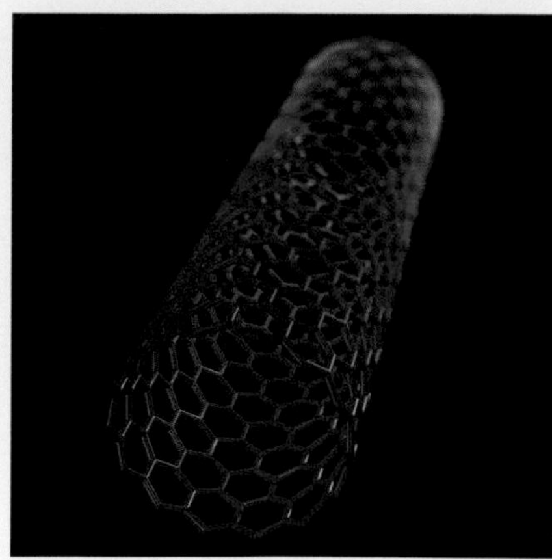

Figure 8 A nanotube

Figure 9 Acticoat antimicrobial wound dressing which uses nanosilver to keep harmful micro-organisms out of wounds

Nanoparticles, because of their small size, show different properties from larger particles. They differ from the larger particles because of their high surface area to volume ratio and the way in which the atoms are arranged. As a result of their small size, nanoparticles are more sensitive to heat, light, magnetism and electricity.

At present, nanomaterials have many uses and there are many more potential uses for the future.

* In Japan, chemists have found that gold particles smaller than 5 nm catalytically convert toxic carbon monoxide to carbon dioxide at −70 °C, a reaction that usually requires a much higher temperature.
* Nanoparticles of silver have antibacterial, antiviral and antifungal properties. They are used in sterilising sprays to clean operating theatres in hospitals and in wound dressings (Figure 9).
* Carbon nanotubes have important uses in miniature electronic devices and smaller and faster computers.
* Ultra-thin, strong coatings of scratch resistant polymer can be used to cover and protect lenses in glasses and cameras and also for contact lenses.
* Nano-sized polymer particles are used to coat fabrics to make them stain resistant. Liquids spilled on to the fabric turn into beads, run off and no stain is left behind.

Risks of nanomaterials

While the discovery of nanomaterials and their important potential uses has brought great excitement to the world of new materials there are also many worries about the effects of nanomaterials in the human body and the environment. There have been conflicting reports about the effects of nanomaterials, some saying they are harmless but others claiming that they may damage human cells.

European Union ministers have called for nanosilver and long-walled carbon nanotubes to be banned in electrical and electronic products. The International Nanotechnology Industries Association recognises the potential dangers of nanomaterials to the environment and health but claim that the 'take back policy' in the Waste Electrical and Electronic Equipment Directive would ensure that no nanomaterials in engineering would end up as waste and therefore that they would not affect the environment. They feel that nanomaterials in personal care products pose a greater problem as we know that these will end up in the environment.

For long multiwalled carbon nanotubes there is some evidence that they may behave like asbestos when inhaled. Engineers would argue against this. They claim that the nanotubes have to be free for inhalation to be a danger to health, but this is not the case as they would be bound up in electrical products. It would seem that the properties of each nanomaterial must be evaluated according to its application, and on a case by case basis.

Questions

12 Nanotechnology involves the use of nano-sized particles.

a) Explain fully the meaning of nanotechnology.

b) Give one important use of nanotechnology.

c) How many nanometres are in 1 metre? Choose the correct answer from the following.

10^{-9} 10^{9} 10^{3} 10^{-3}

13 a) What is the difference between normal silver particles and nanosilver particles?

b) Give three properties that change when normal silver particles are replaced by nanosilver particles.

c) Give one use of nanosilver in medicine.

d) Choose the value which represents a nanometre.

10^{-9} cm 10^{-9} m 10^{-9} mm 0.000000 m 10^{-3} cm

Exam questions

1 a) The table below shows some of the raw materials from which useful materials are made. Copy the table. Choose four useful materials from the list below and place them in their correct position in your table.

oxygen hydrogen
sodium chloride iron
ammonia plastics

Raw material	Useful materials	
air	nitrogen	
rocks		aluminium
crude oil	petrol	
sea		water

(4 marks)

b) Solid sodium chloride is a material which does not conduct electricity; however, when it is molten, it can be electrolysed. This electrolysis produces a metal and a gas.

i) What is meant by the term **electrolysis**? *(2 marks)*

ii) Explain why **solid** sodium chloride does not conduct electricity. *(2 marks)*

c) Aluminium is extracted from its ore by electrolysis. The purified ore is dissolved in molten cryolite and molten aluminium forms at the cathode lining of the electrolysis cell.

i) Name the ore from which aluminium is extracted. *(1 mark)*

ii) Write a half equation for the reaction occurring at the cathode. *(3 marks)*

d) Some modern materials contain nanoparticles. Nano-sized zinc oxide particles are used in sun creams.

i) What is the size range of nanoparticles in metres? *(1 mark)*

ii) Evaluate the risks of using nanoparticles in sun creams. *(1 mark)*

2 The diagram shows the laboratory apparatus used in the electrolysis of lead(II) bromide.

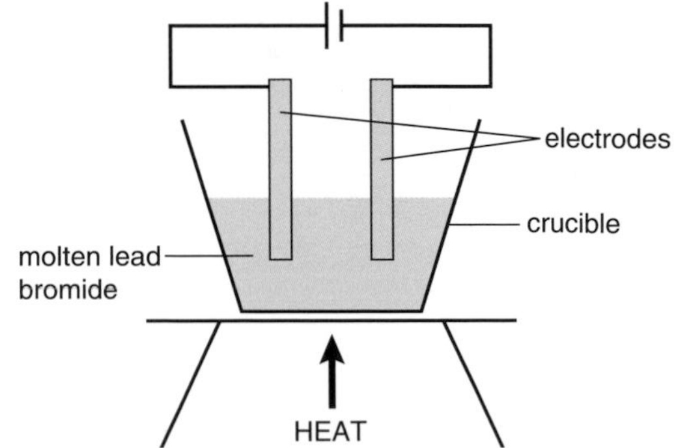

a) i) Why must the lead bromide be molten? *(1 mark)*

ii) Write an ionic equation for the reaction which takes place at the cathode. *(2 marks)*

b) Aluminium metal is extracted from pure aluminium oxide by electrolysis using the cell shown below:

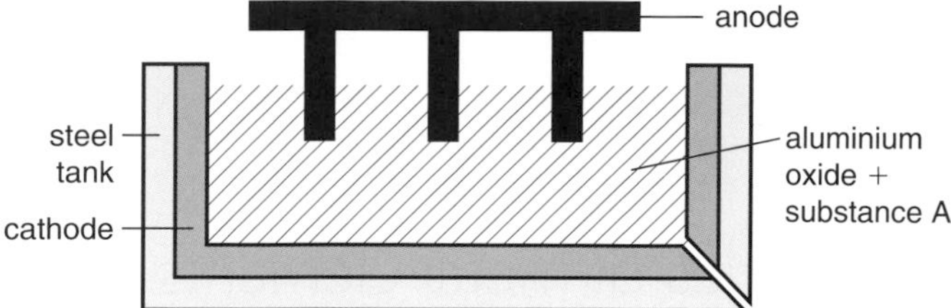

Describe how aluminium is produced in the above cell. Your answer should include:

* the name of the substance A and why it is added to the cell
* a description of what happens to the ions in the cell
* a balanced ionic equation for the reaction occurring at the cathode
* how the aluminium is removed from the cell
* an explanation as to why the anodes need to be periodically replaced.

In this question you will be assessed on using your written communication skills including the use of specialist science terms. *(9 marks)*

3 Ionic compounds like lead(II) bromide conduct electricity when molten.

a) Explain as fully as possible why ionic compounds conduct electricity when molten. *(2 marks)*

b) i) Draw a **labelled diagram** of the assembled apparatus used to carry out the electrolysis of molten lead(II) bromide. *(5 marks)*

ii) Name the material used to make the electrodes in this electrolysis. *(1 mark)*

iii) What would be observed at the positive electrode during the experiment? *(2 marks)*

iv) Name the products of this electrolysis. *(2 marks)*

v) Why does this electrolysis experiment need to be carried out in a fume cupboard? *(2 marks)*

4 The diagram shows the apparatus used in the electrolysis of lithium chloride.

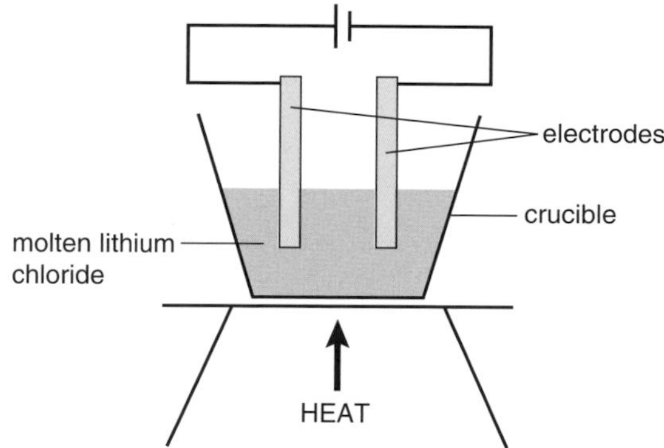

a) Why must the lithium chloride be molten? *(1 mark)*

b) Why does the electrolysis of lithium chloride need to be carried out in a fume cupboard? *(1 mark)*

c) What would you observe happening at the anode? *(1 mark)*

d) Write an ionic equation for the reaction which takes place at the cathode. *(2 marks)*

5 The diagram below shows the apparatus used in the electrolysis of molten lead(II) bromide.

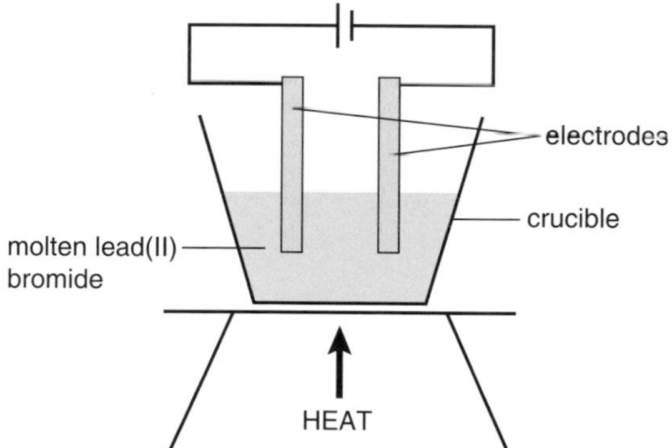

a) Explain fully why lead bromide does not conduct electricity in the solid state. *(1 mark)*

b) Why is the electrolysis of lead bromide carried out in a fume cupboard? *(1 mark)*

c) Describe what is formed at the **negative** electrode during the electrolysis of molten lead(II) bromide. *(1 mark)*

d) Write an **ionic** equation for the reaction which takes place at the **anode** during the electrolysis of molten lead(II) bromide. *(3 marks)*

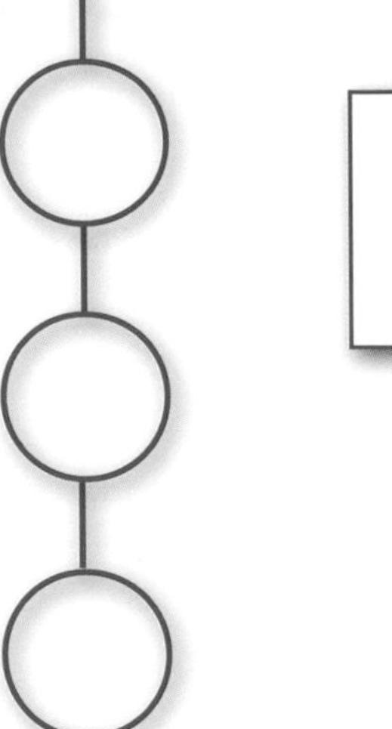

11 Metals, Metal Compounds and the Reactivity Series of Metals

▶ The reactivity series of metal elements

6000BC	4000BC	2000BC	1000AD	2000AD

Gold	Copper	Lead	Iron	Sodium	Aluminium
6000BC	4000–6000BC	3500BC	1200BC	1807AD	1825AD

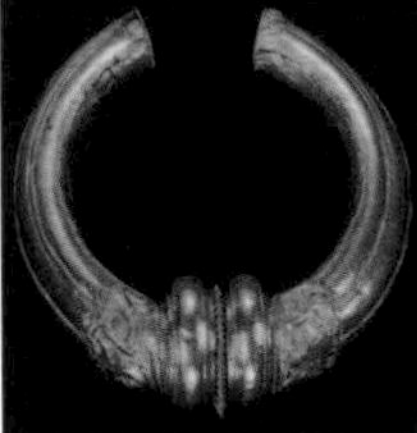

Gold objects have been found in the archaeological digs of the earliest known civilisations. This tubular gold torque was found in the north of Ireland 1st century BC.

Although copper did not come into widespread use until this time it is thought that copper beads found recently in Iraq date back to 9000BC.

Lead water pipes bearing the stamp of Emperors of ancient Rome are found throughout the world.

This iron bridge built in 1816 spans the Liffey. It was the first iron bridge in Ireland. This foot bridge was originally named the Liffey Bridge but is now called the Ha'penny because until 1919 there was a half-penny charge to cross it.

Sodium metal has very few commercial uses but is used as a heat exchanger in nuclear reactors.

Aluminium is one of the most versatile of modern metals yet it was more precious than gold when it was first discovered.

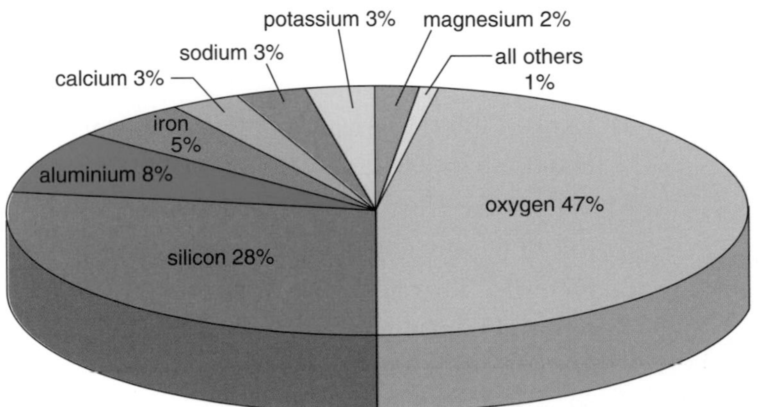

Figure 1 Abundance of elements in the Earth's crust

Gold and silver were known to the ancient civilisations. The timeline above also shows that copper objects were used long before objects were made from iron. The metals sodium and potassium, however, have only been discovered recently. The pie chart in Figure 1 shows the relative amounts of metals available in the Earth's crust. There is much more aluminium than iron; however, iron was in use thousands of years before aluminium was known.

These observations can be explained by the relative reactivity of the metals. Metal elements can be placed in a list beginning with the most reactive and ending with the least reactive: a **reactivity series**.

▶ Constructing a reactivity series of the metals

To construct a reactivity series a set of reactions are carried out on a selection of metals.

1. Reaction with air
2. Reaction with water
3. Reaction with steam
4. Reaction with acids
5. Displacement reactions

Reaction with air

Reaction when left in air	Symbol of metal	Reaction when heated in air	Apparatus
These soft metals can be cut easily with a knife revealing a shiny surface which quickly tarnishes	K	Burns with a lilac flame	deflagrating spoon; metal; heat
	Na	Burns with a bright yellow flame	
Reacts slowly with the air forming a layer of oxide	Ca	Burns with a brick red flame	tongs
	Mg	Burns with a bright white flame leaving a white ash	
	Al	Sheets of aluminium do not burn easily. Powdered aluminium burns with white sparks leaving a white solid	Use tongs to hold the metal in the flame of the Bunsen burner or place the metal in a crucible as in the apparatus below
	Zn	Burns leaving a yellow solid which when cooled changes to white	crucible; metal; pipe clay triangle; tripod; Bunsen burner; heat resistant mat
The oxide layer on iron is easily rubbed off the iron revealing more fresh metal which will continue to react	Fe	Sheets of iron do not burn easily. Iron wool or iron filings burn with white sparks forming a black solid	
	Cu	Sheets of copper quickly form a black layer of copper oxide. The black layer of copper oxide will form without heating	

The metals react with oxygen to form an oxide.

Example: aluminium + oxygen → aluminium oxide

$$4Al + 3O_2 \rightarrow 2Al_2O_3$$

Reaction of metals with water

Metal	Reaction with water	Apparatus	Further tests
K	Floats, moves rapidly around the surface, so much heat is released K bursts into a lilac flame, bubbles of gas released, colourless solution formed	metal; trough; water	Solution changes universal indicator from green to blue
Na	Floats, moves rapidly around the surface, so much heat is released Na melts and forms a sphere of molten metal, may burn with a yellow flame, colourless solution formed		
Ca	Ca granules will sink initially, continually rise to top and sink in turn, bubbles of gas evolved, beaker feels warm to the touch as heat is evolved, a grey gritty powdery solid forms in the water	test tube; beaker; inverted funnel; water; metal	The gas collected burns with a squeaky pop
Mg	Very few bubbles are observed even after leaving for several days		
Al			
Zn	No reaction		
Fe	The iron will rust after a few days		
Cu			

The more reactive metals react with water to form the metal hydroxide and hydrogen.

Example: sodium + water → sodium hydroxide + hydrogen

$$2Na + 2H_2O \rightarrow 2NaOH + H_2$$

Figure 2 Lithium, sodium and potassium react with water vapour in the air. To prevent this reaction, the metals are stored in oil

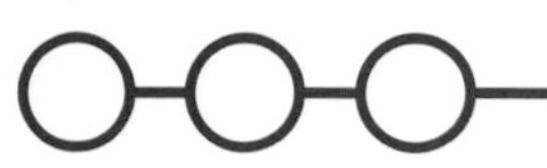

Reaction of metals with steam

Why are sodium, potassium and calcium not reacted with steam?

Metal	Reaction with steam	Apparatus	Further tests
Mg	Reacts when heated. Produces a very bright white light. A white powder remains.	damp mineral wool; metal; delivery tube; gas; gas jar; heat; heat; boiling tube; trough; water; beehive shelf	
Al	Aluminium foil will not react. Small pieces will react when the oxide layer is taken off. Aluminium powder reacts, when heated, to form a white powder.		The gas burns with a squeaky pop.
Zn	Reacts when heated. Glows as steam is passed over producing a yellow powder. Yellow powder becomes white when it is left to cool.		
Fe	Iron must be heated until it glows red before the steam is passed over. Reacts to form a black solid.	1. Heat the metal. 2. Move the Bunsen burner to heat the damp mineral wool to produce steam. Safety: remove the apparatus from the water immediately at the end of the experiment to prevent water from sucking back into the hot boiling tube.	

When a metal reacts with steam the metal oxide and hydrogen gas are formed.

Example: magnesium + steam → magnesium oxide + hydrogen

$$Mg + H_2O_{(g)} \rightarrow MgO + H_2$$

Reaction of metals with acids

Place a piece of the metal into a test tube that is 1/3 filled with dilute hydrochloric acid or dilute sulfuric acid.

Why are only a few granules of calcium used in this experiment?

Metal	Reaction with acid	Rate of reaction
Ca	* bubbles of gas produced * metal disappears quickly * colourless solution formed * test tube feels warm to the touch as heat is evolved. (Powdered aluminium is used as aluminium oxide layer adheres to the surface of the aluminium and protects it from reaction with the acid. Aluminium foil can be used if the aluminium oxide layer is removed with a scouring pad.)	↑ Rate of production of bubbles increases
Mg		
Al		
Zn		
Cu	no reaction	

What apparatus would you use to collect and test the gas produced when an acid reacts with a metal?

When an acid reacts with a metal, a salt and hydrogen are formed.

Example: zinc + hydrochloric acid → zinc chloride + hydrogen

$$Zn + 2HCl \rightarrow ZnCl_2 + H_2$$

zinc + sulfuric acid → zinc sulfate + hydrogen

$$Zn + H_2SO_4 \rightarrow ZnSO_4 + H_2$$

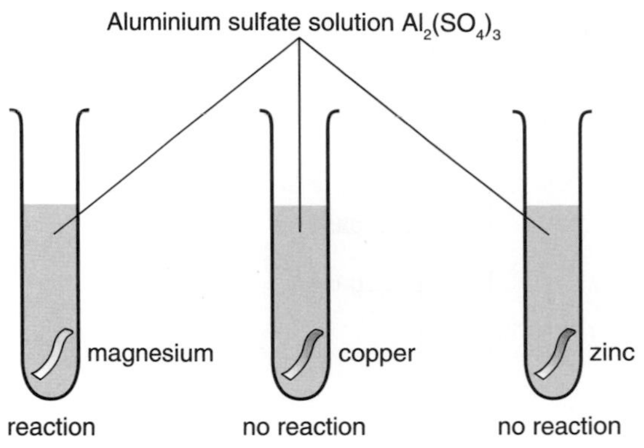

Figure 3 Reaction of metals with aluminium sulfate

Displacement reactions

A displacement reaction is one where a more reactive element displaces a less reactive element from its compound.

The more reactive metal atom forms an ion causing the less reactive metal ion to form an atom. (Displacement reactions are examples of redox reactions. See Chapter 9.)

Displacement reactions are useful when trying to place metals like aluminium into a reactivity series. Aluminium quickly forms an oxide layer in air. This oxide layer adheres (sticks) strongly to the surface of the aluminium protecting it from reacting with other chemicals.

A series of metal samples are placed into a test tube that is 2/3 filled with aluminium sulfate, as shown in Figure 3. A reaction is observed in the test tube containing the sample of magnesium. This indicates that the magnesium is more reactive than the aluminium. It can displace the aluminium from the compound. The copper and the zinc are not as reactive as the aluminium as they cannot displace the aluminium from its compound. Therefore, aluminium is placed below magnesium and above copper and zinc in the reactivity series.

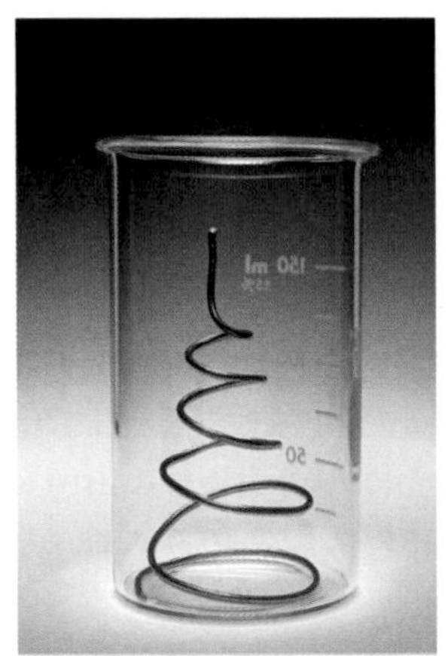
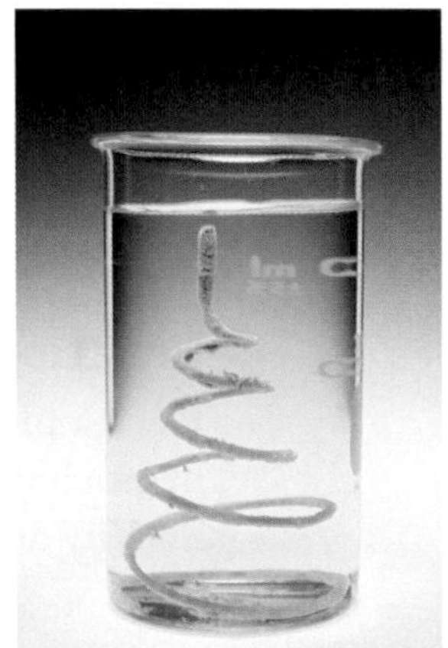

Figure 4 A spectacular displacement reaction! The copper displaces the silver from the silver nitrate. Silver crystals form on the surface of the wire

One way of remembering a list is to construct a sentence which tells a quirky story. Use those in Figures 5 and 6, or make up a better one of your own.

Merging the results of the series of reactions a)–e) produces the following reactivity series.

K	Most reactive ↑	**P**otassium
Na		**S**odium
Ca		**C**alcium
Mg		**M**agnesium
Al		**A**luminium
Zn		**Z**inc
Fe		**I**ron
Cu	Least reactive	**C**opper

Figure 5 Peter Smith Caught Measles And Zits in California!

Figure 6 Penny Savage Caught Mammoths And Zebras in Capetown!

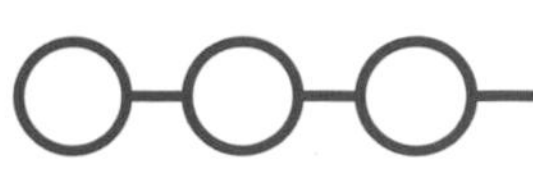

Aluminium is used in thin sheets as cooking foil. It is used in the manufacture of electricity pylons and fizzy drinks cans. These uses all require the aluminium to be unreactive. Yet we now know aluminium is a very reactive metal that is high up in the reactivity series. Objects made from aluminium are much less reactive than predicted by the reactivity series because the aluminium has a protective coating of aluminium oxide on its surface. The oxide layer adheres tightly to the aluminium. The oxide layer is unreactive.

Questions

1 Using your knowledge of the reactivity series predict if a reaction will occur between the following solutions and metals.
   a) aluminium and iron(III) sulfate solution
   b) calcium and sodium chloride solution
   c) zinc and copper(II) sulfate solution.

2 List the observations which can be made during the following displacement reaction: magnesium and copper(II) sulfate solution.

Placing an unfamiliar metal into the reactivity series

Lead and tin are relatively unreactive metals. Use the results of the following displacement reactions to place them into the reactivity series on page 144. (See Table 1 to check if you are correct.)

Metal \ Solution	$CuSO_4$	$ZnSO_4$	Fe_2SO_4	$Pb(NO_3)_2$	$SnCl_2$
Cu		✗	✗	✗	✗
Zn	✓		✓	✓	✓
Fe	✓	✗		✓	✓
Pb	✓	✗	✗		✗
Sn	✓	✗	✗	✓	

✗ indicates that no reaction took place; ✓ indicates a reaction is observed. When a reaction is observed the metal ion in the compound has been displaced by a more reactive metal.

▶ The relationship between the extraction of a metal from its ore and its position in the reactivity series

In general, metals are found combined in a compound in the Earth's crust. The metal must be extracted from the compound, the metal ore. The more reactive a metal is, the more difficult it is to extract from its ore.

The table on the left contains a more comprehensive reactivity series including the non-metal elements carbon and hydrogen.

Which metals will not displace hydrogen from acids? Explain your answer.

Return to the introductory paragraph of this chapter on page 140. Can you now explain the order in which the metallic elements were discovered.

Reactivity Series	Method of extraction
K	Extracted from ore by electrolysis (see Chapter 10)
Na	
Ca	
Mg	
Al	
C	
Zn	Extracted from ore by reduction with carbon or carbon monoxide
Fe	
Sn	
Pb	
H	
Cu	Found uncombined in nature (native) (but nowadays the supply is almost depleted)
Ag	
Au	

Table 1 Reactivity series of metals and carbon and hydrogen

▶ The extraction of iron in the blast furnace

The main ore of iron is an oxide known as haematite, Fe_2O_3.

Iron ore (Fe_2O_3), coke (C), and limestone ($CaCO_3$) are added through large hoppers into the top of the blast furnace. Hot air is blown into the furnace at the bottom.

> The coke burns in air in an extremely exothermic reaction to form carbon dioxide.
>
> coke + oxygen → carbon dioxide
>
> $$C + O_2 \rightarrow CO_2$$
>
> At these high temperatures more coke reacts with the carbon dioxide to form carbon monoxide. Carbon monoxide is the main reducing agent in the blast furnace.
>
> carbon dioxide + coke → carbon monoxide
>
> $$CO_2 + C \rightarrow 2CO$$
>
> 'Production of the reducing agent'

The carbon monoxide reduces the iron ore to iron.

iron(III) oxide + carbon monoxide → iron + carbon dioxide

$$Fe_2O_3 + 3CO \rightarrow 2Fe_{(l)} + 3CO_2$$

'Reduction of the iron ore'

The iron is a liquid at the temperature inside the furnace and falls to the bottom of the furnace where it is tapped off.

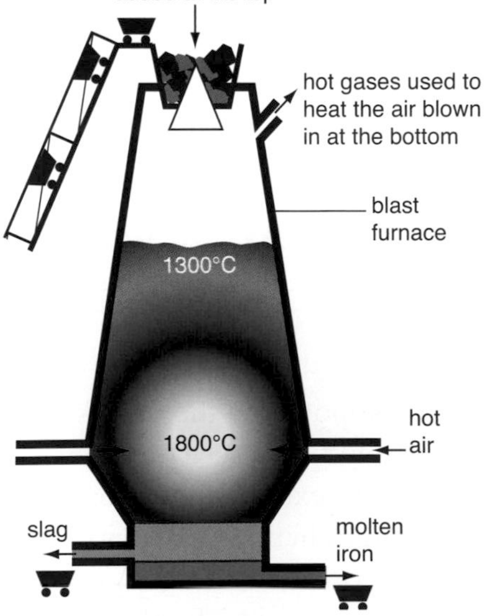

> The iron ore is not pure when it is added; it contains a lot of sand, silicon dioxide (SiO_2). The limestone is added into the furnace to remove the impurities.
>
> The limestone thermally decomposes to form calcium oxide and carbon dioxide.
>
> calcium carbonate (limestone) → calcium oxide + carbon dioxide
>
> $$CaCO_3 \rightarrow CaO + CO_2$$
>
> The basic calcium oxide reacts with the slightly acidic silicon dioxide to form calcium silicate, which is also known as slag.
>
> calcium oxide + silicon dioxide → calcium silicate
>
> $$CaO + SiO_2 \rightarrow CaSiO_{3(l)}$$
>
> 'Removal of the impurities in iron ore'

Figure 7 The blast furnace is a 30 metre tower made from steel and lined with heat resistant brick. It is continually run 24 hours a day for approximately 10 years when it is allowed to cool and the brick lining changed

The cost of producing iron and steel

The iron produced in the blast furnace is known as pig iron. The refining of pig iron into steel is arguably one of the most important technologies ever developed. Iron in the form of steel, an alloy of iron with carbon, has literally thousands of uses: in cars, lorries, trains, bridges, tools, musical instruments, houses, skyscrapers, cutlery, surgical instruments etc. Historians have even named a period of time after it: the Iron Age. However, the reserves of iron ore will not last for ever and the recycling of iron and steel is seen as increasingly important; in addition to preserving reserves of ore for future generations the energy used in recycling is half that required to produce a sample of iron by reduction of the ore in the blast furnace. Recycling also reduces the emission of greenhouse gases, as carbon dioxide is produced as a byproduct of the oxidation, reduction and thermal decomposition reactions occurring in the blast furnace. (See Chapter 14, page 185, The greenhouse effect.)

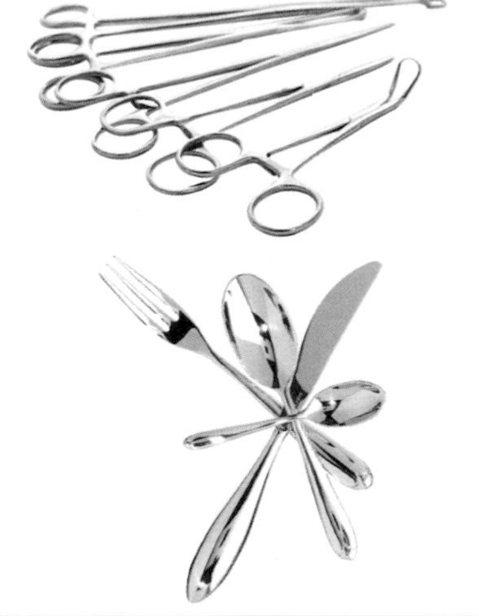

Figure 8 Some of the many uses of iron

Other ways to reduce the economic and environmental cost of the extraction process

The slag produced in the blast furnace is known as a byproduct as it is not the primary product required from the process. It is a useful byproduct as it is used in road building and can be blown in between the cavity walls in buildings as an insulator. The profit made from selling this byproduct reduces the cost of the iron.

The gases which leave the top of the furnace are extremely hot. These gases are captured and the heat is used to heat the blasts of warm air which are blown in at the bottom of the furnace.

The coke used to produce the reducing agent carbon monoxide may contain sulfur. Therefore, the gases are also scrubbed to ensure no sulfur dioxide escapes into the air. (See Chapter 14, page 203, Acid rain.)

Questions

3 Write balanced chemical equations for the following types of reaction which occur in the blast furnace.

a) oxidation b) reduction c) thermal decomposition

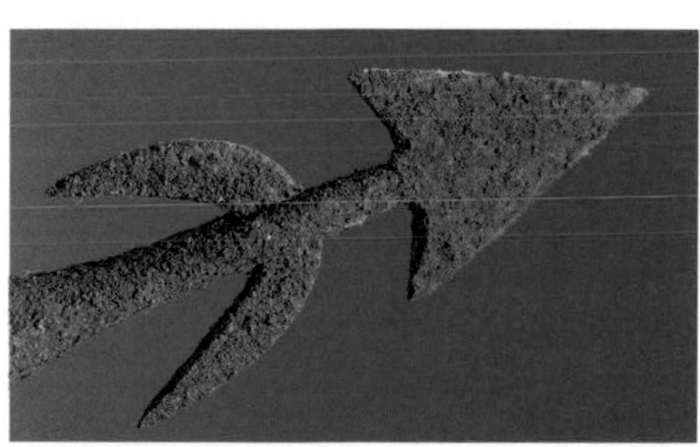

Figure 9 Flakes of hydrated iron(III) oxide falling from iron

Rust

Unlike aluminium, which forms a tightly bound protective oxide layer on its surface, iron forms an oxide layer which falls from its surface exposing more fresh iron to the air. This oxide is commonly known as rust.

It has the chemical name hydrated iron(III) oxide.

Rust **hydrated iron(III) oxide** $Fe_2O_3.xH_2O$

The cost of rusting of iron and steel to the economy is estimated to be hundreds of thousands of pounds every year. Large industries have evolved to try to combat this problem. Preventing rust is possible when the causes of rust are fully understood.

Figure 10 Aluminium oxide adheres tightly to the surface of aluminium

Investigating the causes of rust

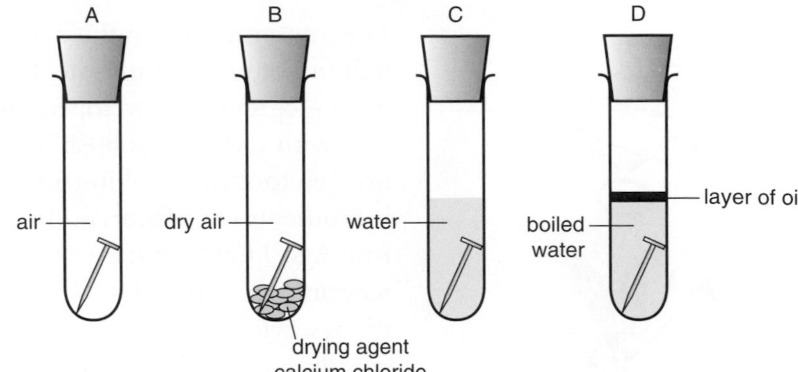

Figure 11 Iron nails in four different environments

Iron nails are left in four different environments as shown in the diagram above. The presence or absence of rust is noted after one week and is recorded in the table below.

Test tube	Environment	Elements present	Presence/absence of rust
A	air	iron, oxygen and water	rust produced
B	calcium chloride is a drying agent and absorbs the water in the air	iron and oxygen	no rust produced
C	water contains dissolved oxygen	iron, oxygen and water	rust produced
D	boiling water removes all the dissolved oxygen. The layer of oil prevents the oxygen from redissolving in the water again.	iron and water	no rust produced

The results of the experiments show that rust is the product of the reaction between iron, water and oxygen.

When metals react with oxygen in the air to form oxides the metal is said to **corrode**. Rusting is the term given to the corrosion of iron or iron in the form of steel.

Methods to prevent rust

Most methods for rust prevention are **barrier methods**. They provide a barrier between the iron and oxygen and water.

Barrier method of rust prevention	Example of use
Painting	
Oiling	

Barrier method of rust prevention	Example of use
Plastic coating	
Metal plating Several different metals are used to plate iron to act as a barrier, thus preventing exposure of iron to water and oxygen. For example, food cans made from iron are plated with tin. Galvanising is the term given to iron which is plated (completely covered) with zinc.	galvanising chromium plating

Figure 12 A 1 kg disc of zinc designed to be bolted on to the **outside** of the hull of a ship. The amazing thing about sacrificial protection is that the more reactive metal will react even if it is not in direct contact with the water and oxygen. It just has to be attached to the iron

Sacrificial protection

In some cases barrier methods of rust prevention can be inappropriate or too costly. Marine oil rigs are massive structures made from steel. They are placed on the sea bed surrounded by water, oxygen and salts which act as a catalyst for the formation of rust. They are prevented from rusting by attaching zinc bars to the steel frame. The zinc, which is higher up in the reactivity series than iron, will react with the water and oxygen first, preventing the iron from reacting. This type of protection is known as sacrificial protection. The iron will not begin to react until the zinc bar is almost corroded. The zinc bars are checked regularly and replaced when necessary. Magnesium bars attached to the hulls of ships and to petrol storage tanks protect the iron in the same way.

Galvanising provides a dual protection against rust. When the iron object is fully covered it acts as a barrier, preventing water and oxygen from reaching the iron. Then if the zinc coating becomes chipped it acts as a sacrificial protection; although the air and water are now in contact with the iron, the zinc reacts first as it is higher up in the reactivity series.

▶ Exam questions

1 Strontium (Sr) is a typical Group II element.

a) Would you expect strontium to react more vigorously or less vigorously than calcium when put in water? Give a reason for your answer. *(2 marks)*

b) When strontium reacts with water an alkaline solution is formed and a gas is given off. What is the alkaline solution and what gas is given off? *(2 marks)*

c) What formula would you expect for the oxide formed when strontium reacts with oxygen? *(1 mark)*

2 A student investigated displacement reactions and recorded some observations in the table below.

Reactants	Some observations
copper + silver nitrate solution	colourless solution turned blue, solid formed
iron + zinc sulfate solution	nothing happened
silver + iron(II) sulfate solution	nothing happened
zinc + copper(II) sulfate solution	blue solution turned colourless, solid formed
iron + copper(II) sulfate solution	blue solution turned colourless, solid formed

a) What colour would you expect for the solid formed when iron reacts with copper(II) sulfate solution? *(1 mark)*

b) Why did the colourless solution turn **blue** when copper powder reacted with silver nitrate solution? *(1 mark)*

c) Use the information in the table to place the metals copper, iron, silver and zinc in order of reactivity, giving the **most** reactive first. *(2 marks)*

d) Which of the metals copper, iron, silver and zinc would you expect to react most quickly with dilute hydrochloric acid? *(1 mark)*

3 This question is about metals and their compounds. You may find your Data Leaflet useful.

a) Calcium and magnesium are both alkaline earth metals.

i) To which group in the Periodic Table do calcium and magnesium belong? *(1 mark)*

ii) Describe **two** things you would observe happening when a piece of magnesium ribbon is burned in the air. *(2 marks)*

iii) Copy and complete the word equation for the reaction of magnesium with oxygen. *(1 mark)*

magnesium + oxygen → ________

b) Calcium metal reacts with water.

i) Describe **three** things you would observe happening when calcium is added to water. *(3 marks)*

ii) Give **one** safety precaution which should be taken when carrying out the reaction between calcium and water. *(1 mark)*

iii) Copy and complete the word equation for the reaction of calcium with water. *(2 marks)*

calcium + water → ______ + ______

c) Magnesium reacts very slowly with water but it reacts quite vigorously with steam.

i) What gas is formed when magnesium reacts with steam? *(1 mark)*

ii) What is the other product of the reaction of magnesium with steam? *(1 mark)*

d) Copper sulfate can be made by reacting solid green copper carbonate powder with dilute sulfuric acid?

i) Describe **two** things you would observe happening when copper carbonate reacts with sulfuric acid. *(2 marks)*

ii) Why can copper sulfate not be prepared by adding dilute sulfuric acid directly to copper? *(1 mark)*

e) Magnesium powder reacts quickly when stirred with copper(II) sulfate solution.

i) Describe the colour change of the solution in this reaction. *(2 marks)*

ii) Write a balanced **symbol** equation for the reaction of magnesium with copper(II) sulfate. *(2 marks)*

iii) What **type** of chemical reaction is the reaction between magnesium and copper sulfate? *(1 mark)*

4 Iron can be protected from rusting by sacrificial protection. This protection can be investigated by wrapping different metals around iron nails and leaving them in water for one week.

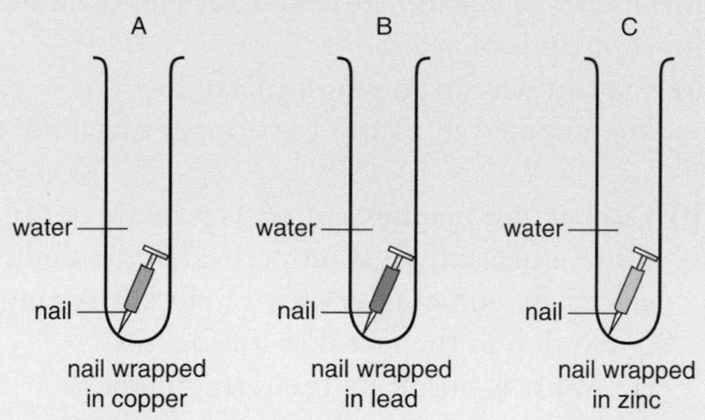

a) In which tube would **no** rusting occur? *(1 mark)*

b) Use the idea of sacrificial protection to explain your answer to part **a)**. *(2 marks)*

5 This question is about metals and their compounds.

a) One physical property of a metal is that it conducts electricity. Give **two** other physical properties of metals. *(2 marks)*

b) Potassium and sodium are alkali metals.

i) How are these metals stored in the school laboratory? *(1 mark)*

ii) What type of base is an alkali? *(1 mark)*

c) A teacher demonstrated the reaction of sodium with water to her class. She made sure that all the pupils were wearing safety glasses. Then she cut a **small** piece of sodium and carefully placed it into a trough of water.

i) Why did the teacher only use a small piece of sodium? *(1 mark)*

ii) Describe three things that the pupils would observe when sodium reacts with water. Your quality of written communication will be assessed in this answer. *(4 marks)*

d) Copy and complete the table below which gives some information about two metal elements. *(4 marks)*

Element	Group	Period	Electronic structure
Magnesium	II		
		4	2,8,8,1

e) i) Beryllium, magnesium and calcium belong to Group II in the Periodic Table. Which of these three metals is the most reactive? *(1 mark)*

ii) Give **two** things you would observe when dilute hydrochloric acid is added to calcium carbonate. *(2 marks)*

iii) Copy and complete the word equation for the reaction of calcium carbonate with dilute hydrochloric acid. *(2 marks)*

calcium carbonate + hydrochloric acid → ____ + ____ + ____

f) Many metal compounds are coloured solids. Others are white. Give the correct colour for each of the four compounds below. Choose from the list of colours. *(2 marks)*

white green red blown blue black

i) copper(II) carbonate

ii) magnesium oxide

iii) hydrated copper(II) sulfate

iv) anhydrous copper(II) sulfate

6 A student investigated the reactivity of magnesium using displacement reactions and recorded her observations in the table below.

Reactants	Observations
magnesium + copper(II) sulfate	blue solution turned colourless and a solid formed
magnesium + iron(II) sulfate	pale green solution turned colourless and a solid formed
iron + zinc sulfate	no reaction
iron + copper(II) sulfate	blue solution went pale green and a solid formed
zinc + copper(II) sulfate	blue solution turned colourless and a solid formed
zinc + magnesium sulfate	no reaction

a) Why did the blue solution turn colourless when zinc was added to copper(II) sulfate? *(1 mark)*

b) Use the information in the table to place the metals iron, copper, magnesium and zinc in order of reactivity, starting with the **most reactive**. *(2 marks)*

c) Which one of the four metals above forms a black layer of metal oxide when it is strongly heated in the air? *(1 mark)*

7 a) Iron is extracted from iron(III) oxide (haematite) in a blast furnace.

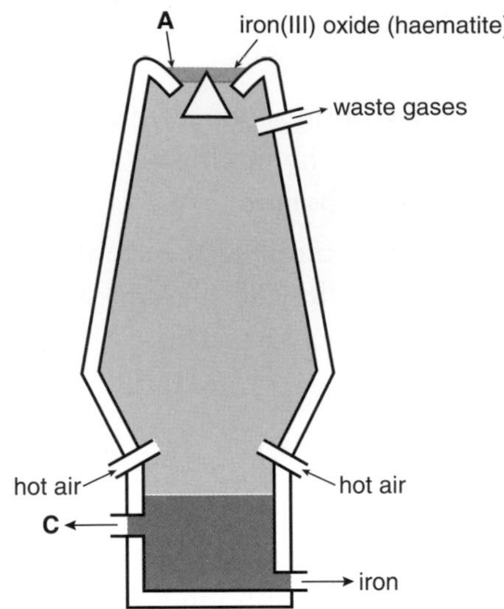

Describe the production of the iron from its ore in the blast furnace.
You should include the following information:

- The name of the two substances added at **A**.
- The name of the substance removed at **C**.
- Descriptions of the main reactions that take place.
- A balanced formula equation to show the reduction of iron(III) oxide to iron. *(8 marks)*

b) At the bottom of the blast furnace coke reacts to form carbon dioxide. Write a balanced symbol equation for this reaction. *(2 marks)*

c) The carbon dioxide reacts with more coke to form carbon monoxide.

i) Write a balanced symbol equation for this reaction. *(3 marks)*

ii) What is the importance of carbon monoxide in the extraction process? *(1 mark)*

iii) Write a balanced symbol equation to show the part played by the carbon monoxide in the extraction process. *(3 marks)*

d) Sand (SiO_2) is an impurity in the raw materials. The sand is removed from the blast furnace by reacting it with calcium oxide.

i) Write a balanced symbol equation to show how calcium oxide is formed in the blast furnace. *(2 marks)*

ii) Write a balanced symbol equation for the reaction of sand with calcium oxide. *(2 marks)*

8 Magnesium metal does not occur uncombined in nature. It was first isolated by Sir Humphrey Davey in 1808 by passing an electric current through molten magnesium chloride. Copper metal does occur in nature and has been known for thousands of years.

a) Explain why magnesium metal does not occur uncombined in nature but copper metal does. *(2 marks)*

b) Copper and magnesium are typical metals and show similar physical properties. Both conduct electricity and copper's use in electric wiring is also due to the fact that it is ductile.

i) What is meant by the term ductile? *(1 mark)*

ii) Explain why metals conduct electricity. *(3 marks)*

iii) Give **two other** physical properties of metals. *(2 marks)*

c) Compounds of copper vary in their colour. Copy and complete the table below, giving the colour of the substances listed.

Substance	Colour
copper(II) carbonate	
copper(II) sulfate solution	

(2 marks)

d) Magnesium metal burns in air with a bright white flame as shown. The product of the reaction is mainly magnesium oxide with about 10% magnesium nitride.

i) Describe the appearance of magnesium oxide. *(2 marks)*

ii) Write a balanced symbol equation for the formation of the magnesium oxide. *(3 marks)*

iii) Give the formula for the magnesium nitride. *(1 mark)*

e) Magnesium metal reacts with dilute hydrochloric acid.

i) What would you observe when magnesium reacts with dilute hydrochloric acid. *(2 marks)*

ii) Write a balanced symbol equation for the reaction between magnesium and dilute hydrochloric acid. *(3 marks)*

iii) Name **one other** metal which reacts **safely** with dilute hydrochloric acid. *(1 mark)*

12 Water

► Ensuring water is fit to drink

Although about 70% of the surface of the Earth is covered in water, very little of it is fit to drink. Water must be treated first, to remove the harmful substances. This is carried out at a water treatment plant.

In many parts of the world the population only have access to dirty water. We are encouraged by charity organisations to fund efficient water pumps so that others have access to drinking water. The San People or Bushmen of the Kalahari desert rarely drink water. There is not a steady supply in this semi-arid area. They obtain all of their water requirements from eating plant roots or desert melons. We are very fortunate to have an almost endless supply of drinking water piped into our homes.

Figure 1 Many populations rely on pumps funded by charity organisations for a meagre supply of drinking water

Figure 2 Tap water is fit to drink but it is not pure in the chemical sense

> Hard water is water which will not lather *easily* **with soap**.

► Hard and soft water

The drinking water we obtain from taps in our homes is not pure water. Although harmful substances are removed from water at water treatment plants and chlorine gas is added to kill any bacteria present, tap water may also contain other naturally occurring dissolved substances. These dissolved substances improve the taste of the water and make it useful to some commercial enterprises, for example in the brewing industry. However, they can also be a nuisance. Some sources of water are said to be **hard** due to the type of substances dissolved.

Hard water is water which does not lather readily with soap.

Disadvantages of hard water		
Wastes soap		It takes more soap to produce a lather, thus it costs more. The scum formed is unsightly.
Causes scum when reacted with soap		
Causes **fur** or **limescale** on hot water pipes, kettles and in hot water tanks; blocks fine pipes in dishwashers and the tiny holes in shower heads. (Temporary hard water only, see page 155.)	 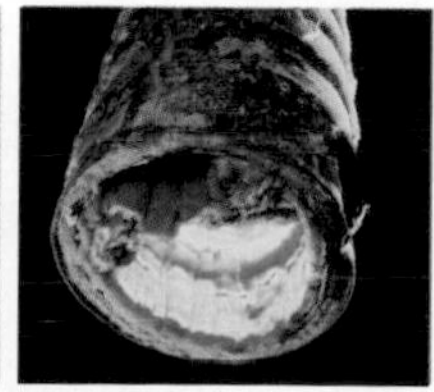	Excessive scale can block hot water pipes and shower heads and prevent dishwashers from working properly. When limescale covers the element of a kettle, energy is used to heat the limescale as well as the water, unnecessarily using extra energy and increasing the cost.

Table 1 Disadvantages of hard water

Advantages of hard water	
Tastes better	
Necessary for brewing beer	
Necessary for tanning leather	
Good for bones and teeth	 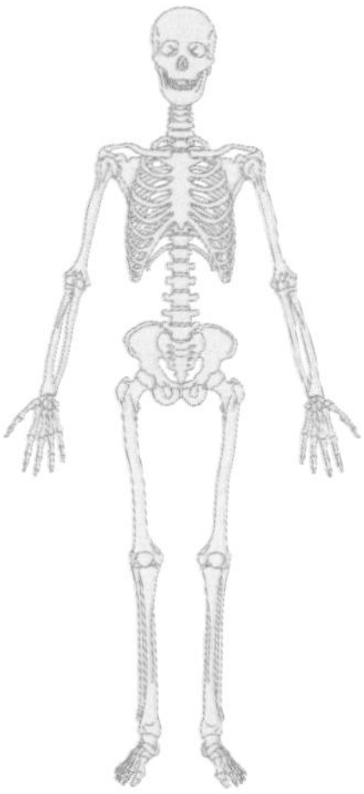
May help to prevent heart disease	

Table 2 Advantages of hard water

Hard water has no adverse effects on detergents. Hard water and soft water will both lather easily with detergents.

Soap substitutes known as detergents were developed to decrease the unwanted effects of soap scum caused by hard water. Hard water has no effect on detergents.

Temporary hardness is hardness that can be removed by boiling.

Permanent hardness is hardness that cannot be removed by boiling.

Temporary and permanent hard water

There are two types of hard water, temporary hard water and permanent hard water.

Temporary hardness is hardness which can be removed by boiling.

Permanent hardness is hardness which cannot be removed by boiling.

Samples of hard water can contain only temporary hardness or only permanent hardness or both types of hardness.

Hardness in water is caused by the presence of dissolved calcium ions Ca^{2+} and/or magnesium ions Mg^{2+}.

Temporary hardness is caused by the hydrogen carbonates of calcium and magnesium.

Permanent hardness is caused by the sulfates of calcium and magnesium.

This information is summarised in the table below.

Type of hardness	Definition	Compounds dissolved in the water	
temporary	hardness which can be removed by boiling	calcium hydrogen carbonate	$Ca(HCO_3)_2$
		magnesium hydrogen carbonate	$Mg(HCO_3)_2$
permanent	hardness which cannot be removed by boiling	calcium sulfate	$CaSO_4$
		magnesium sulfate	$MgSO_4$

Table 3 Temporary and permanent hardness

Return to Table 1 on page 153, on the disadvantages of hard water. Explain why some of the disadvantages are only due to temporary hard water supplies.

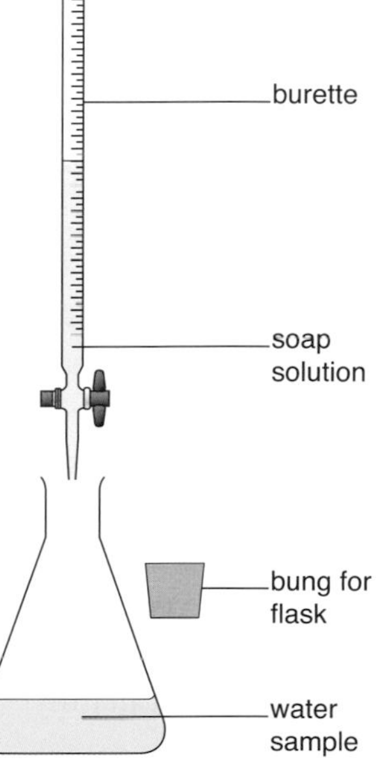

Testing water samples for hardness

1. Place 10 cm^3 of the water sample into a conical flask.
2. Add 1 cm^3 of soap solution from a burette.
3. Stopper the flask and shake.
4. Continue to add soap solution 1 cm^3 at a time and shake until a lather lasting for more than 30 seconds is formed. (This lather is called a permanent lather.)
5. Record the volume of soap solution required to produce a permanent lather.
6. The harder the water sample the greater the volume of soap solution required to produce a permanent lather.

Testing hard water samples for the presence of temporary or permanent hardness

1. Boil the sample for a short time.
2. Once the sample has cooled follow steps 1–5 above.
3. Samples which contain temporary hardness will take ***less*** soap solution after boiling to produce a permanent lather. The temporary hardness is removed by boiling.

Samples which contain only permanent hardness will need the ***same*** volume of soap solution to produce a permanent lather after boiling as before boiling. Boiling the sample has no effect on the hardness.

The word permanent is used in two different ways when discussing hard water. A permanent lather is a lather formed between water and soap which lasts for more than 30 seconds. Permanent hard water is water which cannot be softened by boiling.

▶ How temporary hardness arises in water

Dissolved calcium carbonate is the main cause of temporary hardness in water supplies. It forms when calcium carbonate in limestone rock dissolves in rain water. Rain water is a weak acid, pH~5.5.

Water vapour in the air reacts with carbon dioxide in the air to form carbonic acid.

$$H_2O_{(g)} + CO_{2(aq)} \rightarrow H_2CO_{3(aq)}$$

When this weak acid falls on limestone rock it reacts with the calcium carbonate in the rock to form soluble calcium hydrogen carbonate.

$$H_2CO_{3(aq)} + CaCO_{3(s)} \rightarrow Ca(HCO_3)_{2(aq)}$$

The following equation describes the process in one step.

$$H_2O_{(g)} + CO_{2(g)} + CaCO_{3(s)} \rightarrow Ca(HCO_3)_{2(aq)}$$

As the rain water dissolves the limestone in the rock it leaves spaces in the rock which over many thousands of years become caves. The hard water flows from the caves and ends up in our water supply. Some water drips slowly down from the roof of the cave; some of the water evaporates and deposits tiny particles of solid calcium carbonate. These collect on the roof of the cave and eventually build up into icicle-like fingers of calcium carbonate rock, known as stalactites. Similar fingers of calcium carbonate built up from the floor are known as stalagmites. On very rare occasions, the two formations meet and a pillar of calcium carbonate is formed.

The marble arch caves in County Fermanagh boast spectacular examples of stalactites, stalagmites and pillars. Parts of the cave are open to tourists to view from specially constructed paths. Other parts are open to sports enthusiasts for 'pot-holing'.

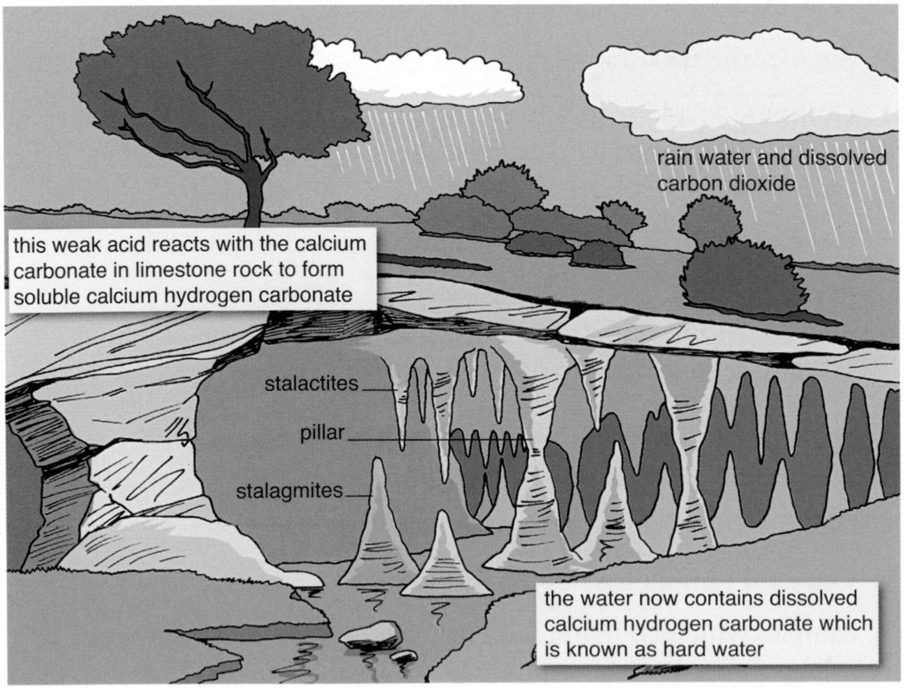

Figure 3 How temporary hardness arises in water

Figure 4 Stalactites in the Marble Arch caves in County Fermanagh

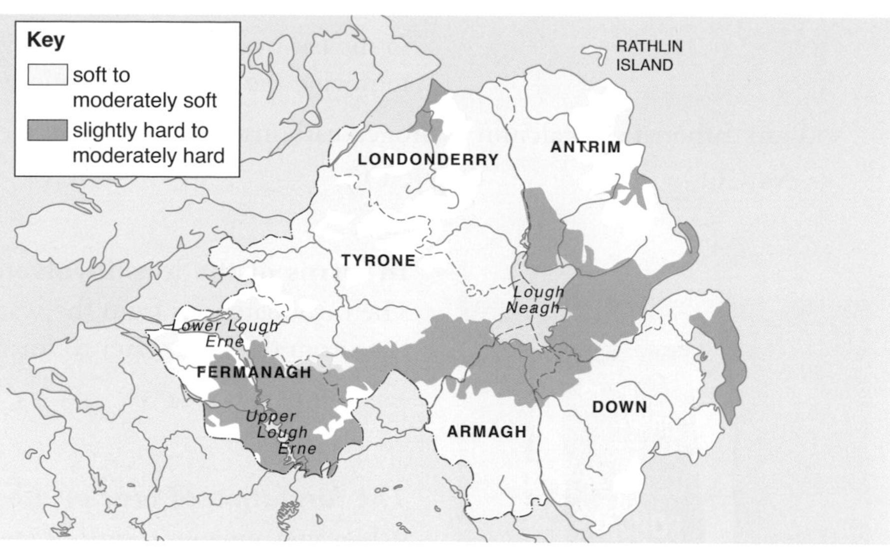

Figure 5 Map of water hardness in Northern Ireland

▶ Methods of removing hardness from water

By boiling (temporary hardness only)

Temporary hard water contains dissolved calcium hydrogen carbonate. When it is heated it thermally decomposes to form solid calcium carbonate (thermal decomposition: the breakdown of a compound using heat). The calcium hydrogen carbonate is no longer present in the water and therefore the water is no longer hard. However, the solid calcium carbonate is left behind. In a kettle this builds up as limescale on the element. In a dishwasher minute particles of solid calcium carbonate block the very fine water jets and prevent the machine from washing the dishes properly. (See the disadvantages of hard water, Table 1, page 153.)

$$\text{calcium hydrogen carbonate} \xrightarrow{\text{heat}} \text{calcium carbonate} + \text{carbon dioxide} + \text{water}$$

$$Ca(HCO_3)_{2(aq)} \xrightarrow{\text{heat}} CaCO_{3(s)} + CO_{2(g)} + H_2O_{(l)}$$

(Look carefully at this balanced chemical equation. It is the reverse of the equation for formation of temporary hard water, page 156.)

In terms of the ions involved

The hydrogen carbonate ions from the hard water are broken down by heat to form insoluble carbonate ions.

$$2HCO_3^-{}_{(aq)} \xrightarrow{\text{heat}} CO_3^{2-}{}_{(s)} + CO_{2(g)} + H_2O_{(l)}$$

Adding washing soda crystals, hydrated sodium carbonate, $Na_2CO_3.10H_2O$

Washing soda crystals are colourless, ice-like crystals of sodium carbonate which contain water of crystallisation. When they are added to water they initially dissolve then react with the dissolved chemicals in the hard water to form a precipitate of calcium carbonate, thus removing the dissolved chemicals which cause the hardness.

sodium carbonate + calcium hydrogen carbonate → calcium carbonate + sodium hydrogen carbonate

$$Na_2CO_{3(aq)} + Ca(HCO_3)_{2(aq)} \rightarrow CaCO_{3(s)} + 2NaHCO_{3(aq)}$$

Figure 6 Hydrated sodium carbonate, washing soda crystals

In terms of the ions involved

The carbonate ions from the washing soda react with the calcium ions from the hard water to form a precipitate of calcium carbonate:

$$CO_3^{2-}{}_{(aq)} + Ca^{2+}{}_{(aq)} \rightarrow CaCO_{3(s)}$$

The formation of precipitates

When two aqueous solutions are mixed sometimes the ions react to form an insoluble substance. This type of reaction is known as a precipitation reaction. The reaction of washing soda with hard water is an example of a precipitation reaction. Other examples include the reaction of sodium hydroxide solution or ammonium hydroxide solution with selected metal ions (see Chapter 6, page 92). The precipitate is the solid which appears when the two solutions are mixed. The photograph shows the reaction between two colourless solutions to form a yellow powdery precipitate.

Figure 7 Formation of lead iodide, a yellow, powdery precipitate

Ions in two solutions reacting together to form a precipitate

Washing soda crystals are one of the ingredients in bath salts. When added to bath water they give the water a smooth and silky texture. Even in regions where the water is only slightly hard putting bath salts into a bath will leave a grey ring of calcium carbonate precipitate around the water level.

Figure 8 Bath salts to soften and scent water

Using an ion exchange resin

By using an ion exchange resin, the ions in the water which cause hardness are removed and replaced with ions which do not cause hardness.

An ion exchange resin is made from tiny sticky resin beads which contain loosely held sodium or hydrogen ions. Sodium ions and hydrogen ions do not cause hardness in water. The resin beads are packed into a column and the water is allowed to trickle through

the column. The calcium ions and magnesium ions which cause the hardness are trapped by the column and are replaced by sodium or hydrogen ions. You may have seen an ion exchange column fitted to one of the taps in your science laboratory.

In terms of the ions involved

Calcium ions which cause hardness in water are removed and replaced with sodium ions which do not cause hardness in water.

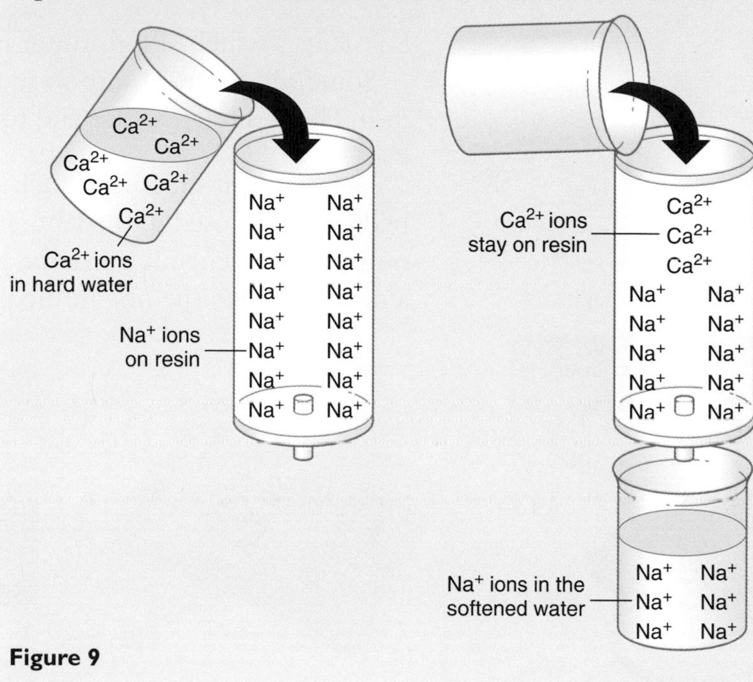

Figure 9

Interpreting tables of results for tests carried out on water samples

Water sample	Volume of soap required to produce a lather lasting for more than 30 seconds		
	Untreated sample	After boiling	After adding washing soda
A	2	2	2
B	23	12	2
C	18	18	2
D	14	2	2
E	4	4	2

The table shows the volume of soap solution required to form a permanent lather with 15 cm^3 of six different water samples before and after various treatments.

Washing soda is added to remove hardness. The final column records the volume of soap solution required to produce a permanent lather for a sample of soft water.

Sample A is soft water.

Sample B is the hardest water because it requires the most soap solution to produce a permanent lather. This should not be confused with sample C. Sample C contains only permanent hard water as it is not removed by boiling.

Sample B contains both temporary and permanent hard water as only some of the hardness is removed by boiling.

Sample D contains temporary hard water only as all of the hardness is removed by boiling.

Sample E contains permanent hardness as it is not removed by boiling.

► Interaction of substances with moist air

Water vapour in the air can damage optical and electronic equipment, such as cameras or computers, and leather goods, such as shoes and handbags. Often they are stored with packets of a substance called silica gel. The silica gel absorbs the water vapour in the air and prevents it from damaging the lenses or the electronics or leaving white marks on leather.

Substances which absorb water from the air are called **desiccants**.

Some substances absorb so much water from the air they dissolve in it. These substances are said to be **deliquescent**.

Deliquescent substances such as calcium chloride and sodium hydroxide are used in the laboratory to protect chemicals from moisture. The chemical may be placed in a piece of glassware called a desiccator like the one in the picture.

Figure 10 A desiccator

Figure 11 A packet of silica gel

Figure 12 Beads of silica gel

Silica gel is also used to dry the air in systems which use compressed air such as the brake system on high speed trains. The silica gel absorbs moisture from the air preventing damage due to condensation or moisture which can lead to brake failure.

► Fluoridation of water supplies

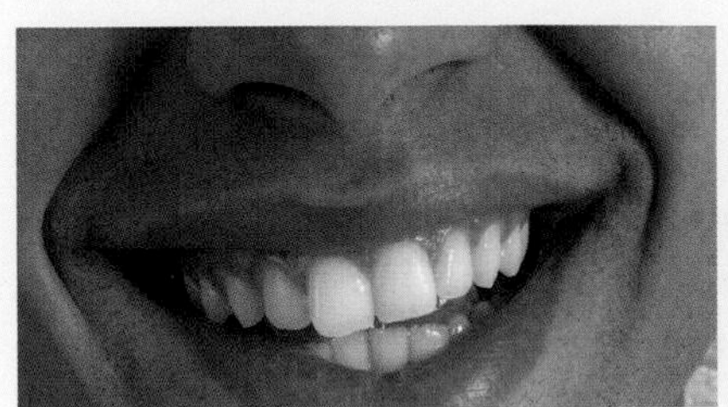

Figure 13 Healthy teeth and gums from use of fluoride toothpaste

Oral hygiene has an impact on appearance, diet, nutrition and speech. It is recommended that everyone visit a dentist twice a year and brush their teeth at least twice a day with a fluoride toothpaste.

Fluoride is the common name given to the substance sodium fluoride, which is the active ingredient in fluoride toothpastes. Sodium fluoride increases the resistance of teeth to attack from acid and can reverse the loss of tooth enamel. Fluoride is most effective when applied directly to teeth. However, in the middle of the last century it was suggested that adding fluoride to public water supplies was an efficient way to ensure all of the population had access to the benefits of fluoride. The suggestion to fluoridate water supplies caused immediate controversy and the debate still rages today.

In the table below are some statements supporting the campaign for fluoridation and some statements against water fluoridation. Use the information to discuss this controversial issue.

Arguments used to support the campaign for fluoridation of water supplies	Arguments used to oppose the campaign for fluoridation of water supplies
Increases the resistance of teeth to acid decay	There are other ways to deliver fluoride other than in the public water supply. Fluoride does not need to be swallowed to prevent tooth decay
Reverses the effects of loss of tooth enamel	Not effective enough to justify cost
Significantly lowers the number of cavities in teeth	High concentrations cause dental fluorosis (which ranges from tiny white specks on the tooth enamel to black stains and cracking of teeth) and skeletal fluorosis (which can lead to very limited joint movement and muscle wasting)
World Health Organisation (WHO) has set a low maximum concentration of fluoride permitted to avoid severe dental fluorosis and skeletal fluorosis	Ethical issues: Many people regard fluoride as a medicine and therefore evidence of its effect should be subject to the same rigorous testing as used for other prescribed drugs The dosage cannot be controlled or monitored The response of the recipient to various doses of fluoride ingested by drinking fluoridated water cannot be monitored Ingestion of fluoride by the very elderly, diabetics or those suffering from kidney failure can lead to very serious health problems Many disagree with the principle of mass medication
Fluoride cannot be a medicine as it occurs in all water supplies in much the same way as hardness occurs in water, although no water source in Northern Ireland contains fluoride at a level likely to affect dental health either negatively or positively. Fluoride is also found in fish and tea	Tooth decay has dropped to the same rate in countries with and without water fluoridation

Table 4 The arguments for and against the fluoridation of water supplies

The debate may be solved by unbiased, up-to-date research. Studies are needed to provide information on the effect of water fluoridation on people's teeth, allowing for the fact that fluoride toothpaste is in general use. Account should be taken of the effect of sugar consumption which has increased dramatically since the first debate on fluoridation of water supplies took place in the mid 20th century.

▶ Exam questions

1 Jane went to visit her friend Jacques who lived in Brussels, a hard water region. Jane noticed that she needed more soap when she washed than she used at home.

a) Why did Jane need more soap when she washed in Brussels? *(1 mark)*

When Jacques boils water, he uses a simple cheap kettle because of the scale which builds up in the kettle.

b) What does this tell you about the **type** of hard water in Brussels? *(1 mark)*

c) Give **one** advantage of hard water. *(1 mark)*

Before putting water in his steam iron, Jacques always passes the water through an ion exchanger.

d) Why does he use an ion exchanger? *(1 mark)*

2 Hard water is water which does not lather easily with soap.

a) What effect does hard water have on detergents? *(1 mark)*

b) Give **two** advantages of hard water. *(2 marks)*

c) Temporary hard water can be softened by boiling the water. Give **one other** way of making hard water soft. *(1 mark)*

3 You are provided with water samples from two different rivers.

a) Describe how you would carry out a fair test to **compare** the hardness of the two samples. *(3 marks)*

b) What is meant by permanent hardness? *(1 mark)*

c) Name **one** method of removing permanent hardness. *(1 mark)*

4 The following experiment was carried out to investigate the hardness of two water samples.

Step 1 Place the two water samples into two separate test tubes.

Step 2 Add 1 cm^3 of Substance A to each test tube and shake.

Step 3 Repeat step 2 until a permanent lather is formed.

a) Name substance A. *(1 mark)*

b) What would you do to ensure that this is a fair test? *(1 mark)*

c) How would you use the results of this experiment to compare the two water samples? *(1 mark)*

d) Name the **type** of water hardness which can be removed by boiling and give **one** disadvantage of this type of hardness. *(2 marks)*

5 Water samples were collected from four towns. The table below gives information about the amount of soap solution that was needed to form a lather with each of the four samples.

Town	Sample (cm^3)	Soap needed if the water sample has not been boiled/cm^3	Soap needed if the water sample has been boiled/cm^3
A	50	4.0	4.0
L	50	15.0	2.0
P	50	23.0	16.0
N	50	2.0	2.0

a) What is meant by the term hard water? *(1 mark)*

b) i) Which of the towns in the table had the hardest water? *(1 mark)*

ii) Give a reason for your answer. *(1 mark)*

c) Water samples from three different regions of Northern Ireland, A, B and C, were tested by shaking with five drops of soap solution. The tests were repeated with samples which had been boiled and with samples which had been treated with washing soda. The observations were recorded in the table below. All water samples tested were 10 cm^3 in volume.

Sample	Untreated	After boiling	After treatment with washing soda
A	no lather	no lather	lather
B	lather	lather	lather
C	no lather	lather	lather

i) Which sample, A, B or C, contains permanent hard water **only**? *(1 mark)*

ii) Name a chemical substance which can cause chemical hardness in water. *(1 mark)*

iii) Explain, **in terms of ions present**, how the addition of washing soda (sodium carbonate) removes hardness in water. *(3 marks)*

6 In some parts of Northern Ireland the tap water is described as **hard water**. Hardness in water can be temporary or permanent.

a) What is meant by the term **hard water**? *(2 marks)*

b) Name a compound which causes **temporary** hardness in water. *(1 mark)*

c) Write a balanced symbol equation to show how **temporary** hardness can be removed from water by boiling. *(2 marks)*

d) Permanent hardness may be removed by adding washing soda to the water. Explain, in terms of ions, how washing soda can soften water. *(5 marks)*

e) State **one** disadvantage associated with hard water. *(1 mark)*

7 a) Many substances dissolve in water. Some of these dissolved substances can cause the water to be hard. What is meant by hard water? *(2 marks)*

b) A student was given a sample of tap water and carried out the following tests on samples of the water in test tubes.

Test	Description of test	Observed result
1	Addition of a solution of soap and shaking	No lather formed
2a	Boiling a sample of the water	No observed change
2b	Addition of a solution of soap to the boiled water and shaking	No lather formed
3	Addition of solid **hydrated sodium carbonate** followed by soap solution and shaking	Lather formed

i) What is the common name for **hydrated sodium carbonate**? *(1 mark)*

ii) What type of hardness is present in this sample of water? *(1 mark)*

iii) Explain your answer to part **ii)** above. *(2 marks)*

8 A sample of hard water is reacted with soap and an insoluble scum forms. Soap is sodium stearate, $C_{17}H_{35}COONa$. The equation for the reaction is as follows:

$$C_{17}H_{35}COONa + Ca(HCO_3)_2 \rightarrow (C_{17}H_{35}COO)_2Ca + 2NaHCO_3$$

a) Using the equation, state what type of hard water is used in this reaction with soap. *(1 mark)*

b) Suggest a name for $(C_{17}H_{35}COO)_2Ca$. *(1 mark)*

9 Hard water causes household problems in terms of its effect on kettles and water pipes. Salt is added to dishwashers to aid the removal of hardness from water by ion exchange.

a) Suggest **two** advantages of hardness in a **household** water supply. *(2 marks)*

b) Name one **industry** which benefits from hardness in a water supply. *(1 mark)*

c) Explain, in terms of the ions involved, how ion exchange removes hardness from water. *(4 marks)*

10 Some football boots and leather bags have a small packet of silica gel included in the packaging.

a) What is the purpose of the silica gel? *(1 mark)*

b) Name another **solid** compound used in the laboratory for the same purpose as the silica gel. *(1 mark)*

13 Rates of Reaction

▶ Chemical reactions

We are familiar with many chemical reactions in everyday life that take place at different rates. In the kitchen not all foods cook at the same rate; for example, it would take about ten minutes to fry chips but only a few minutes to toast bread or boil an egg. A slower, less favourable reaction is milk going sour which takes a few days to happen. An even slower reaction is the ripening of fruit which takes place over a period of several weeks.

Some chemical reactions are very slow and it may take several years for us to notice them. Two common examples are the reaction of acid rain with limestone buildings or rusting of a car. We can also think of some reactions which are very fast and take place in a fraction of a second, for example, baking soda reacting immediately with vinegar giving off bubbles of carbon dioxide, while explosions in quarries to break rock seem to occur instantaneously. In the laboratory we can show the presence of hydrogen in a test tube by putting a lighted splint into it and observing the immediate small 'pop' or explosion taking place.

While the examples opposite show that chemical reactions can take place at very different rates, chemists have found that they can vary the **rate of reaction** by controlling factors such as:

* temperature
* surface area/size of solid particles
* concentration of solutions
* presence of a catalyst
* light.

Rates of reactions are important in the chemical industry as chemists are involved in making many important commercial products. Some examples are the manufacture of ammonia for making fertilisers, sulfuric acid in the production of detergents and polythene for the production of packaging materials.

In this study we investigate the effects of temperature, surface area, concentration and catalysts on the rate of reaction of acids with metals or acids with metal carbonates or metal hydrogen carbonates. In most cases we will measure the loss in mass of a solid in a given time or the volume of gas produced in a given time.

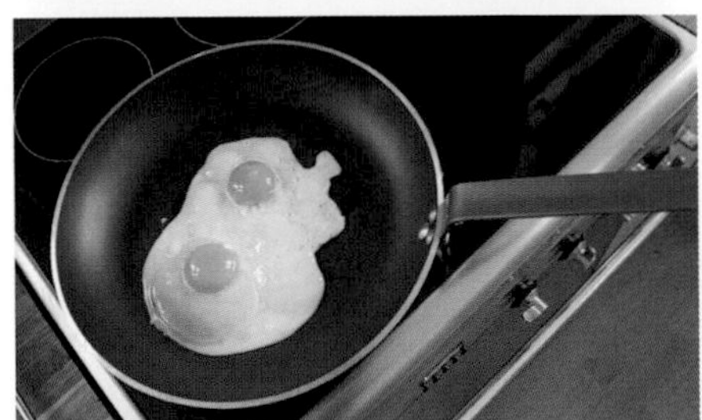

Figure 1 Many reactions take place at very different rates

▶ What is rate?

Some common examples of rate are:

* a car travelling a distance of 160 km in 2 hours is said to be travelling at a rate of 80 km/hour
* 20 litres of diesel are pumped into a tank in 2 minutes; the rate is said to be 10 litres per minute
* a factory produces 1000 bottles of sparkling water every 20 minutes; the rate is 50 bottles per minute.

From the above three examples it is seen that rate is the change in a measured quantity divided by the time taken:

Rate = change in a measured quantity/time taken

Thus in the example above, for a car travelling at 160 km in 2 hours the rate is obtained by dividing 160 km by 2 and this gives a value of 80 km per hour.

We can now say that the rate of reaction is the speed at which a reaction takes place. It can be measured as the rate of formation of a product or the rate of removal of a reactant.

▶ Measuring the rate of a reaction

The rate of reaction tells us how fast or how slow a reaction is taking place. Take for example the reaction between magnesium and dilute sulfuric acid producing hydrogen gas and magnesium sulfate.

$$\text{magnesium} + \text{sulfuric acid} \rightarrow \text{magnesium sulfate} + \text{hydrogen}$$

$$Mg_{(s)} + H_2SO_{4(aq)} \rightarrow MgSO_{4(aq)} + H_{2(g)}$$

As the reaction progresses the rate of reaction can be measured in terms of:

a) **the amount of reactant used up in a given time**

In the above reaction this could be the mass of magnesium used up per minute; or

b) **the amount of product produced in a given time**

For this reaction this would be the mass of magnesium sulfate or the volume of hydrogen formed per minute.

Thus if 0.1 gram of magnesium was added to dilute sulfuric acid and it took 20 seconds for the magnesium to completely react and give 100 cm^3 hydrogen gas, the rate of reaction can be expressed as:

$$\text{rate} = \frac{\text{change in mass of magnesium or volume of hydrogen given off}}{\text{time taken}}$$

The rate with respect to magnesium is 0.1/20 = 0.005 g/s; or, in terms of hydrogen it is 100/20 = 5 cm^3/s.

The rate calculated above is the **average rate** over 20 seconds for all the magnesium to react or for the total volume of hydrogen to form.

For some reactions the rate is directly proportional to the concentration of the reactant or reactants, i.e. the rate doubles when the concentration of a reactant is doubled. We can say that the rate of reaction will be inversely proportional to the time taken for the reaction to reach completion.

rate of reaction $\propto$ concentration of reactant

rate of reaction $\propto \frac{1}{\text{time}}$ (unit = s^{-1})

Using a change in mass of reactant to investigate how surface area affects the rate of a chemical reaction

Consider the following chemical reactions:

* **Cooking**: potatoes take a shorter time to cook when they are cut into smaller pieces.
* **Combustion**: it is easier to light a fire with small pieces of stick, rather than by using large blocks of wood.
* **Combustion**: some modern coal-fired power stations burn powdered coal rather than lumps of coal.
* **Metals reacting with acids:** zinc powder will react much more quickly with dilute sulfuric acid than zinc granules do.

All of the reactions above occur more quickly because the surface area of the solid has been increased. The surface area is the amount of solid surface that is available for reaction.

A fixed mass of solid in a single block has a smaller surface area than the same mass of solid cut into smaller pieces. As the solid is broken into even smaller pieces more of the solid is exposed and the surface area increases.

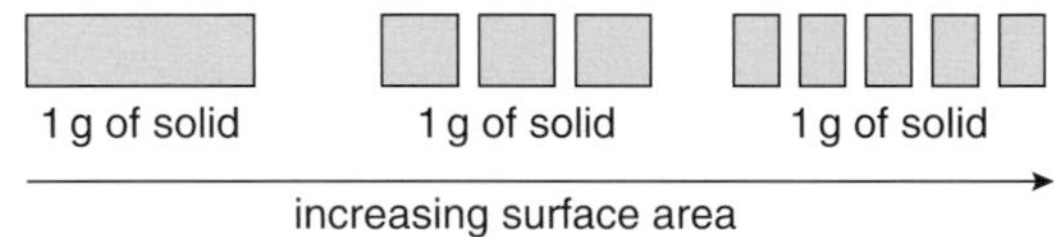

A study of the reaction between marble chips and dilute hydrochloric acid shows that when the surface area of a solid is **increased** so too is the rate of reaction. Marble chips (calcium carbonate) react with hydrochloric acid to produce calcium chloride, water and carbon dioxide:

$$CaCO_{3(s)} + 2HCl_{(aq)} \rightarrow CaCl_{2(aq)} + H_2O_{(l)} + CO_{2(g)}$$

The rate of reaction can be studied using the apparatus shown in Figure 2.

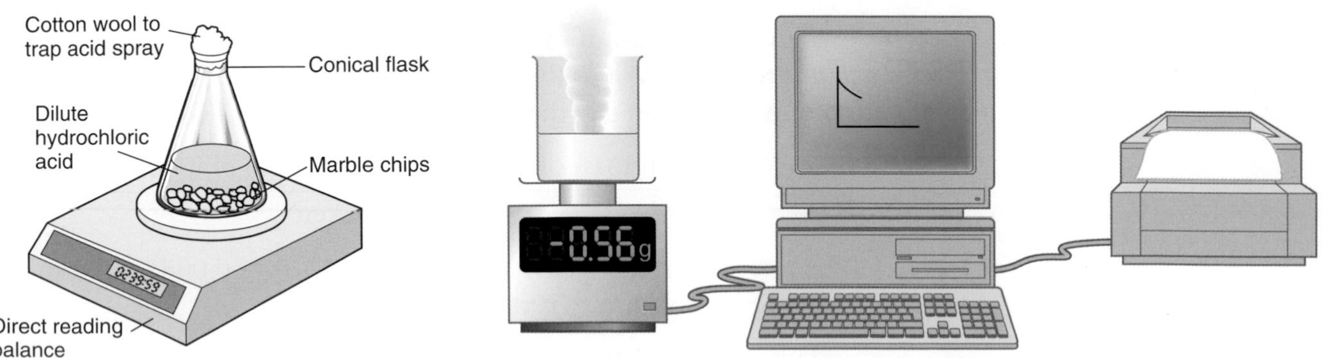

Figure 2 Measuring the rate of reaction between marble chips and hydrochloric acid

In this experiment a given mass of large marble chips (excess) is added to a given volume of dilute hydrochloric acid. As carbon dioxide gas escapes the mass of the flask and its contents decreases. The cotton wool stops any loss of liquid from the flask. The loss in mass of the flask and its contents is measured and recorded each minute until the reaction is over. The experiment is repeated again using the same volume and concentration of hydrochloric acid and the same temperature. The same mass of marble chips is used but this time medium-sized chips are used. A third experiment using exactly the same conditions but small marble chips is also carried out.

The results for the three different sizes of marble chips are given in Table 1 while Figure 3 shows graphs for the three sets of results.

Time/min	Total mass loss/g		
	Large pieces	Medium pieces	Small pieces
0	0.00	0.00	0.00
1	1.00	1.48	2.96
2	1.80	2.52	3.68
3	2.52	3.20	3.85
4	3.00	3.58	3.93
5	3.29	3.73	3.98
6	3.50	3.85	3.99
7	3.66	3.92	4.00
8	3.76	3.96	4.00
9	3.82	3.99	4.00
10	3.88	4.00	4.00
11	3.93	4.00	4.00
12	3.97	4.00	4.00
13	3.99	4.00	4.00
14	4.00	4.00	4.00
15	4.00	4.00	4.00

Table 1 Results for the three sizes of marble chips

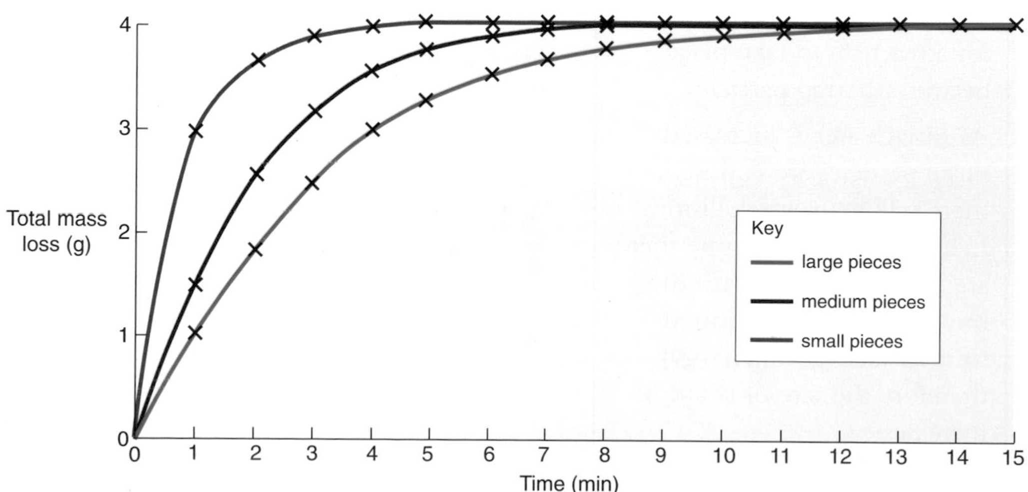

Figure 3 How the surface area of the marble chips affects the rate of reaction with hydrochloric acid

Questions

1 This question refers to the results given in Table 1 and Figure 3.

a) Look at the results in Table 1 and calculate in which reaction there was the greatest loss in mass after 5 minutes.

b) Calculate the average rate of reaction for each reaction after 5 minutes and work out which reaction is fastest.

c) From the graphs in Figure 3 decide which reaction was taking place most quickly after 5 minutes. Explain your answer.

d) Look closely at the results and decide which reaction stops first. Write down how long it takes for the reaction to reach completion.

e) What mass of carbon dioxide is formed at the end of each reaction?

f) For each graph what happens to the reaction rate as time progresses?

The above results show that for each experiment there is the same loss in mass of carbon dioxide. The slopes of the graphs also show the same pattern in that each time the rate of reaction starts off fast, then slows down and eventually stops. Most importantly, the graphs demonstrate that the rate of reaction is fastest when small marble chips are used. The steeper the slope or the greater the gradient then the faster the reaction is taking place.

Explaining the effect of surface area on reaction rate

Collision Theory is used to explain how different factors affect the rate of a reaction. Collision Theory states that for a reaction to take place between the reacting particles (ions, molecules or atoms) it is necessary that they collide. Additionally, particles must have sufficient energy to react; otherwise they simply bounce off each other without reacting. The minimum amount of energy that reacting particles must possess to react is called the **activation energy** and this energy is used to break bonds in the reacting particles in order that products can form (see Figure 4).

Collision Theory states that for a reaction to take place, reacting particles must collide with sufficient energy.

Activation energy is the minimum energy required for a reaction to take place betwen reacting particles.

As surface area is increased more particles are exposed, so there will be more collisions. In a fixed period of time there are more collisions with the minimum energy required to react (activation energy), therefore the rate of reaction increases.

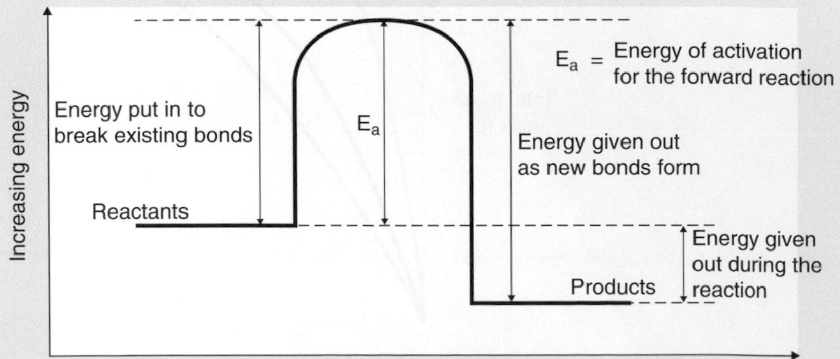

Figure 4 Activation energy for a chemical reaction

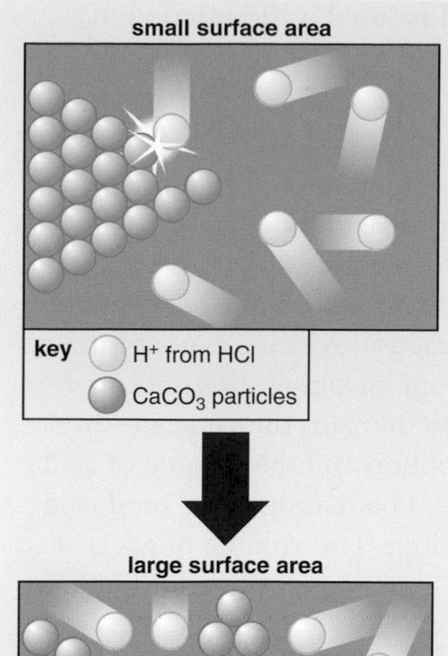

more particles of $CaCO_3$ available for collisions when the surface area is increased

Figure 5 Marble chips reacting with hydrochloric acid

In the reaction between marble chips and hydrochloric acid, it is the hydrogen ions of the hydrochloric acid that react with the carbonate ions on the surface of the marble chips. The hydrogen ions are moving freely throughout the acid solution and a reaction can take place when hydrogen ions with sufficient energy collide with the carbonate ions. As a result of these successful collisions, bubbles of carbon dioxide are produced:

$$CO_3^{2-} + 2H^+ \rightarrow CO_2 + H_2O$$

Each time there is a successful collision, hydrogen ions are used up. Due to the decreasing concentration of hydrogen ions as time progresses, the rate of reaction decreases. If marble chips are in excess then the reaction ends when all the hydrogen ions are used up and no more bubbles of carbon dioxide are given off.

When marble chips in the above reaction are broken up into smaller pieces they have a greater surface area as shown in Figure 5. This means there will be more particles available for reaction. In a given time there will be more successful collisions between the hydrogen ions and the carbonate ions of the marble chips and as a result the rate of reaction will be faster.

Explaining the effect of concentration of a solution on the rate of reaction

The effect of changing the concentration of a solution on the rate of reaction can be followed by measuring the volume of a gas given off over a period of time. The following apparatus, in Figure 6, can be used to measure the volume of gas given off over a period of time.

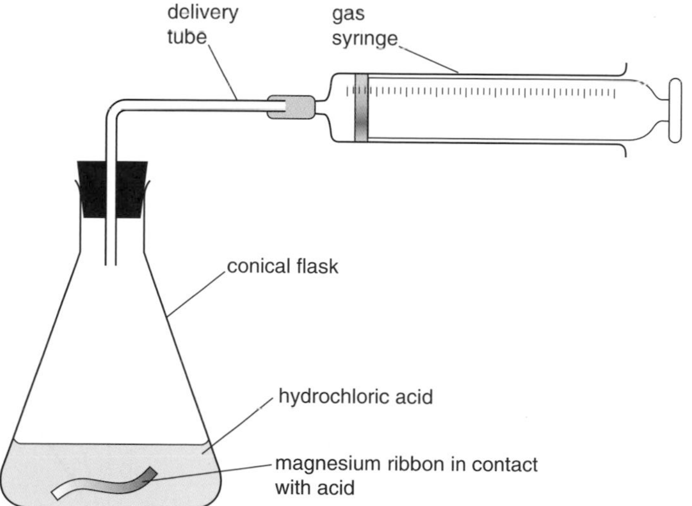

Figure 6 Apparatus used to investigate the rate of reaction by measuring the volume of gas produced

The reaction between marble chips and different concentrations of hydrochloric acid would be a suitable reaction to study the effect of concentration of acid on reaction rate. During the course of this reaction we could measure how much carbon dioxide gas is produced over a period of time.

An alternative reaction which could be used is the reaction of magnesium with excess hydrochloric acid:

$$Mg_{(s)} + 2HCl_{(aq)} \rightarrow MgCl_{2(aq)} + H_{2(g)}$$

In this investigation we will use two different concentrations of hydrochloric acid. In the first reaction we will use excess 1 mol/dm^3 hydrochloric acid and in the second reaction we will use the same volume but the hydrochloric acid will be at a concentration of 0.5 mol/dm^3. The acid in the first reaction is twice as concentrated as that in the second reaction. Apart from changing the concentration of the hydrochloric acid, everything else remains the same, i.e. the temperature, the mass of magnesium ribbon and the volume of acid must be the same for the two reactions. The hydrogen gas produced in this reaction is collected in a gas syringe. The volume of gas is measured at regular time intervals of 10 seconds as shown in Table 2.

Time/s	0	10	20	30	40	50	60	70	80	90	100	110	120	130
Reaction 1 (1 mol/dm^3 HCl) Volume H_2/cm^3	0	18	32	45	53	58	60	60	60	60	60	60	60	60
Reaction 2 (0.5 mol/dm^3 HCl) Volume H_2/cm^3	0	9	16	23	30	36	42	47	51	55	57	59	60	60

Table 2 Results for the two different concentrations of hydrochloric acid reacting with magnesium ribbon

Figure 7 shows the graphs of volume of hydrogen produced against time for the two different concentrations of hydrochloric acid.

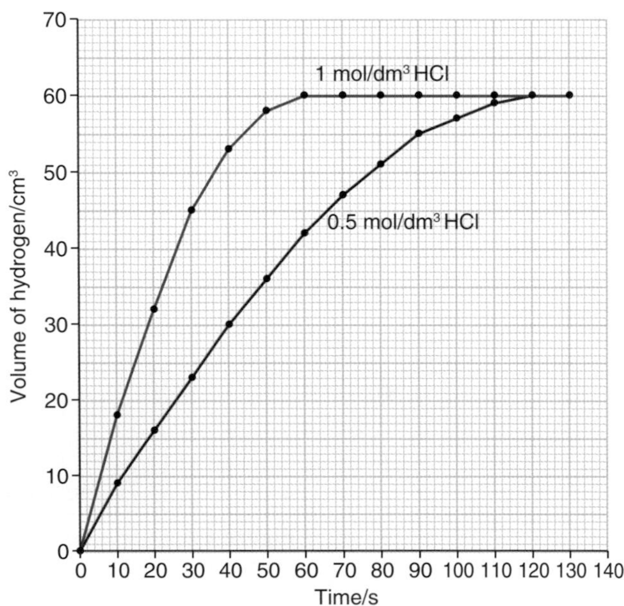

Figure 7 The graph shows the volume of hydrogen against time for the two different concentrations of hydrochloric acid

The above graphs highlight some important points about the effect of concentration on the rate of reaction.

* The curve for 1.0 mol/dm^3 hydrochloric acid is steeper than that for 0.5 mol/dm^3 hydrochloric acid. This tells us that the reaction of the more concentrated acid with magnesium proceeds at a faster rate than the reaction with the lower concentration of hydrochloric acid.
* The curve for the 1.0 mol/dm^3 hydrochloric acid starts off twice as steep as that for the 0.5 mol/dm^3 hydrochloric acid. This shows that initially the rate of reaction for 1.0 mol/dm^3 hydrochloric acid is twice that for 0.5 mol/dm^3 hydrochloric acid. So initially doubling the concentration of the acid doubled the rate of reaction.
* For each reaction the same volume of hydrogen gas is produced; however, it is produced much faster for the 1.0 mol/dm^3 hydrochloric acid.

As concentration of a solution is increased there are more reacting particles in the same volume of solution. In a fixed period of time there are more collisions, therefore there are more collisions with the minimum energy required to react (activation energy) and the rate of reaction increases.

Using collision theory to explain the effect of concentration on the rate of reaction

Collision theory can be used to explain why the rate of reaction increases when the concentration of a reactant is increased. Figure 8 shows that when the concentration of hydrochloric acid is low then there are only a small number of collisions between the H^+ ions of hydrochloric acid and the magnesium atoms in a given time. Considering that only some of the collisions have enough energy for a reaction to occur it is not surprising that the rate of reaction is slow. As the concentration of hydrochloric acid (H^+) increases there are more H^+ ions to collide with the magnesium atoms in a given time and the rate of reaction is faster as there are more successful collisions in this fixed period of time.

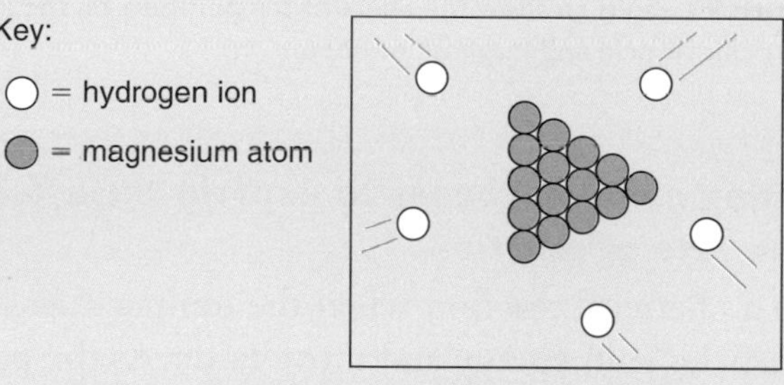

Low concentration of hydrochloric acid (H^+) – slow reaction as there are few collisions in a given time.

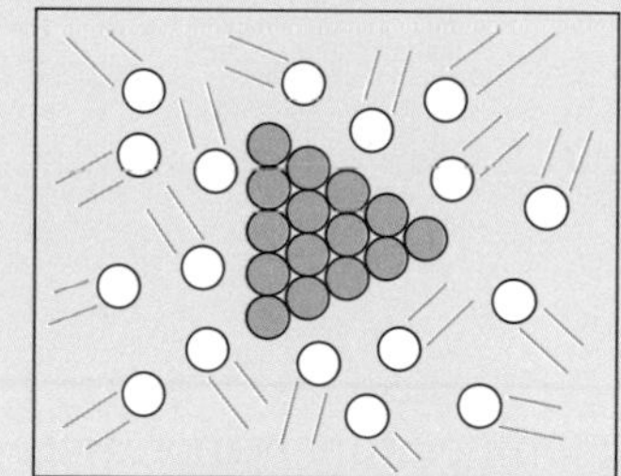

High concentration of hydrochloric acid (H^+) – faster reaction as there are more collisions in a given time.

Figure 8 The number of collisions increase as the concentration increases

Explaining the effect of temperature on the rate of reaction

The effect of temperature on the rate of reaction can be studied for the reaction of magnesium ribbon with hydrochloric acid. The reaction is carried out at 15 °C and 25 °C and each time the same volume of 0.5 mol/dm^3 hydrochloric acid (excess) and the same mass of magnesium ribbon (0.07 g) is used. Table 3 gives a typical set of results:

Time/min	0	0.5	1	1.5	2	2.5	3	3.5	4	4.5	5	5.5
Volume of hydrogen at 15 °C/cm^3	0	9.5	18	26.5	33.5	41.5	48	54	59	62	63	63
Volume of hydrogen at 25 °C/cm^3	0	19	35	50	60	62	63	63	63	63	63	63

Table 3 Results for the reaction of hydrochloric acid and magnesium at 15 °C and 25 °C

When the two graphs are plotted, Figure 9, it is seen that as the temperature is increased the rate of reaction is increased and the time for the reaction is decreased. At the higher temperature, the magnesium reacts much faster and the reaction is over in a shorter time.

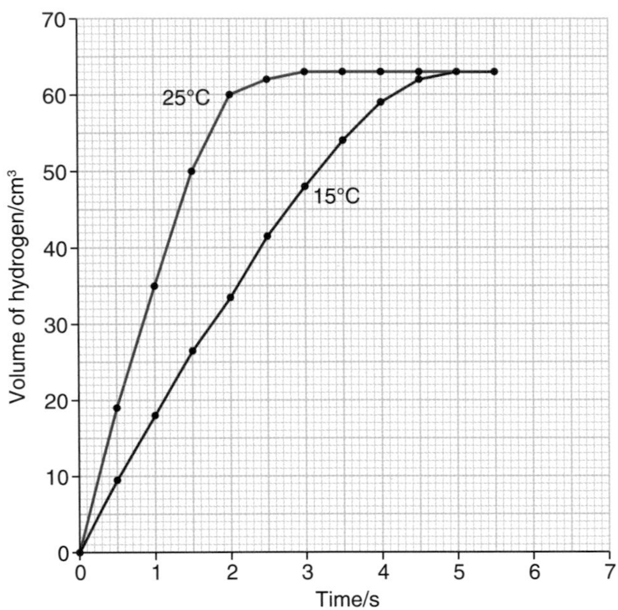

Figure 9 Graphs to show the effect of temperature on the rate of reaction between hydrochloric acid and magnesium ribbon

As temperature is increased the particles gain energy and move faster. In a fixed period of time there are more collisions with the minimum energy required (activation energy), therefore rate of reaction increases.

Using collision theory to explain the effect of temperature on the rate of reaction

In a chemical reaction when the temperature is increased the reacting particles gain energy and move faster. As the particles are moving faster there are more collisions in a given time. Since the collisions are more energetic, it is not surprising that when the temperature is increased the rate of reaction is markedly increased. In this reaction when the acid solution is heated the H^+ ions from the hydrochloric acid gain energy. They collide more often with the magnesium atoms in a given time and since the collisions are more energetic there are many more successful collisions. This means that the rate of reaction increases. For most reactions the rate is approximately doubled when the temperature is increased by only 10 °C. The reason for this is that a rise of ten degrees approximately doubles the number of particles with energy equal to the activation energy. This means that there are twice as many successful collisions in a given time and the rate is approximately doubled.

Questions

These questions relate to the graph shown opposite. The graph shows the volume of hydrogen gas produced against time for the reaction of zinc with excess dilute hydrochloric acid (0.5 mol/dm³) at 25 °C.

2 At what time did the reaction end?

3 What volume of gas had been produced at 50 seconds?

4 Copy the graph and then sketch on it the line you would expect to obtain if the temperature was increased to 40 °C, and all other factors were kept the same. Label this 'A'.

5 If the concentration of the acid was reduced to 0.4 mol/dm³ and the same mass of zinc was added at 25 °C, sketch a second line on your graph that you would expect to obtain if all the zinc is again used up. Label this 'B'.

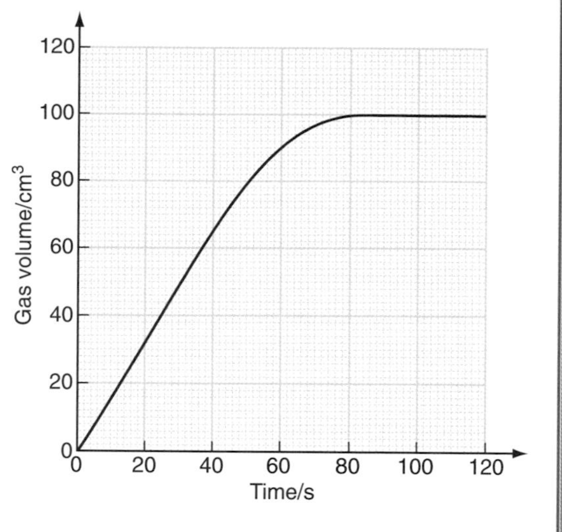

Explaining the effect of a catalyst on the rate of a chemical reaction

There are many chemical reactions that are speeded up using a **catalyst**. Catalysts are used in the contact process to produce sulfuric acid, in the Haber process for the manufacture of ammonia and also in the manufacture of nitric acid.

A catalyst is a substance that increases the rate of a reaction without being used up.

Figure 10 shows a catalytic converter in a car.

As catalysts are not used up in chemical reactions, it means that only small amounts of catalysts are required to speed up reactions. A small amount of catalyst is capable of speeding up the conversion of an infinite amount of reactant to product.

Consider the decomposition of hydrogen peroxide using the catalyst manganese(IV) oxide, MnO_2. At room temperature, and without a catalyst, this reaction is very slow; however, when a small amount of solid manganese(IV) oxide is added the decomposition is very fast and oxygen is given off rapidly.

$$2H_2O_{2(aq)} \rightarrow 2H_2O_{(l)} + O_{2(g)}$$

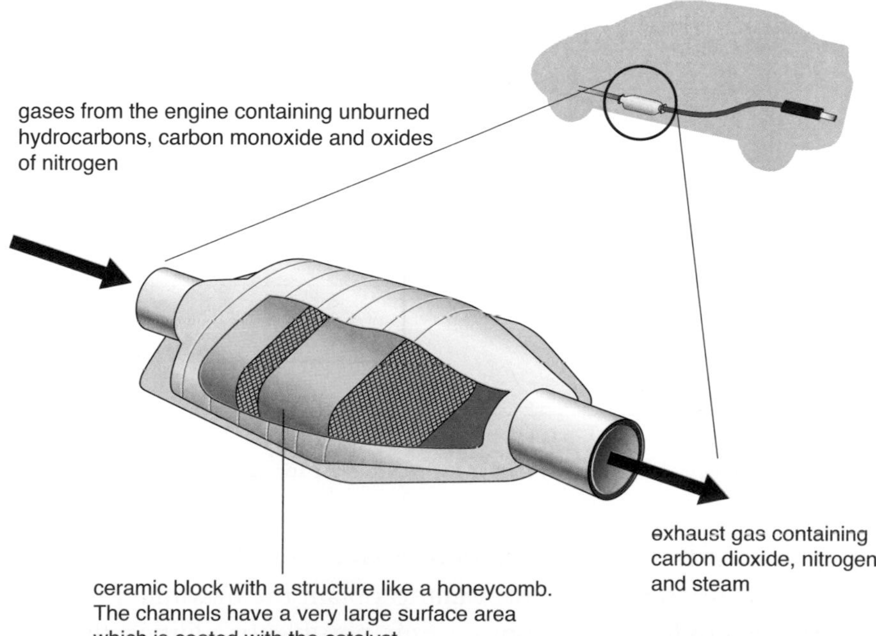

Figure 10 A catalytic converter in a car

Figure 11 shows the effect of changing the amount of manganese(IV) oxide on the time to produce 50 cm^3 oxygen gas from hydrogen peroxide.

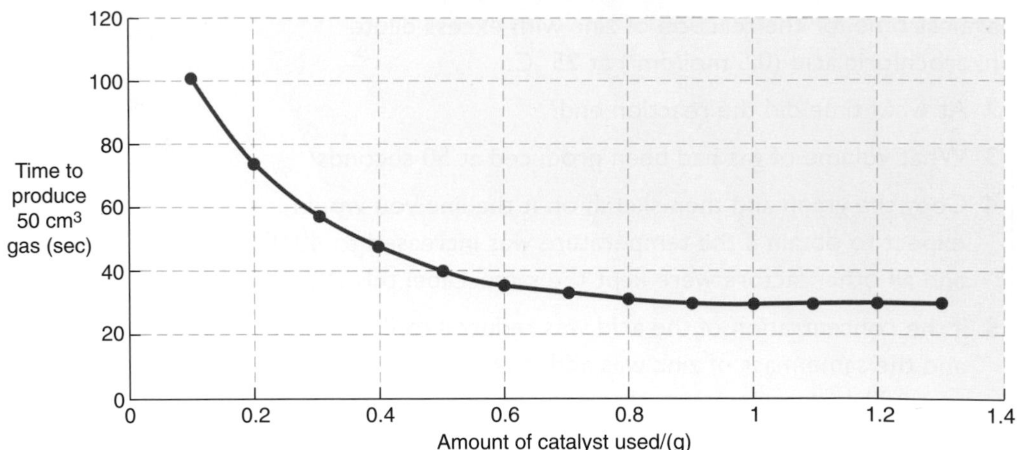

Figure 11 The effect of the amount of manganese oxide on the rate of reaction

From Figure 11, it is seen that the rate of reaction increases as the mass of manganese(IV) oxide increases. This occurs up to 0.9 g but after this value the rate does not increase when the amount of catalyst increases.

Why catalysts speed up the rate of reaction

For a reaction to take place particles must collide and they must have sufficient energy to overcome the activation energy of the reaction. If not, they merely collide and bounce off each other. Catalysts increase the rate of reaction by lowering the activation energy of a reaction. This means that in a catalytic reaction when particles collide more of them have sufficient energy to overcome the energy barrier to form products and the reaction is faster. This is shown in Figure 12.

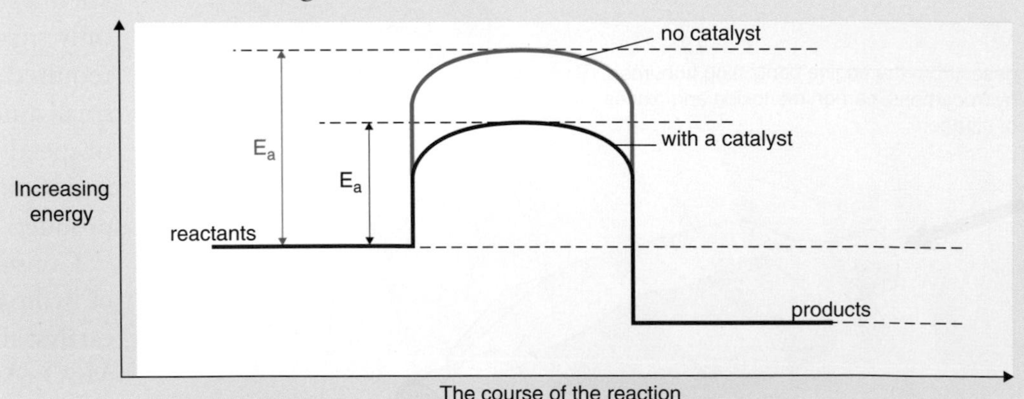

Figure 12 An energy level diagram showing why a catalyst speeds up a reaction

Using catalysts in the chemical industry to save energy

In chemical reactions, chemists want to obtain the maximum yield of desirable product in the shortest time possible. In addition they want to use the minimum amount of energy to obtain the product.

The development of better catalysts plays an important part in finding new, lower energy routes to obtain larger yields of products. An additional advantage of developing new catalysts is that there are fewer waste products and this saves resources.

A good example of the development of new catalysts is in the production of ethanoic acid. In 1970, it was made by the oxidation of hydrocarbons from crude oil in the presence of cobalt(II) ethanoate. The reaction was carried out at 180 °C and 50 atmospheres of pressure. The reaction produced around 35% ethanoic acid with 65% of unwanted products.

A new catalytic method to make ethanoic acid has now been discovered. There is a **high yield** of 94% ethanoic acid (previously 35%) with only a small amount of waste products.

$$CO + CH_3OH \rightarrow CH_3COOH$$

The catalyst used is based on an iridium compound which has a very long lifetime. The process is carried out at 180 °C and 50 atmospheres. Much less energy and fewer steps are needed than in the older process based on the oxidation of hydrocarbons. Also, as there is a greatly increased yield, it means there are fewer harmful chemicals for disposal and less chemical pollution.

▶ Exam questions

1 A student wanted to investigate the rate of the reaction between zinc and sulfuric acid. He put 1 g zinc powder into a conical flask containing 50 cm^3 dilute sulfuric acid and shook the flask carefully. After 10 seconds the reaction had finished.

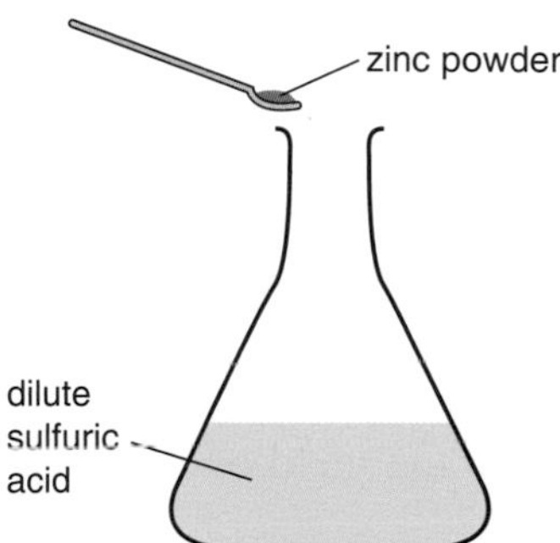

a) Give **three** ways in which the student could change the investigation, using the same mass of zinc, to **slow down** the reaction. *(3 marks)*

b) How could the student tell when the reaction of zinc with dilute sulfuric acid had ended? *(1 mark)*

2 The following diagram shows part of the label from a packet of antacid tablets.

fizzers
Antacid Tablets
Ingredients
Citric acid
Calcium carbonate
Sodium saccharin
Lemon flavouring

a) When added to water the tablet fizzes, partly due to the reaction between calcium carbonate and citric acid.

i) Citric acid forms salts called citrates. Copy and complete the word equation:

Calcium carbonate + citric acid → *(1 mark)*

ii) Use the equation in **a) i)** to explain what causes the fizz. *(1 mark)*

b) In an experiment one Fizzer tablet was added to 50 cm³ of water in a conical flask at a temperature of 20 °C. The flask was loosely stoppered with a cotton wool plug and placed on a balance and a stop watch started. The mass was recorded every 20 seconds.

i) Sketch the diagram of the apparatus used for this experiment, as shown below, and complete it. Label the diagram. *(3 marks)*

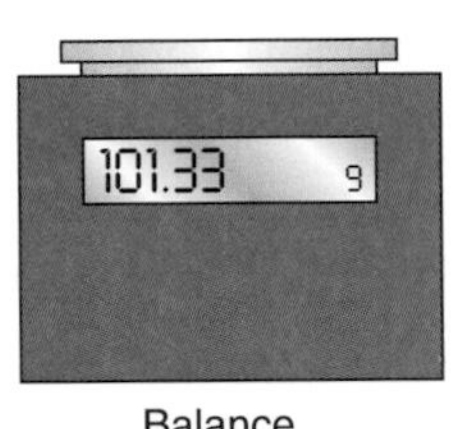

ii) Explain why the mass of the flask and its contents decreases during the experiment. *(2 marks)*

iii) What is the purpose of the cotton wool plug? *(2 marks)*

c) The table below shows the results for the experiment.

Times/s	0	20	40	60	80	100
Total mass/g	101.33	101.12	101.00	100.92	100.90	100.90

i) Plot these results on graph paper and use the graph to answer the following questions. *(3 marks)*

ii) At what time does the reaction stop? *(1 mark)*

iii) What loss in mass would be expected if half a tablet is used in 50 cm³ of water at 20 °C? State clearly how you obtained your answer. *(2 marks)*

iv) If the experiment was repeated using one crushed tablet in 50 cm³ of water at 20 °C, state and explain in terms of particles the effect this would have on the rate of the reaction. *(3 marks)*

v) The experiment was repeated using the same volume of water and one whole tablet at 40 °C. On the same axes as you drew in part **i)**, sketch the graph for this experiment and label it **B**. *(4 marks)*

3 The Haber process is used to produce ammonia in industry. The amount of ammonia gas produced (% yield) from this reaction is affected by both the temperature and the pressure at which the process is carried out. The following graph shows how the amount of ammonia produced from the reaction changes with both temperature and pressure.

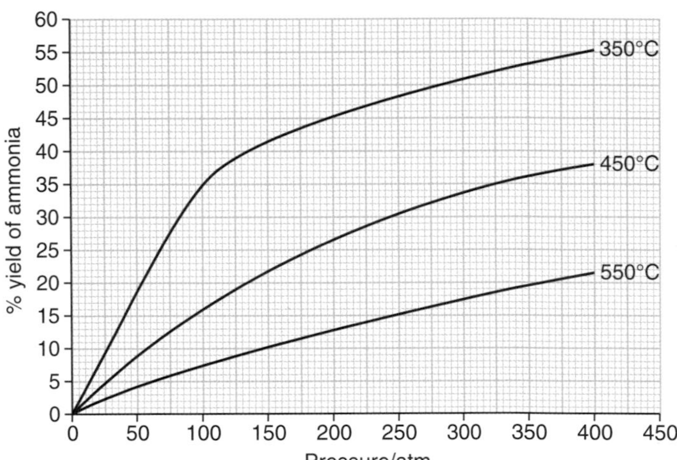

Use the graph to answer the following questions.

a) What happens to the percentage yield of ammonia if the pressure is increased at constant temperature? *(1 mark)*

b) State the temperature and pressure at which the greatest yield of ammonia gas is produced. *(2 marks)*

c) The conditions usually used in the production of ammonia are a temperature of 450 °C and a pressure of 200 atmospheres. What is the percentage yield of ammonia using these conditions? *(1 mark)*

4 a) Some students investigated the rate of reaction between marble chips and 100 cm³ of dilute hydrochloric acid. They used excess marble chips and recorded the loss in mass of the flask and its contents every 30 seconds.

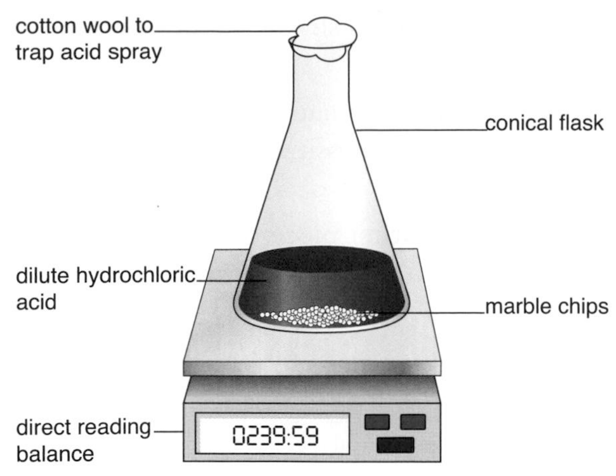

The results obtained during the experiment are given in the following table.

Time/s	0	30	60	90	120	150	180	210	240	270
Loss in mass/g	0.0	1.1	2.0	2.7	3.2	3.6	3.8	3.9	4.0	4.0

i) On graph paper, plot the results given in the table. Draw a curve of best fit. *(3 marks)*

ii) Label the *y*-axis on your graph. *(1 mark)*

iii) The students repeated the experiment, but the only change was to add 20 cm^3 of water to the hydrochloric acid to make it more dilute. On the same axes as you draw in part **i)**, **sketch** the curve you would expect for this reaction and label this curve with an X. *(2 marks)*

iv) Use the idea of collisions to explain the effect of increasing the concentration on the rate of reaction. *(3 marks)*

b) The following equation shows how ammonia is made industrially in the Haber process. The conditions are 450 °C, 250 atmospheres and an iron catalyst.

$$N_2 + 3H_2 \rightarrow 2NH_3$$

i) Give **one** reason why a temperature of more than 450 °C is **not** used in this industrial reaction. *(1 mark)*

ii) A pressure of 1000 atmospheres would give a higher yield of ammonia than 250 atmospheres. Give **one** reason why pressures of 1000 atmospheres are not used. *(1 mark)*

5 Hydrogen peroxide decomposes in the presence of solid manganese(IV) oxide to produce water and oxygen. The apparatus shown below was used to investigate the rate of decomposition of hydrogen peroxide solution.

a) 20 cm^3 of hydrogen peroxide solution were added to 1.0 g of solid manganese(IV) oxide at 20 °C.

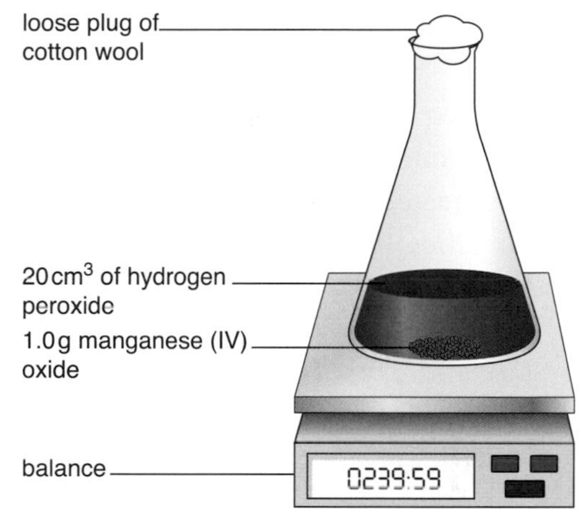

The following results were obtained.

Time/mins	Mass of oxygen lost/g
0	0.0
1	0.23
2	0.34
4	0.45
5	0.47
6	0.48
7	0.48

i) Write a balanced symbol equation for the decomposition of hydrogen peroxide. *(3 marks)*

ii) What is the purpose of the cotton wool plug? *(1 mark)*

iii) Plot a graph of mass of oxygen lost (g) against time (minutes) on graph paper. *(3 marks)*

iv) Use the graph to determine the mass of oxygen lost after 3 minutes. *(1 mark)*

v) How could you experimentally investigate the rate of reaction without measuring the mass of oxygen lost? *(1 mark)*

b) At the end of this experiment the manganese(IV) oxide can be recovered.

i) Draw a **labelled diagram** of the assembled apparatus which could be used to recover the manganese(IV) oxide at the end of the experiment. *(3 marks)*

ii) How would you experimentally prove that the manganese(IV) oxide was not used up in this experiment? *(2 marks)*

c) To investigate the effect of temperature on this reaction, 20 cm^3 of hydrogen peroxide were heated to 40 °C and added to 1.0 g of manganese(IV) oxide in the same apparatus as shown in part **a)**.
The reaction was over in 4 minutes.
State and explain, **in terms of particles**, the effect of increasing the temperature of the hydrogen peroxide on the rate of the reaction. *(4 marks)*

6 Different factors affect the speed of a chemical reaction. Light and the presence of a catalyst are two of these factors.

a) Photographic film is a gel containing silver(I) ions. When light reaches the photographic film, the silver(I) ions are converted to silver and the silver appears as dark spots.
Write an ionic equation for the conversion of silver(I) ions to silver. *(2 marks)*

b) A solution of hydrogen peroxide may be decomposed using a catalyst.
The diagram below shows the assembled apparatus used to carry out the decomposition and measure the volume of oxygen gas produced.

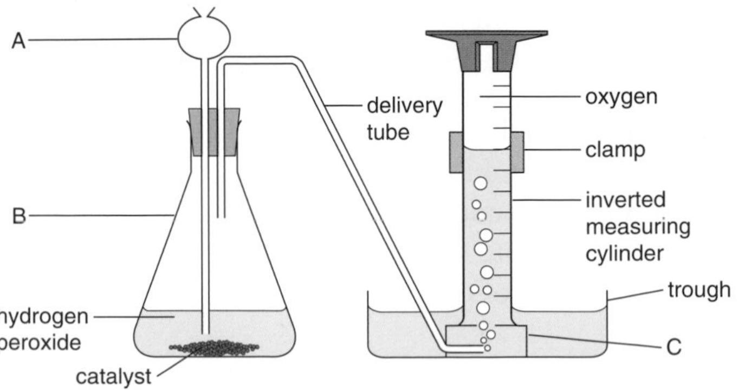

i) What labels should be in positions A, B and C? *(3 marks)*

ii) What is the name of the catalyst used in the decomposition of hydrogen peroxide? *(1 mark)*

iii) What other piece of apparatus could be used to measure the volume of oxygen produced? *(1 mark)*

iv) What is meant by the term **catalyst**? *(3 marks)*

v) Write a balanced symbol equation for the decomposition of hydrogen peroxide. *(3 marks)*

c) The volume of oxygen produced by decomposing 25.0 cm^3 of a 0.1 mol/dm^3 solution of hydrogen peroxide at 10 °C, 25 °C and 40 °C was measured and plotted on the graph below.

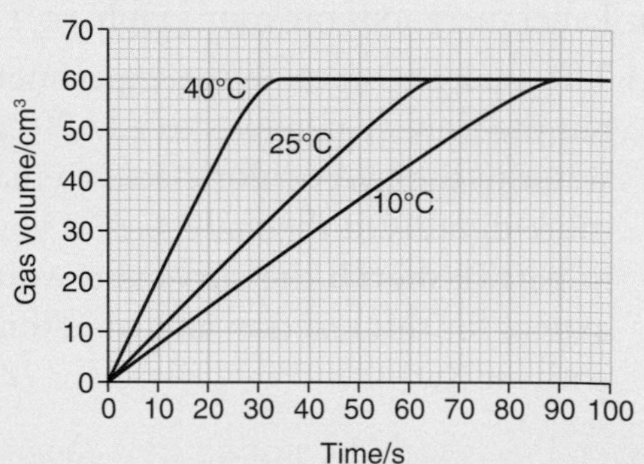

State and explain fully, in terms of particles, the effect of temperature on the rate of the catalytic decomposition of hydrogen peroxide. *(4 marks)*

14 Non-Metals and Their Compounds

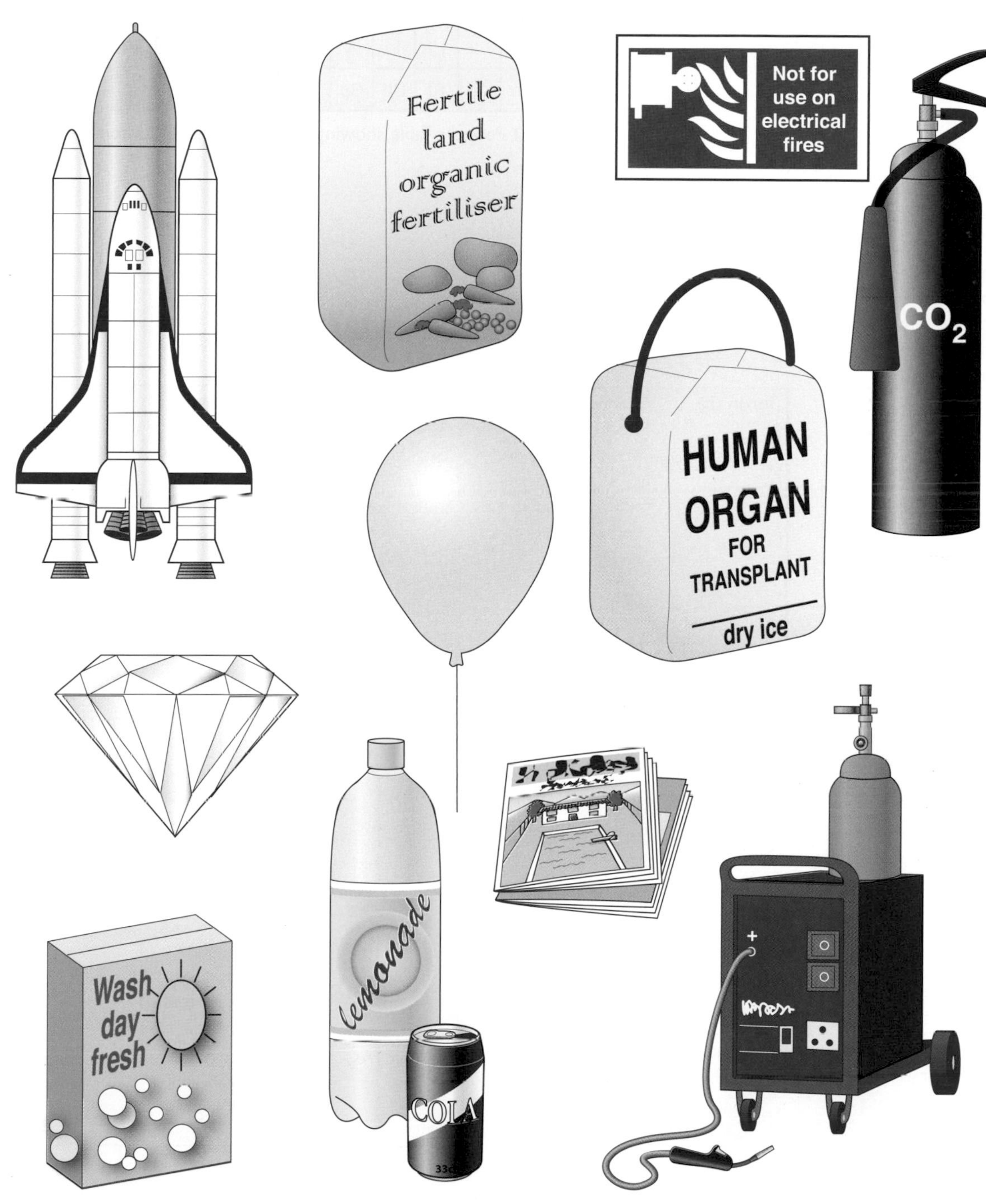

Figure 1 A selection of objects

Look carefully at this series of images of familiar substances and objects. Do you know which elements have been used in their manufacture?

Many of the images are of substances which are vital to our modern day survival.

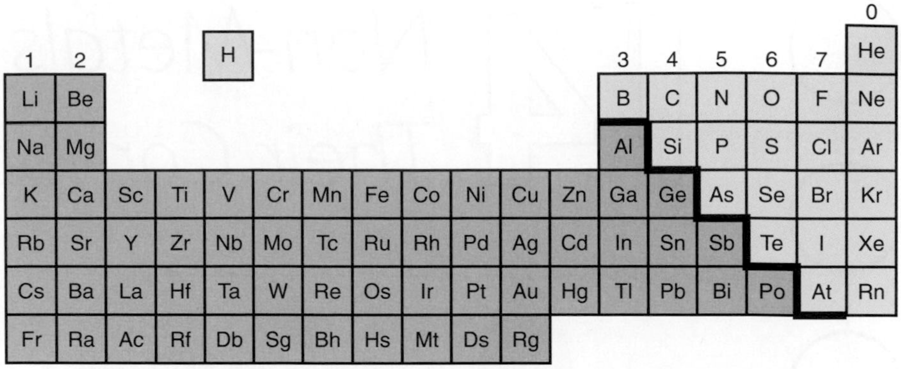

1	2											3	4	5	6	7	0
				H													He
Li	Be											B	C	N	O	F	Ne
Na	Mg											Al	Si	P	S	Cl	Ar
K	Ca	Sc	Ti	V	Cr	Mn	Fe	Co	Ni	Cu	Zn	Ga	Ge	As	Se	Br	Kr
Rb	Sr	Y	Zr	Nb	Mo	Tc	Ru	Rh	Pd	Ag	Cd	In	Sn	Sb	Te	I	Xe
Cs	Ba	La	Hf	Ta	W	Re	Os	Ir	Pt	Au	Hg	Tl	Pb	Bi	Po	At	Rn
Fr	Ra	Ac	Rf	Db	Sg	Bh	Hs	Mt	Ds	Rg							

Figure 2 Periodic Table showing metals (orange) and non-metals (blue)

Hydrogen (H) Potential for use as a clean fuel: in meteorological balloons, in rocket engines and in production of ammonia.						**Helium (He)**
	Boron (B)	**Carbon (C)** Combustion products: CO and CO_2. As CO_2 in: fire extinguishers, carbonated drinks, dry ice.	**Nitrogen (N)** As a coolant in: food packaging, manufacture of ammonia and production of ammonia. As NH_3 in: manufacture of fertilisers, manufacture of nylon and production of nitric acid.	**Oxygen (O)** In breathing apparatus, in welding gases, in rocket engines and in steel making.	**Fluorine (F)**	**Neon (Ne)**
		Silicon (Si)	**Phosphorus (P)**	**Sulfur (S)** Vulcanisation of rubber, fungicides. As SO_2 in bleach. As H_2SO_4: in manufacture of car batteries, in manufacture of detergents, in manufacture of fertilisers and in manufacture of pigments.	**Chlorine (Cl)**	**Argon (Ar)**
			Arsenic (As)	**Selenium (Se)**	**Bromine (Br)**	**Krypton (Kr)**
				Tellurium (Te)	**Iodine (I)**	**Xenon (Xe)**
					Astatine (At)	**Radon (Rn)**

Figure 3 Non-metals and their uses

Figure 4 Natural rubber eraser

Figure 5 Bicycle tyre

The eraser in the photograph is soft and pliable and small pieces break off when rubbed across the surface of a piece of paper. These properties make it useful for correcting mistakes made with a pencil but quite useless for manufacture of a bicycle tyre, yet both the objects shown are made from natural rubber.

How can this compound be employed for two such different uses?

The natural rubber used to manufacture the tyre has been heated with sulfur, a solid yellow non-metal element. The addition of this element renders the rubber harder and more durable and the elasticity of the rubber is retained. The process of adding sulfur to rubber is known as vulcanisation.

This chapter will investigate the non-metal elements:

* Hydrogen
* Carbon
* Nitrogen
* Oxygen
* Sulfur

and some of their compounds to illustrate the importance of chemistry and the place of industrial chemical processes in our modern world.

Hydrogen

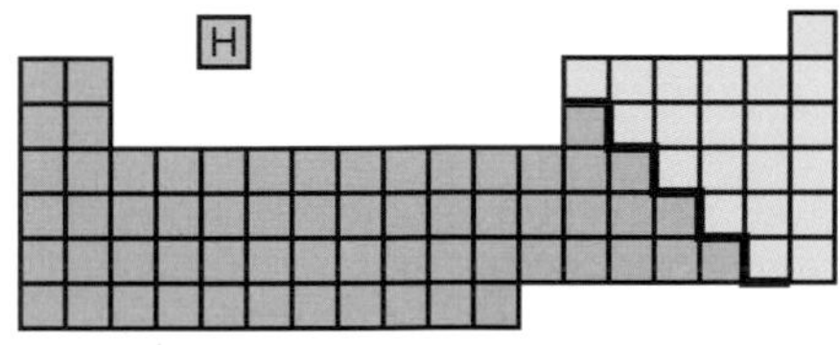

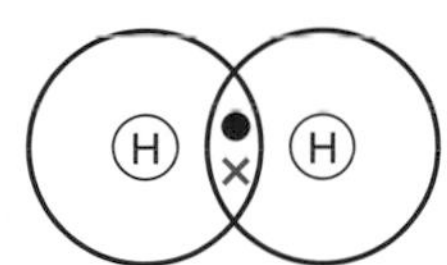

Figure 6 A representation of a molecule of hydrogen

Hydrogen is a	colourless odourless gas	Physical properties of hydrogen
which is	lighter than air insoluble in water	
and	burns explosively in air.	

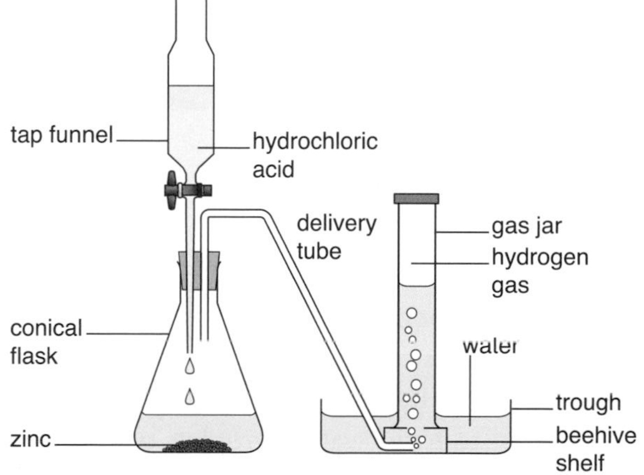

Figure 7 The laboratory preparation of hydrogen gas

Hydrogen is prepared in the laboratory by the action of dilute hydrochloric acid on zinc metal (see also reaction of metals with acids, Chapter 11) as illustrated in Figure 7. The hydrogen can be collected 'over water' as it is not soluble in water.

$$\text{zinc} + \text{hydrochloric acid} \rightarrow \text{zinc chloride} + \text{hydrogen}$$

$$Zn + 2HCl \rightarrow ZnCl_2 + H_2$$

Observations:

* bubbles of a colourless gas are evolved
* the zinc metal disappears
* heat can be felt at the bottom of the conical flask/the temperature of the reaction mixture rises.

The chemical reactions of hydrogen

Hydrogen as a reducing agent

Oxidation	Reduction
Addition of oxygen	Loss of oxygen
Loss of hydrogen	Gain of hydrogen
Loss of electrons	Gain of electrons

Recall the definitions of oxidation and reduction in Chapter 9.

Reaction with oxygen

hydrogen + oxygen → water

$$2H_2 + O_2 \rightarrow 2H_2O$$

The oxygen is reduced as it has gained hydrogen. The addition of hydrogen to a substance is known as reduction.

The hydrogen in this reaction is known as the **reducing agent** as it has caused the reduction to take place.

Possibly the most dramatic use of hydrogen was in hydrogen balloons in the Franco-Prussian war in Europe. In September 1870 during a siege Paris became completely surrounded by the Prussians. French aeronauts suggested to the head of the Post Office that hydrogen balloons should be used to communicate with the outside world and with the provisional government at Tours. The Post Office accepted the suggestion, and on September 23, the professional aeronaut Jules Durouf departed from the Place St. Pierre in Montmartre in *Le Neptune* with 227 pounds (103 kilograms) of mail. He landed his balloon safely three hours and fifteen minutes later behind enemy lines at the Chateau de Craconville. On his way, Durouf dropped visiting cards on the enemy position as he flew above the reach of enemy guns.

Reaction with copper oxide

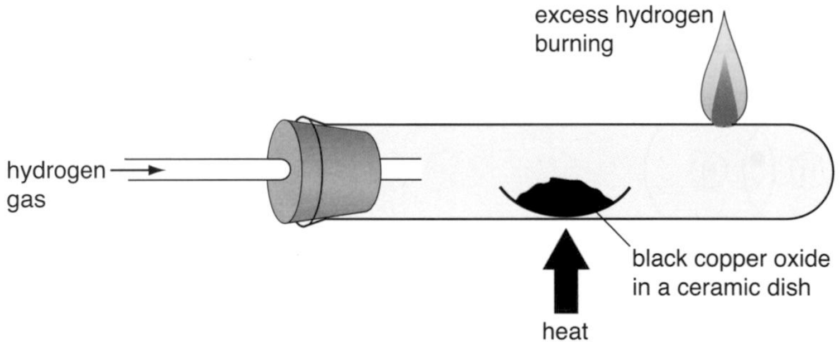

Figure 8 Apparatus for the reaction of copper oxide with hydrogen

When hydrogen gas is passed over heated copper oxide the black copper oxide turns to the red/pink colour of freshly formed copper as the hydrogen removes the oxygen from the copper oxide compound to form water. Droplets of condensation may be seen at the sides of the test-tube.

hydrogen + copper oxide → copper + water

$$H_2 + CuO \rightarrow Cu + H_2O$$

The copper oxide is reduced as it has lost oxygen. The loss of oxygen is known as reduction.

The hydrogen in this reaction is known as the reducing agent as it has caused the reduction to take place.

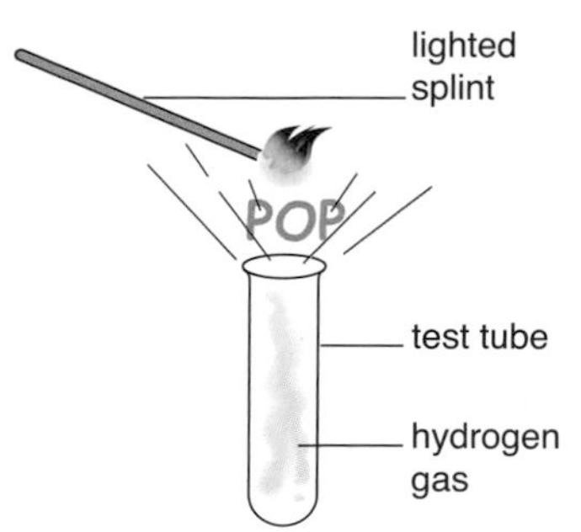

Figure 9 The 'pop' test for hydrogen

A clean fuel is one which when burned does not produce any toxic or polluting products.

Test for hydrogen gas

Place a lit splint at the mouth of a test tube of hydrogen held right way up. The gas will burn in air with a squeaky pop. (The test tube is held the right way up as hydrogen is lighter than air. It will flow out of the mouth of the test tube and mix with oxygen in the air and burn.)

Hydrogen as a fuel

At present fossil fuels, such as oil, coal and natural gas, are extensively used to provide energy. These fuels burn producing useful quantities of heat but also produce toxic gases, some of which add to the greenhouse effect. (For an explanation of this effect, see page 185.) Fossil fuels cannot be replaced and the reserves are already low. Scientists searching for an alternative fuel are considering hydrogen.

Hydrogen is considered a 'clean fuel' because when it burns it produces no toxic waste products. It produces only water which does not add to global warming.

$$\text{hydrogen} + \text{oxygen} \rightarrow \text{water}$$
$$2H_2 + O_2 \rightarrow 2H_2O$$

Hydrogen has been used to provide electricity for the NASA space shuttle for over twenty years. Hydrogen is combined safely with oxygen in an apparatus known as a fuel cell. The water produced is used by the crew as drinking water.

The storage and supply of hydrogen for use as a fuel

Hydrogen does not occur in any great quantity naturally and must be manufactured. Unfortunately, this production process uses energy and can lead to high emissions of carbon dioxide.

Hydrogen can be used safely in fuel cells, but fuel cells are expensive to produce and can only run on 99.999% pure hydrogen.

Pure hydrogen must be liquified or kept under very high pressures if it is to be stored on board a vehicle in the same way as petrol or diesel is stored in vehicles at present. Both the process of condensation of hydrogen and keeping hydrogen under pressure are energy intensive. The storage tanks must be well insulated to prevent the hydrogen returning to a gas as it warms.

Metal containers are suitable storage tanks but hydrogen can diffuse through metals. This weakens the metal container and can cause cracks allowing large quantities of hydrogen to leak. To slow the diffusion down the metal containers need to be coated with non-porous materials. As hydrogen is an extremely inflammable gas, large leaks will inevitably lead to an explosion not just a flame. This is particularly dangerous in a tunnel or an underground car park. Hydrogen is a colourless, odourless gas so leaks would be difficult to detect.

Hydrogen will leak very slowly from metal containers even when internally coated. These slow leaks will not cause an explosion. However, evidence is emerging that molecules of hydrogen gas become atoms in the upper atmosphere and can cause damage to the ozone layer.

If hydrogen is used as a fuel for family cars and other road vehicles, a distribution system similar to that for oil, gas, petrol and diesel will be required. The initial cost of this distribution system will be enormous and economic climates in different countries will dictate whether there is enough money for investment.

Figure 10 A hydrogen powered vehicle

Using hydrogen as a fuel is not a new concept. In 1860, Etienne Lenoir of France invented a vehicle which was fuelled by hydrogen sourced from decomposing water using an electric current.

In 1933, the Norsk Hydro power company converted small trucks to run on hydrogen gas produced from ammonia (NH_3). It had the distinct disadvantage of smelling as if it was run on concentrated urine!

During World War II, the Nazis had surrounded Leningrad, Russia, and cut off supplies. Petrol was running low. So, military technician Boris Shelishch stepped in and converted a truck to run on hydrogen gas. After receiving orders from top commanders, Boris Shelishch and his crew were able to convert 200 trucks in 10 days to run on hydrogen and demonstrated that they burned cleaner and longer than those that had run on petrol.

The combustion of carbon, Part I

A combustion reaction is one where a fuel reacts with oxygen to produce oxides and energy.

Carbon is one of the main components in fossil fuels, such as coal, oil and natural gas (see Chapter 15).

A combustion reaction is one where a fuel reacts with oxygen to produce oxides and energy. Carbon and carbon-containing compounds burn in a plentiful supply of air to form carbon dioxide.

$$\text{carbon} + \text{oxygen}_{(\text{excess})} \rightarrow \text{carbon dioxide}$$
$$C + O_2 \rightarrow CO_2$$

The air naturally contains less than 0.04% carbon dioxide. Over the last 100 years human activity has increased the concentration of carbon dioxide in the atmosphere. The increasing need for energy has increased the burning of fossil fuels thus increasing the production of carbon dioxide. At the same time many trees have been cut down and less carbon dioxide is removed from the air by photosynthesis. The concentration of carbon dioxide in the atmosphere has increased dramatically. This has caused an increase in the greenhouse effect which leads to global warming.

The greenhouse effect

The Earth is surrounded by several layers of gases, the atmosphere. The heat from the Sun passes through these layers to reach the Earth and warm it up. The heat from the Earth travels back to the atmosphere where some of it is prevented from escaping into space by atmospheric gases, such as carbon dioxide, water vapour and methane.

This effect of trapping the energy from the Sun is called the greenhouse effect. It is an important natural process. Without this effect the average temperature of the atmosphere at the surface of the Earth would be 60 °C lower and the Earth would not be able to sustain life.

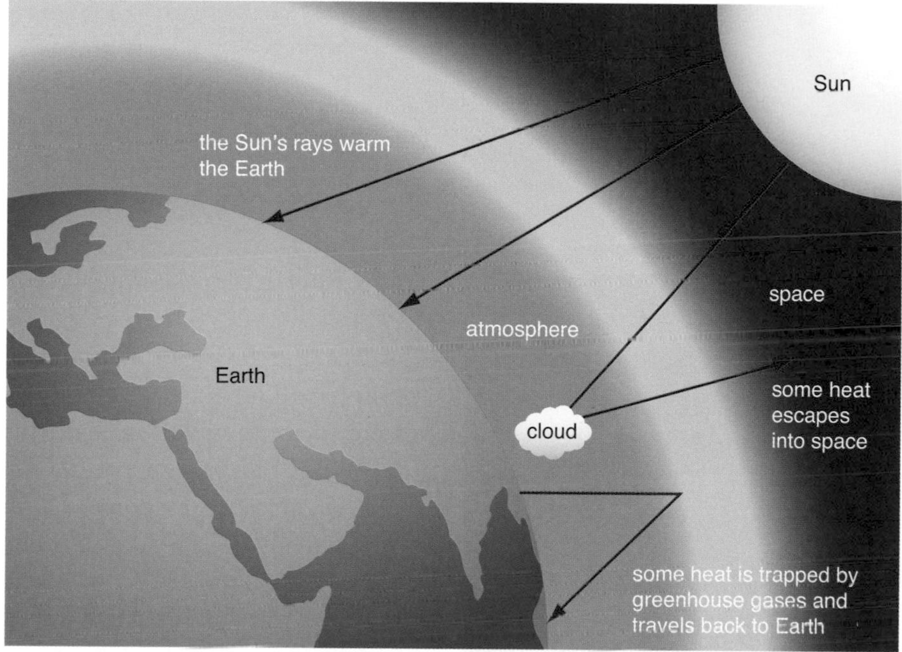

Figure 11 The greenhouse effect

Global warming

Global warming is the term given to the increasing average temperature of the atmosphere at the surface of the Earth. It is caused by changing the balance of the concentration of the greenhouse gases shown in Table 1. Human activity has increased the concentration of these gases very quickly over the last 100 years, thus trapping more of the heat from the Sun and increasing the Earth's temperature.

The greenhouse gases	
water vapour	occurs naturally in the atmosphere
carbon dioxide	produced during respiration by plants and animals, and as a product of combustion of wood and fossil fuels
methane	produced as a product of digestion by ruminant animals such as cows, sheep

Table 1 The greenhouse gases

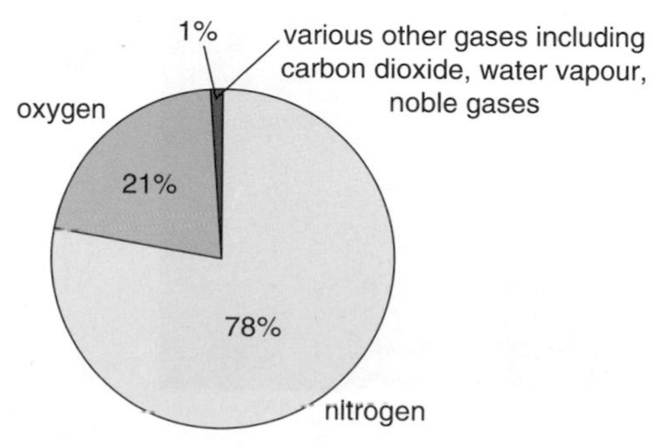

Figure 12 The percentage of gases in the air at present

The effects of global warming

It has taken millions of years for life to become established on Earth. Different species of plants and animals have adapted to different environments. Even small changes in the environment can threaten their survival.

Effects of global warming	Causes	Leads to
polar ice caps will melt	rise in sea levels	flooding of low-lying coastal areas
changes in weather patterns	affect the types of crops grown in different parts of the world	leading to food shortages
	affect plant growth	
	habitats changed	plant and animal species become extinct

Table 2 The effects of global warming

The effect of high concentrations of carbon dioxide in the atmosphere

Figure 13 An active volcano

The current average temperature of the atmosphere at the surface of the Earth is 14 °C. 2.7 billion years ago, the average temperature was 70 °C. This was due to the high concentration of the greenhouse gases in the atmosphere. During this period of the Earth's history, there was intense volcanic activity which released vast quantities of carbon dioxide into the atmosphere. Bacteria and plants slowly turned the CO_2 into carbonates, organic material and oxygen via photosynthesis. The concentration of CO_2 gradually decreased, thus decreasing the temperature.

During the last 100 years the average temperature of the atmosphere at the surface of the Earth has risen by 1 °C. This rise in temperature has been enough to cause unprecedented flooding, drought and destruction of habitats. The hottest average temperatures recorded, since records began in 1850, have been recorded in the years since 1998. This has prompted climate scientists to explain the process to the public and to obtain support for measures to reduce the levels of CO_2 in the atmosphere.

Figure 14 Flooded land

The photograph of the drought was taken on the African continent. However, the photograph of the flood is not of a far away continent but of County Fermanagh, here in Northern Ireland in 2010.

Figure 15 Land in severe drought

▶ Theory of Continental Drift

In 1912, Alfred Wegener put forward the theory of continental drift. He put forward the idea that originally all our present continents were joined together in a single landmass which he called Pangaea. About 200 million years ago the landmass started to break up and form continents. These continents were able to move and drift apart. They ploughed through the weaker crust of the ocean floor like icebergs through the sea.

Wegener showed that the continents fitted together like a jigsaw, especially in the case of South America and Africa. Figure 16 shows the break-up of Pangaea and the jigsaw-like fit between the continents.

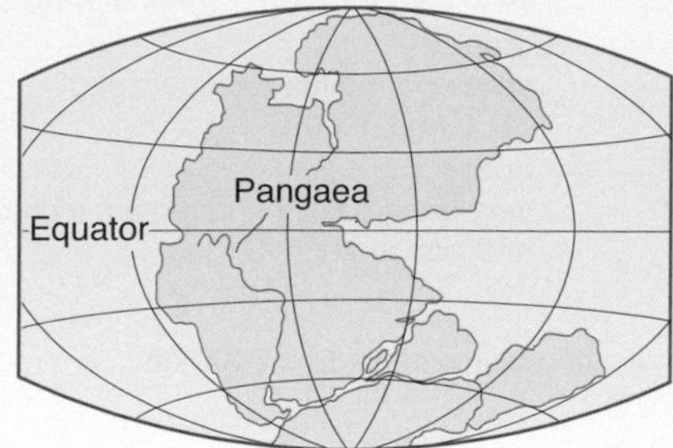

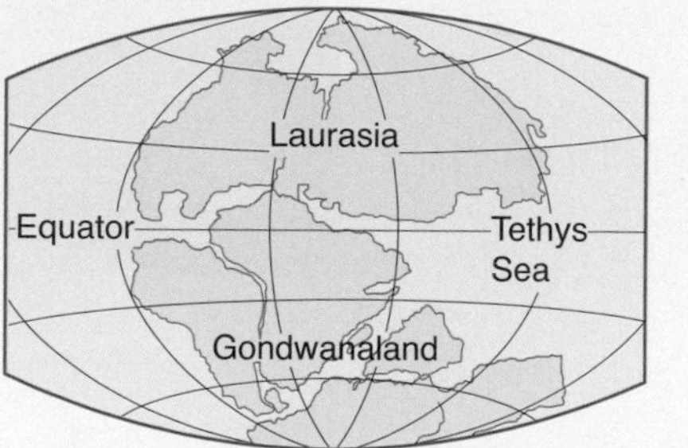

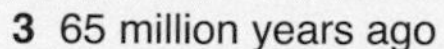

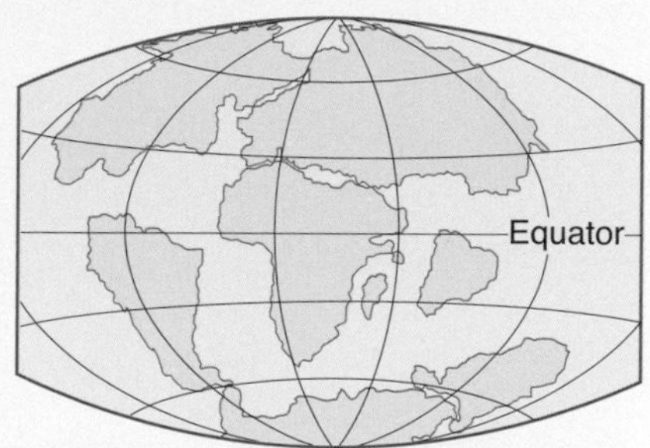

Figure 16 The break-up of Pangaea and the jigsaw-like fit between the continents

Wegener further highlighted the following points as evidence for continental drift:

* The geology of adjacent continents matches; for example, there is a good fit between the ancient rock types and structures between the eastern coast of South America and the western coast of Africa (see Figure 17).

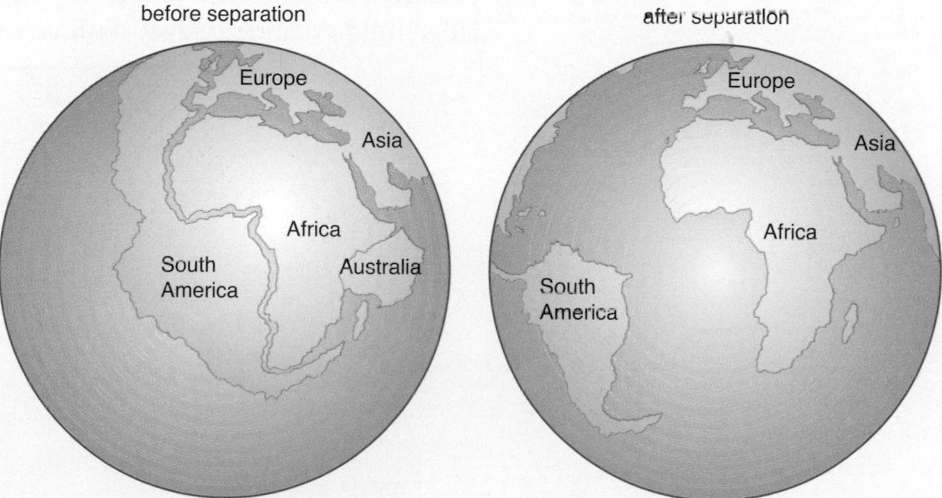

Figure 17 The jigsaw-like fit between South America and West Africa

* The remains of animals and plants found on different continents match up across the 'joint'; for example, similar and identical fossils are found in Brazil and West Africa.

Even though Wegener provided much evidence for his theory of continental drift, his ideas were not accepted. Geologists did not accept his theory as they did not believe that continents could move. Wegener could not explain how or why the continents could move apart. Wegener died in 1930 and it was not until the 1950s and 60s that new discoveries were made. It was found that continents could move due to **convectional currents** in the mantle. Figure 18 shows the layered structure of the Earth with the core, mantle and crust. The mantle is mostly a moderately dense solid with some molten rock and is almost 2900 km thick.

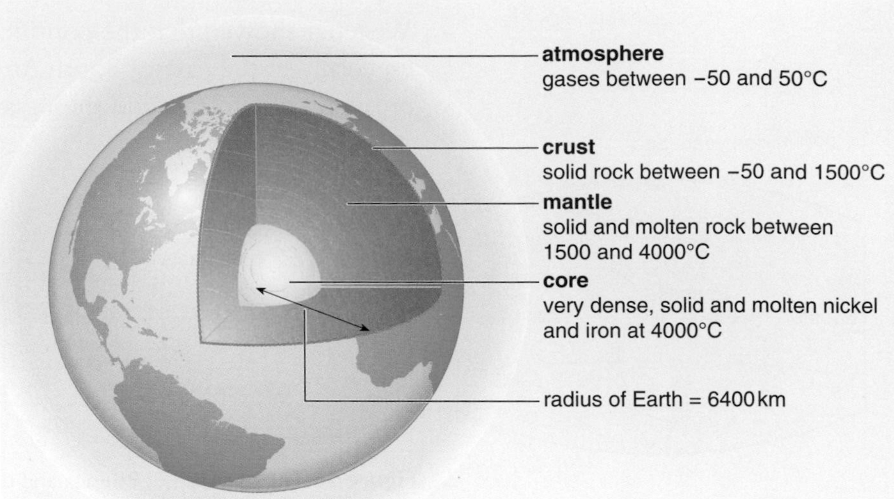

Figure 18 The layered structure of the inside of the Earth

The detailed studies of the Atlantic Ocean in the 1950s and 60s provided evidence that continental drift was caused by convection currents in the mantle. The studies showed that in the centre of the Atlantic Ocean there is a huge mountain range called a mid-ocean ridge (mid-Atlantic Ridge) with volcanoes (Figure 19).

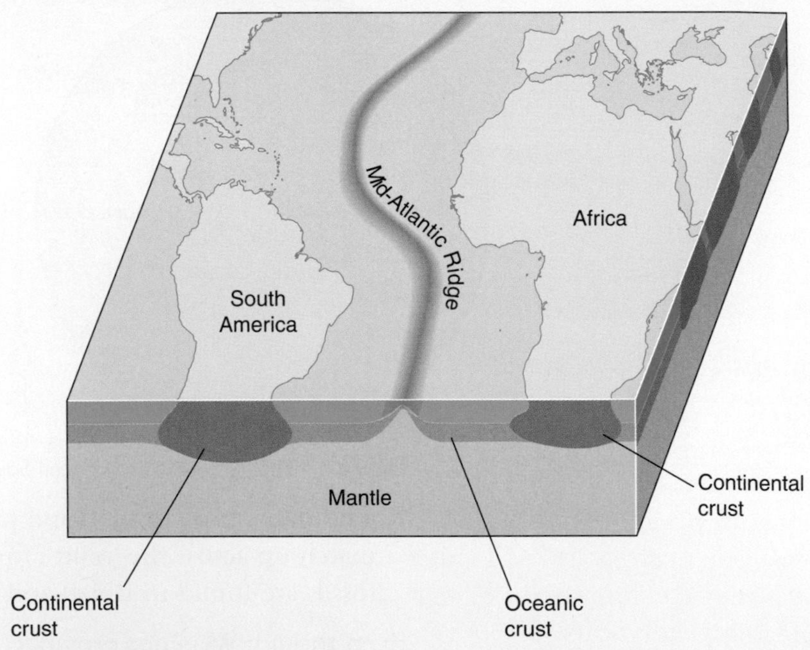

Figure 19 The mid-Atlantic Ridge

* On either side of the ridge there is a similar pattern of humps and hollows.
* The rocks at the top of the ridge are the youngest and the further away the rocks are from the ridge the older they are.

The results of the studies indicate that molten lava was flowing out from volcanoes onto both sides of the mid-ocean ridge and this was a result of convection currents in the mantle.

In 1963, Wegener's theory of continental drift was further supported by studies into the magnetism in rocks. Geologists have found that as molten rocks cool and solidify, any iron in the rocks becomes magnetised in line with the Earth's magnetic field. Additionally, it was found that about every 500 000 years the Earth's magnetic field flips. This means that the North Pole becomes a South Pole and the South Pole becomes a North Pole. The studies on the magnetic properties of rocks along the mid-Atlantic Ridge clearly showed that the magnetism of the rocks on one side of the ridge was a reflection of those on the other side of the ridge (Figure 20).

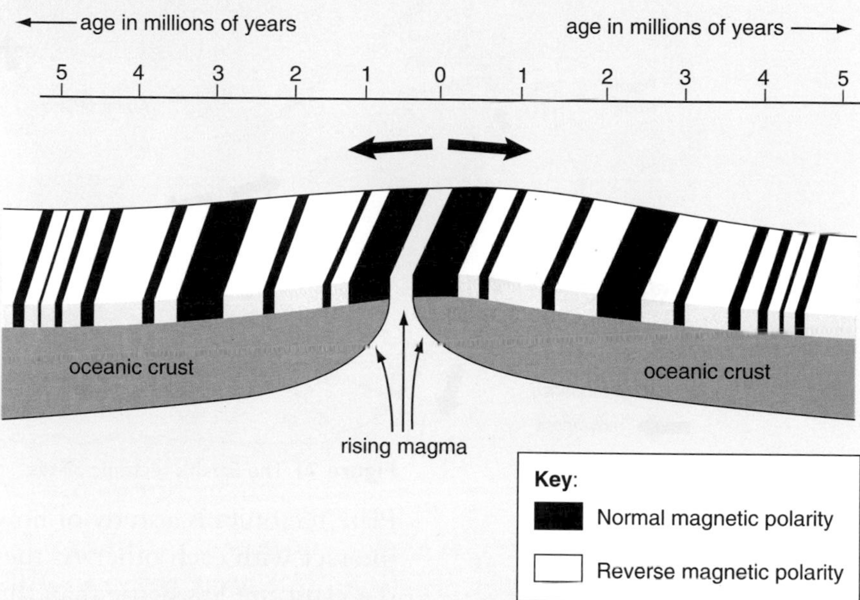

Figure 20 Magnetic patterns in rocks on both sides of the mid-Atlantic Ridge

From the findings it is seen that rocks now hundreds of kilometres apart were formed at the same time as the magma erupted out of the volcano. Over millions of years new rocks were formed by further volcanic activity and the existing rocks were pushed further and further apart. As these rocks move further and further apart so do the continents, in this case Africa and South America. The research into the formation of the mid-Atlantic Ridge and the magnetic patterns of rocks on the ocean floor provided evidence for Wegener's continental drift theory. It convinced scientists that most of the ideas were correct. Geologists now accepted Wegener's belief that, over time, the ocean floor could move. Convectional forces could move the continents through the ocean floor. The idea that continents were in fixed positions was thrown out, and the continental drift theory became accepted. Wegener's theory has now been replaced by the theory of **plate tectonics**. Plate tectonics explains many of the features on the Earth's surface and how it is still changing, including volcanoes and earthquakes which occur at boundaries of plates.

▶ Plate tectonics

In this theory, the Earth's crust is not considered to be a continuous shell of rock. Instead, it is envisaged as cracked and broken into a number of large tectonic plates, as shown in Figure 21. There are two types of tectonic plates: **continental plates** and **oceanic plates**.

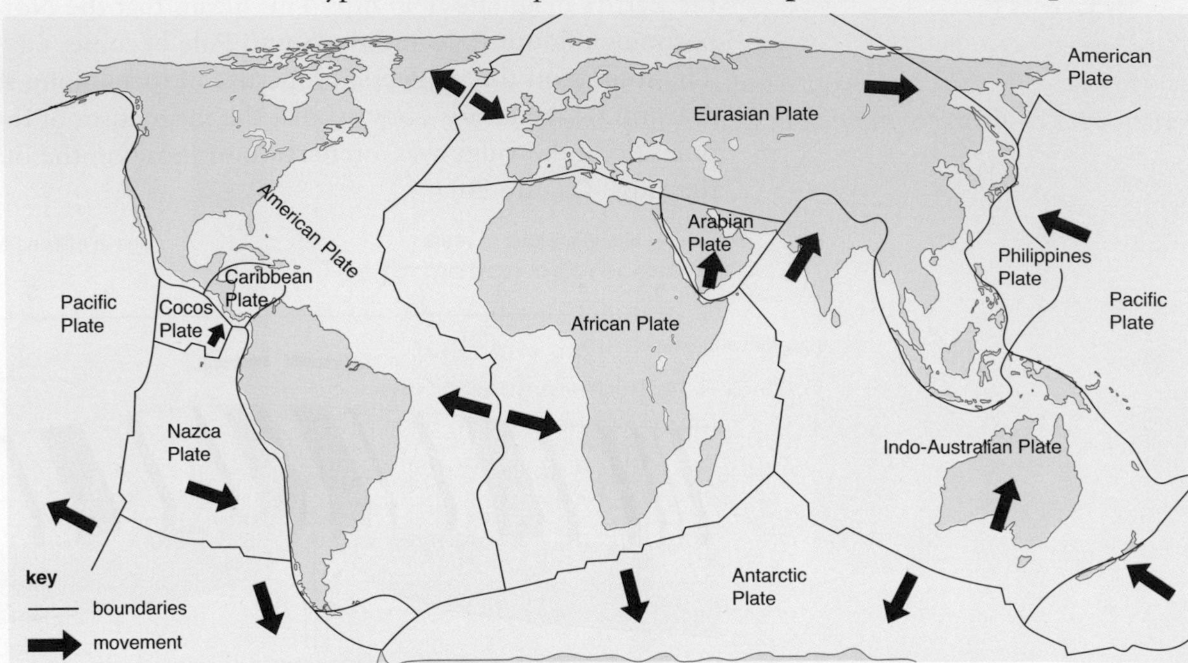

Figure 21 The Earth's tectonic plates

Plate tectonics is a study of how plates move and how they interact with each other. As these large plates, which make up the crust, are less dense than the mantle, they float on it. With the Earth's core at a temperature of 4000 °C, this causes slow-moving convection currents in the mantle. These convection currents cause movement in the plates, which float on the mantle. Space satellite measurements show that such movement is causing North America and Europe to move apart at a rate of about 4 cm per year.

▶ Earthquakes and volcanoes

Earthquakes and volcanoes generally occur around plate boundaries where there are weaknesses in the crust. We will look at what happens when plates slide past each other and when they move apart. Plate movement is generally very slow; however, at times the movement may be sudden and disastrous.

Earthquakes

An earthquake is caused by the stresses and strains that are set up when two continental plates move past each other. This means that they generally occur at plate boundaries, where the plates slide past each other or where one plate slides under another. The forces involved in these processes are very large. Figure 22 shows what happens when two plates slide past each other.

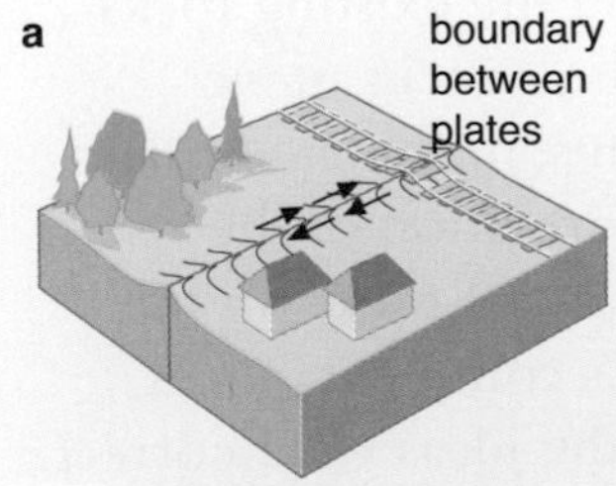

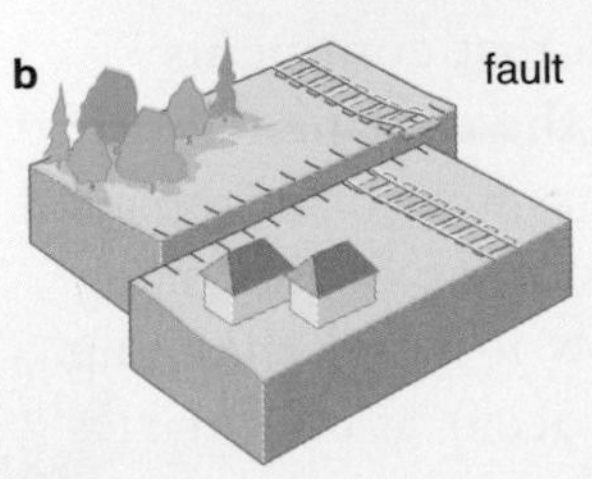

Figure 22 How an earthquake happens

Figure 23 New Zealand after the earthquake in 2011

As the plates slide past each other they may even bend. If these forces are suddenly released, then an earthquake occurs. The ground shakes violently, and this causes breaks and cracks to develop in the ground. This often produces damage to buildings, bridges and other structures (Figure 23), and may result in serious injuries and loss of life.

The breaks in the ground that form due to the horizontal movement of the plates are known as tear faults. Two well-known examples are the San Andreas Fault in California and the Great Glen Fault in Scotland (Figure 24).

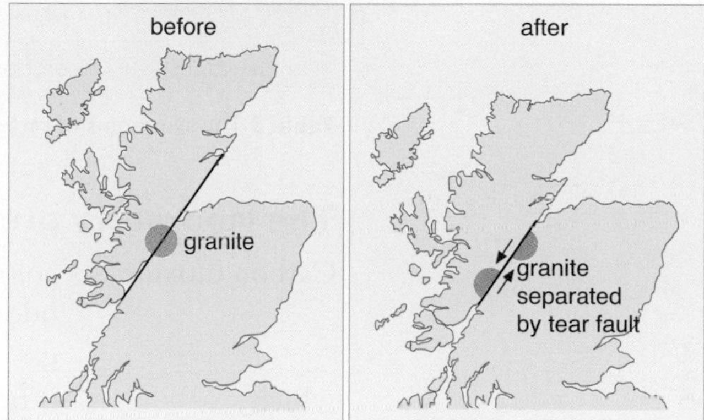

Figure 24 Scotland before and after the Great Glen Fault

Earthquakes vary greatly in scale or magnitude. The magnitude of an earthquake is determined by the intensity of the **seismic wave** it produces. Seismic waves are vibrations from the earthquakes that travel through the Earth. The **Richter scale** is a scale that indicates the magnitude of the earthquake and the damage that it can cause.

Volcanoes

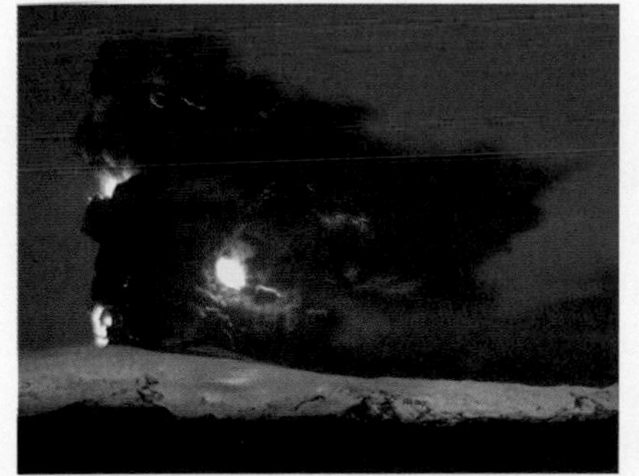

Figure 25 A volcano erupting

Volcanoes are caused by plates moving apart. When this takes place the Earth's crust is stretched. In areas of weakness, the crust may crack. Molten magma and gases can escape through the cracks, resulting in a volcano (Figure 25).

Approximately 80% of volcanoes occur along plate boundaries in the ocean floor. An important difference between volcanoes and earthquakes is that volcanoes are predictable. Prior to eruption, there are usually rumblings from the volcano indicating that an eruption is about to take place. Although there are signs, it is not easy to say how violent the eruption might be.

▶ The combustion of carbon, Part II

Carbon and carbon-containing compounds burn in a limited supply of air to form carbon monoxide.

$$\text{carbon} + \text{oxygen}_{\text{(limited)}} \rightarrow \text{carbon monoxide}$$
$$2C + O_2 \rightarrow 2CO$$

Carbon monoxide is a toxic, colourless, odourless gas often referred to as the 'Silent Killer'. Carbon monoxide reacts with the red blood cells in your body preventing them from carrying the oxygen your body

Figure 26 Carbon monoxide detector

needs to survive. Carbon monoxide is absorbed by the human body 200 times faster than oxygen and is very difficult to eliminate.

Many homes using gas as a fuel for cooking or heating are fitted with a carbon monoxide detector similar to the one shown in Figure 26. All gas fuelled appliances should be regularly maintained to prevent the formation of carbon monoxide due to a lack of oxygen present for combustion.

mild exposure	Slight headache, nausea, vomiting, unusual tiredness
medium exposure	Severe throbbing headache, drowsiness, disorientation, confusion, fast heart rate
extreme exposure	Unconsciousness, convulsions, cardio-respiratory failure, **death**

Table 3 The symptoms of carbon monoxide poisoning

The laboratory preparation of carbon dioxide

Carbon dioxide is a	colourless odourless gas	Physical properties of carbon dioxide
which	is heavier than air is slightly soluble in water does not support combustion	
and	is an acidic gas.	

The carbon dioxide molecule can be represented by:

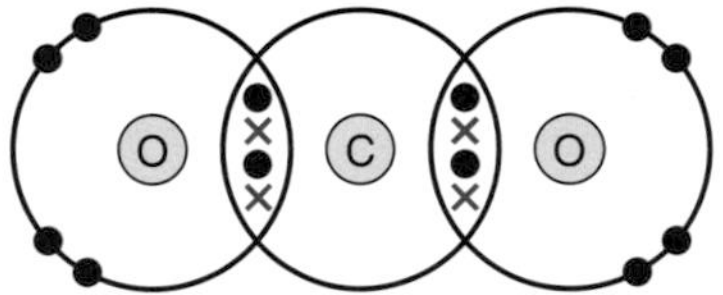

Figure 27 Carbon dioxide molecule

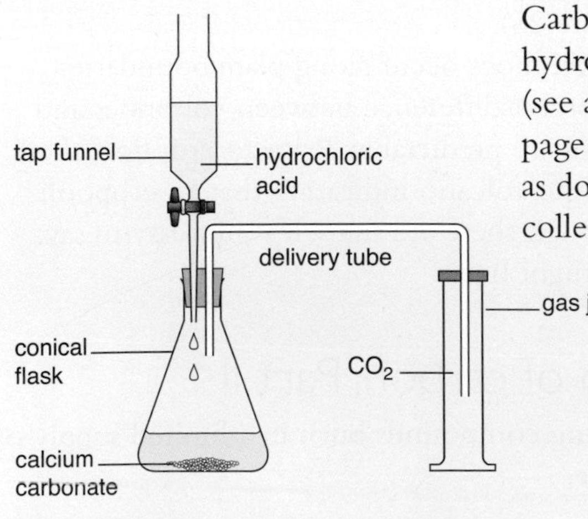

Figure 28 Apparatus for the preparation of carbon dioxide

Carbon dioxide is prepared in the laboratory by the action of dilute hydrochloric acid on calcium carbonate as illustrated in Figure 28 (see also reaction of metal carbonates with acids, Chapter 6, page 87). The carbon dioxide is collected by a method known as downward delivery as it is heavier than air. (CO_2 may also be collected 'over water' as it is only slightly soluble in water.)

Observations:

* a colourless gas is evolved
* the calcium carbonate disappears
* fizzing of the reaction mixture in the conical flask
* heat can be felt at the bottom of the conical flask/the temperature of the reaction mixture rises.

calcium carbonate + hydrochloric acid → calcium chloride + water + carbon dioxide

$$CaCO_3 + 2HCl \rightarrow CaCl_2 + H_2O + CO_2$$

The chemical reactions of carbon dioxide

Reaction with water

Carbon dioxide will react with water to form carbonic acid. Carbonic acid is a weak acid.

$$\text{water} + \text{carbon dioxide} \rightarrow \text{carbonic acid}$$
$$H_2O + CO_2 \rightarrow H_2CO_3$$

The water vapour and the carbon dioxide in the atmosphere react to form rain water. Rain water is a solution of the weak acid, carbonic acid, pH~5 (see Chapter 12, page 156).

Sparkling drinks contain carbon dioxide dissolved under pressure in the water. When the pressure is released most of the carbon dioxide bubbles out of solution. Some of the carbon dioxide reacts with the water causing the sparkling drink to be slightly acidic.

Figure 28 Carbon dioxide bubbling out of sparkling water

Reaction with calcium hydroxide solution

Calcium hydroxide solution, $Ca(OH)_{2(aq)}$, is known as limewater. When carbon dioxide is bubbled through limewater, the limewater changes from colourless to milky white. As the carbon dioxide continues to bubble through the limewater, the milky white precipitate disappears and leaves a colourless solution.

This reaction is used as the basis for the test for carbon dioxide.

$$\text{calcium hydroxide (limewater)} + \text{carbon dioxide} \rightarrow \text{calcium carbonate} + \text{water}$$
$$Ca(OH)_{2(aq)} + CO_{2(g)} \rightarrow CaCO_{3(s)} + H_2O_{(l)}$$

$$\text{calcium carbonate} + \text{carbon dioxide} + \text{water} \rightarrow \text{calcium hydrogen carbonate}$$
$$CaCO_{3(s)} + CO_{2(g)} + H_2O_{(l)} \rightarrow Ca(HCO_3)_{2(aq)}$$

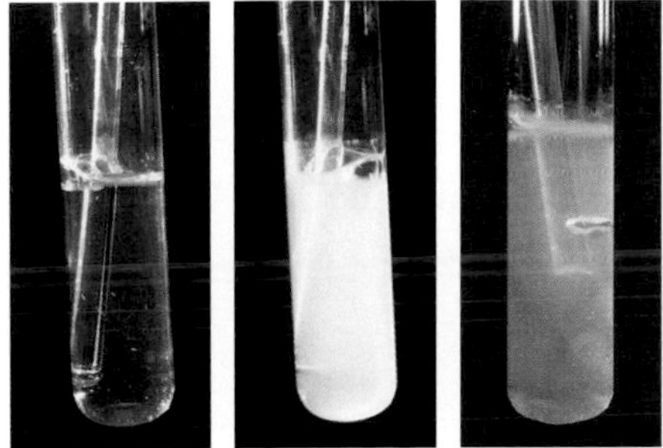

Figure 29 Bubbling carbon dioxide through calcium hydroxide solution first precipitates calcium carbonate, which subsequently dissolves to form calcium hydrogen carbonate

Reaction with burning magnesium

When burning magnesium is plunged into a gas jar of carbon dioxide it continues to burn despite the lack of oxygen. It forms magnesium oxide and carbon in the form of a black sooty powder.

Observations:

* The burning magnesium continues to burn with a bright white light.
* Black soot forms on the inside walls of the gas jar.
* A white ash forms.

$$\text{magnesium} + \text{carbon dioxide} \rightarrow \text{magnesium oxide} + \text{carbon}$$
$$2Mg + CO_2 \rightarrow 2MgO + C$$

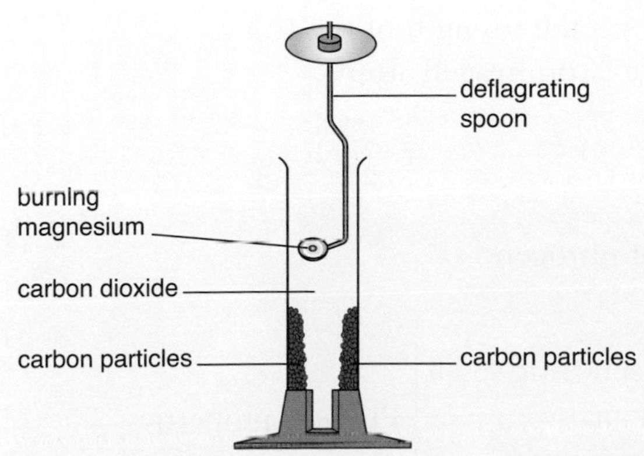

Figure 31 Magnesium burning in carbon dioxide

Figure 32 Sodium hydroxide reagent

Reaction with sodium hydroxide solution

The reagent bottle of sodium hydroxide in Figure 33 has a white crust around the rim. This white crusty solid is the product of the reaction of sodium hydroxide and the carbon dioxide in the air.

sodium hydroxide + carbon dioxide → sodium carbonate + water

$$2NaOH + CO_2 \rightarrow Na_2CO_3 + H_2O$$

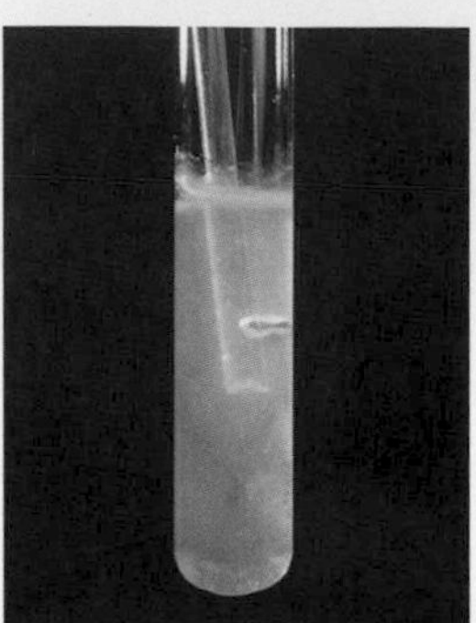

Figure 33 Test for carbon dioxide

Test for carbon dioxide gas

Bubble carbon dioxide through a solution of limewater.

The gas will turn the limewater from colourless to milky white.

▶ Nitrogen

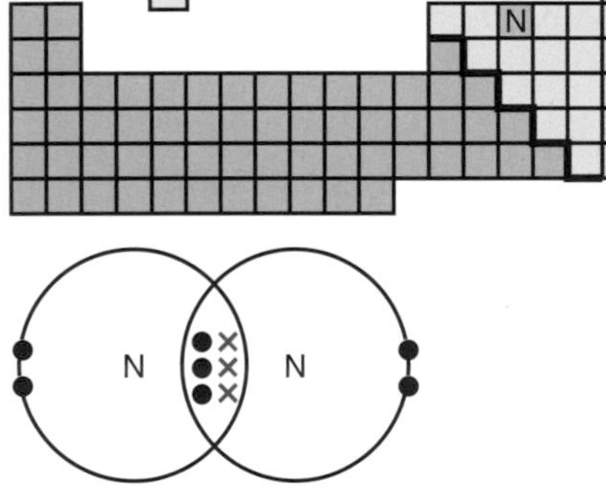

Figure 34 Nitrogen gas is a diatomic molecule

Nitrogen is a	colourless	Physical properties of nitrogen
	odourless	
	gas	
which is	the same weight as air	
	insoluble in water	
and	does not burn.	

Nitrogen is extremely unreactive.

Nitrogen gas is a diatomic molecule with the formula N_2.

Nitrogen is unreactive due to the strength of the triple covalent bond between the two nitrogen atoms.

▶ Ammonia

Ammonia is a compound of nitrogen.

Ammonia is a	colourless gas	Physical properties of ammonia
	with a characteristic smell	
which is	lighter than air	
	very soluble in water	
and	produces an alkaline solution.	

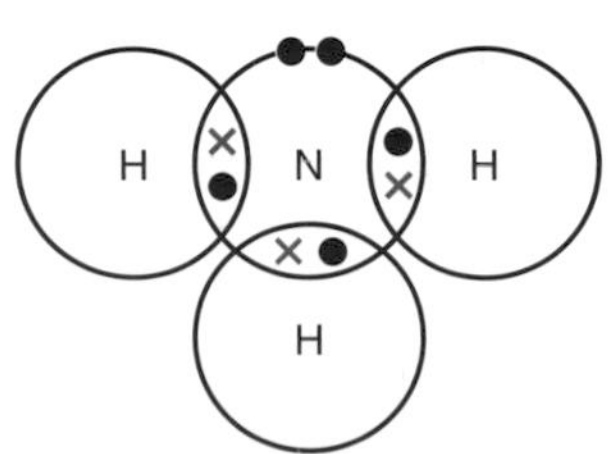

Figure 35 Ammonia

Ammonia is a covalent molecule with the formula NH_3.

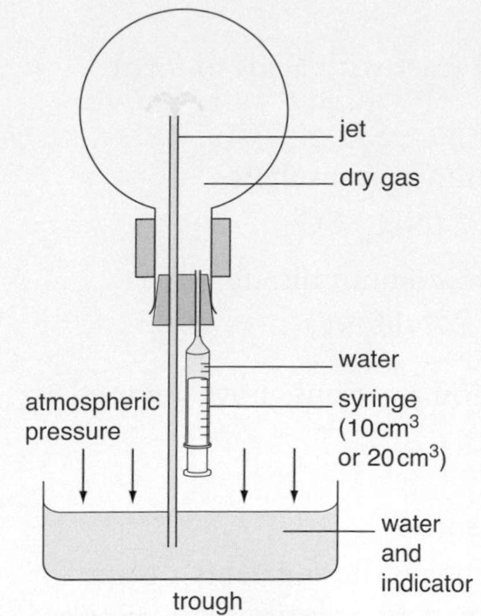

Figure 36 The ammonia fountain

The ammonia fountain experiment

The solubility of ammonia can be shown spectacularly by this experiment, the ammonia fountain. Ammonia gas dissolves in water to form a solution of ammonium hydroxide.

The round flask is filled with dry ammonia gas. The end of the glass jet is immersed in a trough of water to which universal indicator is added. A small amount of water is introduced into the flask by the syringe to start the jet. The ammonia in the flask is so soluble it quickly dissolves. So much of it dissolves that the pressure inside the flask decreases dramatically and water rushes up from the trough to replace the gas. As the ammonia dissolves in the water at the tip of the jet the water changes colour to blue, due to the alkaline nature of ammonia.

ammonia + water → ammonium hydroxide

$$NH_{3(g)} + H_2O_{(l)} \rightarrow NH_4OH_{(aq)}$$

Ammonia and water are molecules formed by sharing electrons between the atoms in the compound. The solution formed contains the ammonium ion, NH_4^+, and the hydroxide ion, OH^-.

Figure 37 Test for ammonia gas

Test for ammonia gas

Dip a glass rod into a solution of concentrated hydrochloric acid.

Bring the glass rod close to the ammonia gas.

White fumes/smoke of ammonium chloride confirm the presence of ammonia gas.

The chemical reactions of ammonia

Reaction with hydrogen chloride

Ammonia reacts with hydrogen chloride to form white fumes of ammonium chloride as the only product. This reaction forms the basis for the test for ammonia gas.

Ammonia and hydrogen chloride are molecules formed by sharing electrons between the atoms in the compound. Ammonium chloride is an ionic compound. It contains the ammonium ion, NH_4^+, and the chloride ion, Cl^-.

ammonia + hydrogen chloride → ammonium chloride

$$NH_{3(g)} + HCl_{(g)} \rightarrow NH_4Cl_{(s)}$$

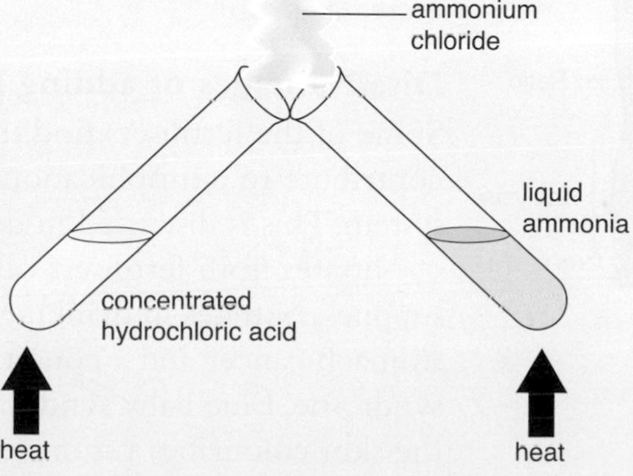

Figure 38 Reaction of ammonia with hydrogen chloride

Reaction with acids

Ammonia is an alkaline gas and will react with acids to form ammonium compounds.

$$\text{ammonia} + \text{sulfuric acid} \rightarrow \text{ammonium sulfate}$$
$$2NH_3 + H_2SO_4 \rightarrow (NH_4)_2SO_4$$
$$\text{ammonia} + \text{nitric acid} \rightarrow \text{ammonium nitrate}$$
$$NH_3 + HNO_3 \rightarrow NH_4NO_3$$

The products of the two neutralisation reactions above are used as commercial artificial fertilisers.

The action of nitrogenous fertilisers

A fertiliser is a compound which supplies the nutrients a plant needs for growth. Fertilisers can be natural or artificial. Nitrogen is important for plant growth as it is present in the structure of the plant, is in chlorophyll, and is involved in the chemical reactions needed for a healthy plant.

Figure 39 a) a healthy plant and
b) a plant showing the effects of lack of nitrogen in the soil

The photograph on the right of Figure 39 shows a plant which has been grown in soil containing much less nitrogen in the form of nitrates. The healthy plant on the left is larger, with larger, greener leaves.

Advantages of adding fertilisers to the soil

Adding fertilisers to the soil results in greater nitrogen uptake by the plant, which produces larger, healthier plants. For a commercial food producer this increases crop yield and thus increases profit.

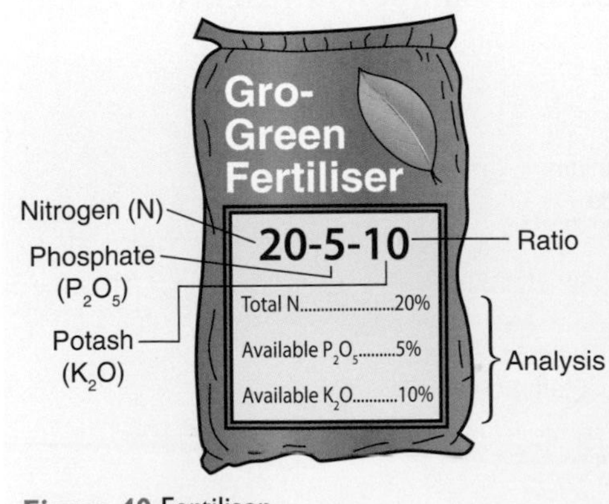

Figure 40 Fertiliser

Disadvantages of adding fertilisers to the soil

Some of the fertilisers find their way into rivers and lakes and contribute to eutrophication, the premature aging of a water system. This is discussed in detail in Chapter 7, page 100.

Nitrates from fertilisers can find their way into drinking water supplies. Nitrates in drinking water can cause some forms of stomach cancer and a condition in infants known as blue baby syndrome. Blue baby syndrome is characterised by a blue tint to the skin colouring, a shortness of breath and an unusual tiredness due to a lack of oxygen in the blood. It can be fatal if not treated.

▶ The importance of nitrogen

All life on Earth depends on the element nitrogen. It is essential to produce amino acids which produce proteins and is also an important part of DNA. Although the atmosphere surrounding the Earth contains approximately 80% molecular nitrogen (N_2) at the surface of the Earth, it is unusable by the majority of plant species. Legumes, such as peas, beans and lentils, and nitrogen-fixing bacteria can add nitrogen from the air into the soil in a form usable by plants. Organic fertiliser, such as manure, and lightning striking the Earth can also add this form of nitrogen to the soil. However, at the beginning of the 20th century, scientists warned that these processes were not able to supply the amount of nitrogen needed to grow food for the expanding world population.

The following chemical process is therefore arguably one of the most important discoveries of the last 100 years.

The Haber process

The Haber process takes nitrogen from the air and changes it to a form which can be used by plants, enabling the mass production of food supplies.

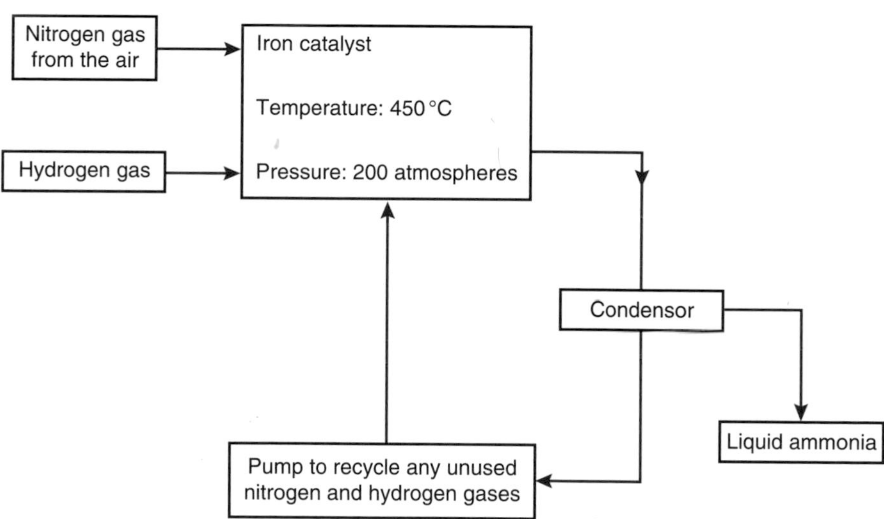

Figure 41 The Haber process for the production of ammonia

Note: The reaction of nitrogen with hydrogen is a reduction reaction. The nitrogen is reduced as it gains hydrogen. The gain of hydrogen is defined as reduction.

Nitrogen, from the air, and hydrogen are compressed to a pressure of 200 atmospheres and heated to 450 °C and passed over an iron catalyst. About 20% of the gases react to form ammonia. As the three gases are pumped through a cooler the ammonia condenses and is tapped off as a liquid. The unreacted hydrogen and nitrogen are recycled and passed over the catalyst once again to produce more ammonia.

$$\text{nitrogen} + \text{hydrogen} \rightleftharpoons \text{ammonia}$$
$$N_2 + 3H_2 \rightleftharpoons 2NH_3$$

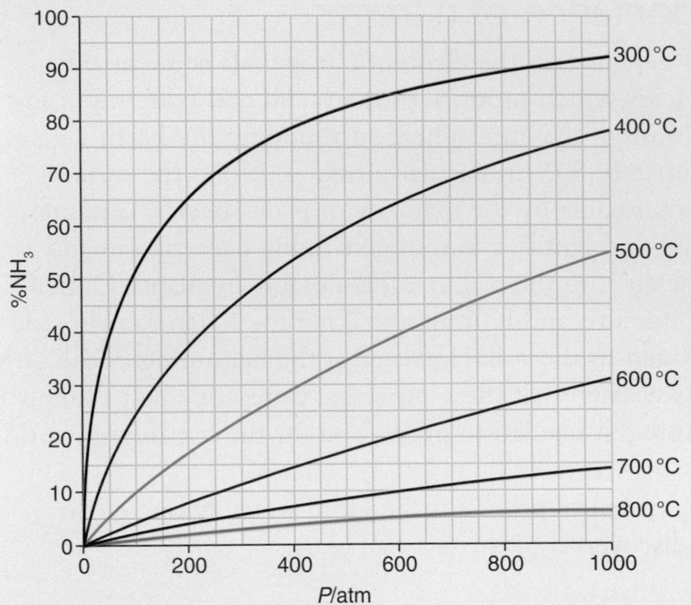

Figure 42 Percentage yield of ammonia depends on the temperature as the pressure is increased

The reaction between nitrogen and hydrogen is reversible. Look carefully at the arrow used in the previous equations. This type of arrow is used to signify a reversible reaction. Once a certain amount of ammonia molecules have formed some will decompose and form hydrogen and nitrogen again. The conditions imposed on the reaction give the optimum (best) yield of ammonia without incurring too much extra cost or slowing the reaction down.

The following graphs illustrate what happens to the percentage of ammonia formed under different conditions of temperature and pressure.

The highest percentage yield of ammonia is achieved at high pressure. The attainment of high pressures in industry is expensive and can be extremely dangerous. The percentage yield of ammonia decreases sharply as the temperature is increased. A low temperature would increase the yield. However, the catalyst will not work below 450 °C and the rate of the reaction will be extremely slow. Considering all of these factors, a compromise is reached to produce the best possible yield of ammonia at the lowest possible cost, in a safe environment with a catalyst working at an optimum rate. The conditions used are given below:

* iron catalyst
* temperature: 450 °C
* pressure: 200 atmospheres.

Figure 43 Fritz Haber, who developed the Haber process

Fritz Haber: two very different applications from the same knowledge

Fritz Haber was born into a German Jewish family in the late 1800s. He became a respected research chemist and at one time was a pupil of Robert Bunsen, the inventor of the Bunsen burner. His discovery of the production of ammonia by circulating nitrogen and hydrogen over an iron catalyst at 450 °C and 200 atmospheres of pressure led to the production of artificial fertilisers and powerful explosives. The fertilisers were used to mass produce food to sustain life and the explosives were used to prolong World War I where so many died. Haber received the Nobel Prize for Chemistry in 1918 for his development of the process.

Using ammonia solution to identify cations

Cations are ions with a positive charge. Metal cations can be identified by reacting a solution of the cation with ammonia solution.

ammonia + water → ammonium hydroxide

$$NH_3 + H_2O \rightarrow NH_4OH$$

The presence of the hydroxide ion in the solution of ammonia causes the formation of the metal hydroxide. Many of the metal hydroxides have distinctive colours which identify the metal cation.

The table below details the observations which are made when ammonia solution is added to a selection of metal cations in solution; first drop by drop and eventually to excess.

Name and charge of cation	Initial reaction as ammonia solution is added drop by drop	Reaction as ammonia is added to excess
Copper(II) ion, Cu^{2+}	Forms a pale blue gelatinous precipitate $Cu^{2+} + 2OH^- \rightarrow Cu(OH)_{2(s)}$	Pale blue precipitate dissolves to form a dark blue solution
Iron(II) ion, Fe^{2+}	Forms a dark green gelatinous precipitate (which slowly turns red-brown as it sits) $Fe^{2+} + 2OH^- \rightarrow Fe(OH)_{2(s)}$	No further reaction. The precipitate does not re-dissolve
Iron(III) ion, Fe^{3+}	Forms a red-brown gelatinous precipitate $Fe^{3+} + 3OH^- \rightarrow Fe(OH)_{3(s)}$	No further reaction. The precipitate does not re-dissolve
Aluminium ion, Al^{3+}	Forms a white gelatinous precipitate $Al^{3+} + 3OH^- \rightarrow Al(OH)_{3(s)}$	No further reaction. The white precipitate does not re-dissolve
Zinc ion, Zn^{2+}	Forms a white gelatinous precipitate $Zn^{2+} + 2OH^- \rightarrow Zn(OH)_{2(s)}$	The white precipitate re-dissolves to form a colourless solution
Magnesium ion, Mg^{2+}	Forms a white gelatinous precipitate $Mg^{2+} + 2OH^- \rightarrow Mg(OH)_{2(s)}$	No further reaction. The white precipitate does not re-dissolve.

Table 4 Using ammonia solution to identify cations

Identifying the ammonium cation, NH_4^+

When sodium hydroxide solution is added to an ammonium compound, ammonia gas is evolved. The gas can be identified as an alkaline gas using damp universal indicator paper. The damp universal indicator paper will turn blue.

sodium hydroxide	+	ammonium chloride	→	sodium chloride	+ water +	ammonia
NaOH	+	NH_4Cl	→	NaCl	+ H_2O +	NH_3
NaOH	+	NH_4^+	→	Na^+	+ H_2O +	NH_3

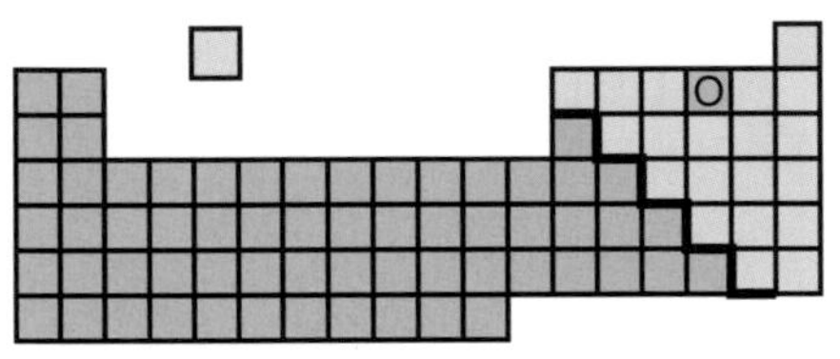

Oxygen

Oxygen is a colourless odourless gas which is approximately the same weight as air, slightly soluble in water and supports combustion (recall combustion is the reaction of a fuel with oxygen to form oxides and heat energy). — Physical properties of oxygen

Oxygen is a diatomic molecule with the formula O_2.

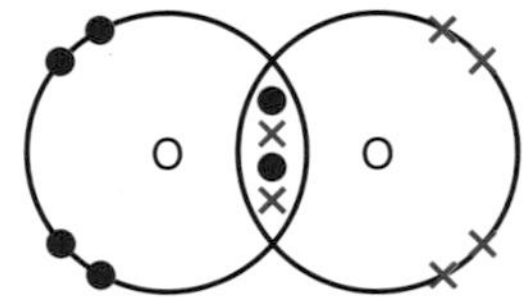

Figure 42

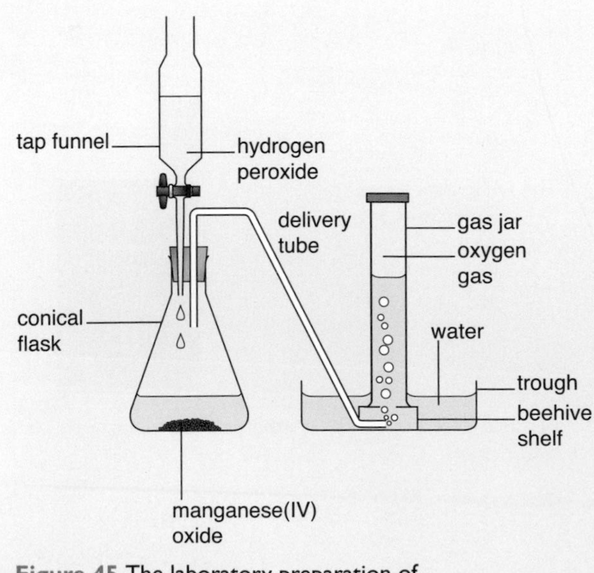

Figure 45 The laboratory preparation of oxygen gas

Oxygen is prepared in the laboratory by the action of manganese(IV) oxide on hydrogen peroxide, as illustrated in Figure 45. The oxygen can be collected 'over water' as it is not very soluble in water.

Manganese(IV) oxide, MnO_2, acts as a catalyst in this reaction. It speeds up the rate of the reaction but remains chemically unchanged at the end. The hydrogen peroxide is decomposed by the action of the catalyst.

hydrogen peroxide → water + oxygen

$$2H_2O_2 \rightarrow 2H_2O + O_2$$

Observations:

* Bubbles of a colourless gas are evolved.
* The black solid remains unaffected at the bottom of the conical flask.
* Heat can be felt at the bottom of the conical flask. The temperature of the reaction mixture rises.

The chemical reactions of oxygen

Reaction with hydrogen

hydrogen + oxygen → water
$H_2 + O_2 \rightarrow H_2O$

For the reaction of hydrogen and oxygen as a clean fuel, see page 183.

For the reaction of hydrogen and oxygen as a reduction, see page 182.

This is an example of a combustion reaction. The hydrogen has reacted with oxygen to form an oxide and heat energy.

Reaction with carbon

carbon + oxygen (excess) → carbon dioxide
$C + O_2 \rightarrow CO_2$

carbon + oxygen (limited) → carbon monoxide
$2C + O_2 \rightarrow 2CO$

See pages 184 and 191 for a detailed discussion of the formation of the two oxides of carbon, carbon dioxide and carbon monoxide.

Reaction with sulfur

sulfur + oxygen → sulfur dioxide
$S + O_2 \rightarrow SO_2$

See page 202 for a detailed discussion of the reaction of sulfur with oxygen.

Reaction with magnesium

Figure 46 Reaction of magnesium with oxygen in the air

Magnesium burns in air with a bright white flame leaving a grey–white ash, magnesium oxide. When burning magnesium is plunged into a gas jar of oxygen the magnesium burns more vigorously with a brighter white flame and a white cloud of particles of magnesium oxide form in the air.

magnesium + oxygen → magnesium oxide
$2Mg + O_2 \rightarrow 2MgO$

Reaction with copper

Copper reacts when heated in an oxygen atmosphere to form black copper(II) oxide.

copper + oxygen → copper(II) oxide
$2Cu + O_2 \rightarrow 2CuO$

Reaction with zinc

Zinc reacts when heated in an oxygen atmosphere to form white zinc oxide. The zinc oxide turns yellow when heated for a prolonged period of time and returns to white as it cools.

zinc + oxygen → zinc oxide
$2Zn + O_2 \rightarrow 2ZnO$

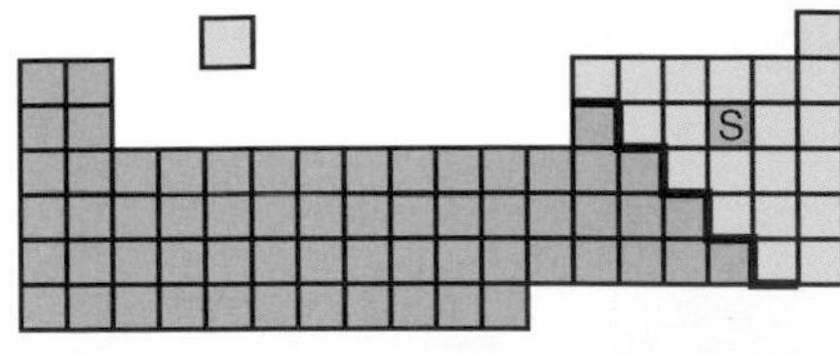

Figure 47 Sulfur

Allotropes are different forms of the same element in the same physical state.

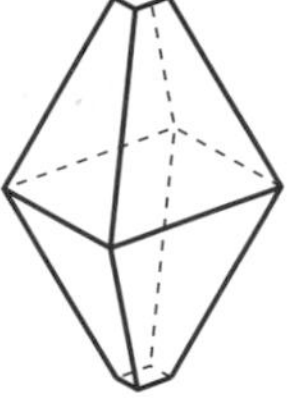

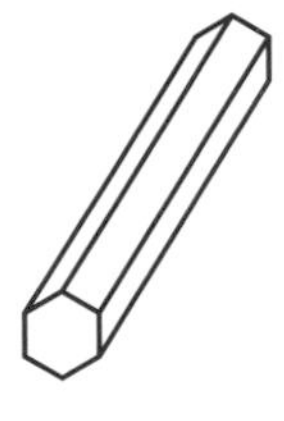

The different crystal shapes are formed because the sulfur (S_8) molecules pack/stack together in different ways.

Sulfur

Sulfur is a yellow solid which burns in air with a blue flame to form sulfur dioxide gas. There are three allotropes of sulfur: rhombic sulfur, monoclinic sulfur and plastic sulfur. **Allotropes are different forms of the same element in the same physical state.**

The chemical reactions of sulfur

Reaction with iron

iron + sulfur → iron sulfide

$Fe + S \rightarrow FeS$

This reaction is often used to illustrate the differences between the properties of elements, compounds and mixtures. See Chapter 3.

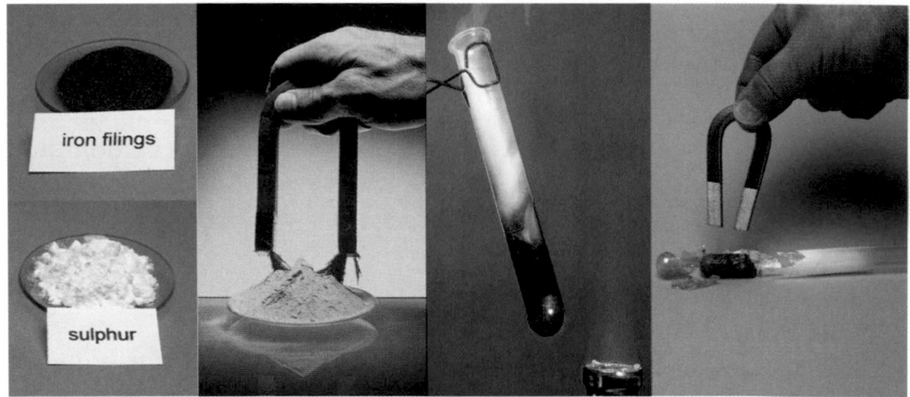

Figure 48 Reaction of sulfur with iron

Yellow sulfur powder is mixed thoroughly with the iron filings. The iron in the mixture is magnetic just as pure iron metal is. The mixture is heated strongly in a Bunsen flame. After the flame is extinguished the hot mixture continues to glow, showing that a chemical reaction is taking place. The product, a brittle grey solid, is removed from the test tube and is not attracted to the magnet.

Reaction with oxygen

sulfur + oxygen → sulfur dioxide

$S + O_2 \rightarrow SO_2$

The yellow solid melts to a brown viscous liquid which burns with a blue flame to form the pungent smelling gas sulfur dioxide.

Figure 49 a) Sulfur melts to form a brown viscous liquid and b) sulfur burning in oxygen

▶ Sulfur dioxide

Sulfur dioxide is a	yellow pungent gas	Physical properties of sulfur dioxide
which is	heavier than air soluble in water	
and	forms an acidic solution.	

The reaction of sulfur dioxide with water

Sulfur dioxide reacts with water to form a weakly acidic solution, sulfurous acid (H_2SO_3).

> Note: the formula of sulfurous acid is H_2SO_3.
> It should not be confused with sulfuric acid, H_2SO_4.

sulfur dioxide + water → sulfurous acid

$$SO_2 + H_2O \rightarrow H_2SO_3$$

Sulfurous acid is a weak acid (see Chapter 6) and is quite unstable. It decomposes to sulfur dioxide and water at room temperature.

Sulfur is present in fossil fuels (see Chapter 15) and sulfur dioxide is formed when fossil fuels are burned. Excess sulfur dioxide in the air causes a phenomenon known as acid rain.

▶ Acid rain

Rain water is a weak acid, pH~5.5. Acid rain is rain water which is more acidic than this, with a pH lower than 5.5.

When fossil fuels are burned in power stations or in vehicle engines, the sulfur content burns to form sulfur dioxide gas. The gases rise into the air where they react with water and more oxygen to form a solution of sulfuric acid, H_2SO_4. When this solution of sulfuric acid falls as rain it is known as acid rain.

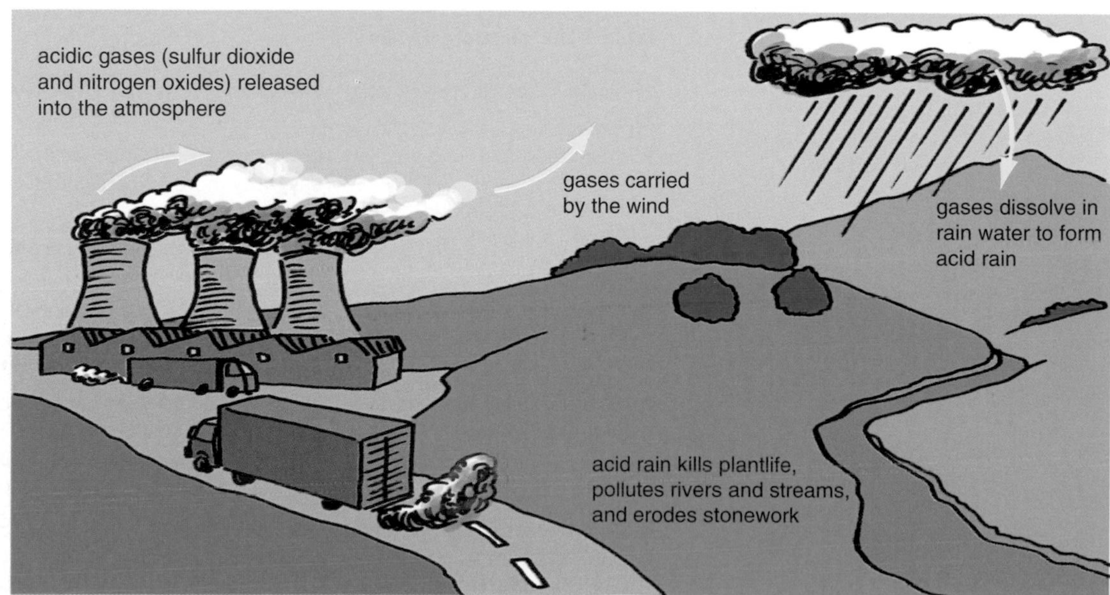

Figure 50 Acid rain

Figure 50 shows how acid rain may fall far from the source of the polluting gases spreading the effect of the acid rain to many other areas. When acid rain falls to earth, it flows across the surface in runoff water, enters water systems, and sinks into the soil.

Where acid rain falls	Effect of acid rain
forests	acid rain harms the leaves making it difficult for the plant to produce glucose by photosynthesis
	leaches nutrients from the soil leaving unhealthy plants which are more susceptible to disease
	severe acid rain pollution can result in complete deforestation
rivers, streams and lakes	water becomes acidic; most fish cannot live in acidic water and die
	acidic water also absorbs poisonous metal ions like aluminium which can also kill fish
limestone rocks, buildings, pavements	acid rain reacts with the calcium carbonate in the limestone, corroding it

Table 5 The effect of acid rain

Measures taken to prevent acid rain	Examples of how these measures work
Burn less fossil fuel	In areas where electricity is produced using fossil fuels, use electricity more efficiently, leading to the production of less electricity
	Produce electricity using renewable sources such as wind power and solar power
Remove sulfur from fossil fuels	Remove sulfur and sulfur-containing compounds from supplies of petrol and diesel used to fuel cars, vans and lorries
Remove the acidic gases from the combustion products before allowing the gases to escape into the atmosphere	In older coal fuelled power stations chemical scrubbers are fitted to the chimney stacks. These neutralise the acidic gases before they escape into the atmosphere

Table 6 Measures used to prevent acid rain

Sulfuric acid present in rain is a distinct disadvantage. However, sulfuric acid is an extremely useful substance and is produced industrially on a massive scale.

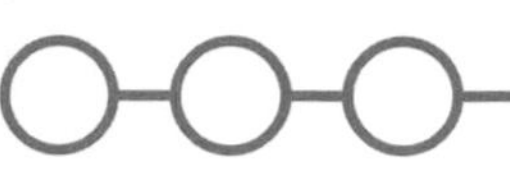

The industrial manufacture of sulfuric acid – the contact process

Sulfuric acid is manufactured from sulfur, oxygen and water. There are four main stages in the contact process.

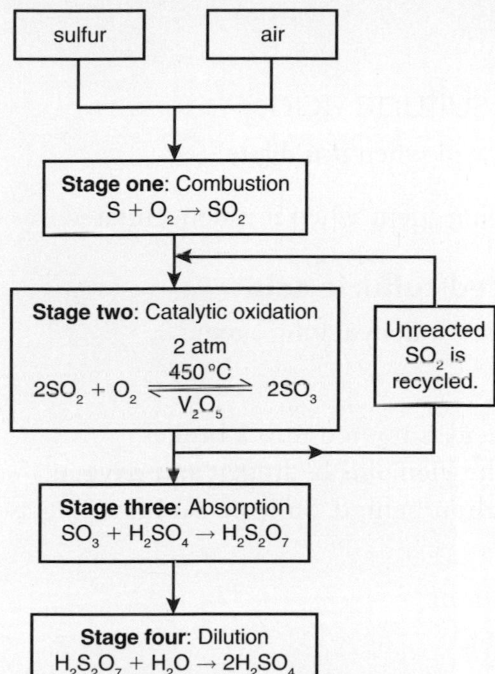

Note: The reaction of sulfur dioxide with oxygen is an oxidation reaction. The sulfur dioxide is oxidised as it gains oxygen. The gain of oxygen is defined as oxidation.

Stage one: The combustion of sulfur
Sulfur is burned in air in an exothermic reaction to form sulfur dioxide gas.

sulfur + oxygen → sulfur dioxide

$$S + O_2 \rightarrow SO_2$$

Stage two: The catalytic oxidation of sulfur dioxide
The sulfur dioxide is mixed with more air at a pressure of 2 atm and heated to 450 °C and passed over a catalyst of vanadium(V) oxide (V_2O_5). Under these conditions the sulfur dioxide reacts with the oxygen in the air to produce sulfur trioxide gas.

$$\text{sulfur dioxide} + \text{oxygen} \underset{V_2O_5}{\overset{2\text{ atm},\ 450\,^{\circ}\text{C}}{\rightleftharpoons}} \text{sulfur trioxide}$$

$$2SO_2 + O_2 \rightleftharpoons 2SO_3$$

Stage three: Absorption of sulfur trioxide into sulfuric acid
(Sulfuric acid may be produced by simply adding water to the sulfur trioxide. However, this reaction is extremely exothermic and forms a corrosive sulfuric acid mist which is difficult to contain.)

In the contact process the sulfur trioxide is mixed with concentrated sulfuric acid to form oleum, a colourless, viscous, oily liquid with an unpleasant characteristic odour.

sulfur trioxide + sulfuric acid → oleum

$$SO_3 + H_2SO_4 \rightarrow H_2S_2O_7$$

Stage four: Dilution of the oleum
The oleum is carefully mixed with water to produce sulfuric acid.

oleum + water → sulfuric acid

$$H_2S_2O_7 + H_2O \rightarrow 2H_2SO_4$$

The reaction between sulfur dioxide and oxygen is reversible. Look carefully at the arrow used in the chemical equations above. This type of arrow is used to signify a reversible reaction. Once a certain amount of sulfur trioxide molecules have formed, some will decompose and reform sulfur dioxide and oxygen again. The conditions imposed on the reaction give the optimum (best) yield of sulfur trioxide without incurring too much extra cost or slowing the reaction down.

The highest percentage yield of sulfur trioxide is achieved at high pressure. The attainment of high pressures in industry is expensive and can be extremely dangerous. The percentage yield of sulfur trioxide decreases sharply as the temperature is increased. A low temperature would increase the yield. However, the catalyst will not work below 450 °C and the rate of the reaction will be extremely slow. Considering all of these factors a compromise is reached to produce the best possible yield of sulfur trioxide at the lowest possible cost, in a safe environment with a catalyst working at an optimum rate.

Vanadium(V) oxide catalyst

Temperature: 450 °C

Pressure: 2 atmospheres

▶ The reactions of sulfuric acid

Sulfuric acid reacts as a typical acid when it is dilute.

Sulfuric acid acts as a dehydrating agent when it is concentrated.

Reactions of concentrated sulfuric acid

Concentrated sulfuric acid acts as a dehydrating agent.

Reaction with sugar

When concentrated sulfuric acid is poured into a beaker containing sugar, it removes the elements hydrogen and oxygen, forming water and leaving carbon behind. Sulfuric acid is acting as a dehydrating agent.

$$\text{sugar} \rightarrow \text{water} + \text{carbon}$$

$$C_6H_{12}O_6 \rightarrow 6H_2O + 6C$$

Figure 51 Reaction of concentrated sulfuric acid and sugar

Observations:

* Sulfuric acid darkens at the beginning.
* The sugar turns black.
* At this stage, the reaction appears to stop.
* Eventually, a black column rises from the beaker.
* A lot of heat is released.
* Steam pours out of the top of the beaker.
* The smell of burned caramel can be detected.

Reaction with hydrated copper sulfate

When concentrated sulfuric acid is added to small blue crystals of hydrated copper sulfate, it removes the water of crystallisation, leaving white anhydrous copper sulfate.

$$\text{hydrated copper sulfate} \rightarrow \text{dehydrated copper sulfate} + \text{water}$$

$$CuSO_4.7H_2O \rightarrow CuSO_4 + 7H_2O$$

Figure 52 Reaction of concentrated sulfuric acid and hydrated copper sulfate

Observations:

* The blue crystals will eventually turn white.
* The white solid will dissolve in the water formed.
* This forms a blue solution.

In all well run science rooms
In a cupboard to remove the fumes
All the best chemists do as they ought a'
And slowly add the acid to the water!

Diluting sulfuric acid

The reaction between sulfuric acid and water is extremely exothermic and unless it is carried out in a carefully controlled manner a dangerous vapour of sulfuric acid can form. Adding the water to the acid causes the concentrated acid to heat up and eventually vaporise producing dangerous acidic fumes. Concentrated sulfuric acid is diluted by the following method.

In a fume cupboard, slowly add concentrated sulfuric acid to water. Stir gently using a glass rod. Wait until the heat evolved has dissipated before adding the next portion of acid.

Reactions of dilute sulfuric acid

Dilute sulfuric acid is a typical acid.

Reaction with metals

sulfuric acid + zinc → zinc sulfate + hydrogen

$$H_2SO_4 + Zn \rightarrow ZnSO_4 + H_2$$

Observations:

* The grey zinc metal disappears.
* Bubbles of a gas are given off.
* Heat is evolved.

What would be observed if magnesium metal was used instead of the zinc in this reaction?

Reaction with metal oxides

sulfuric acid + zinc oxide → zinc sulfate + water

$$H_2SO_4 + ZnO \rightarrow ZnSO_4 + H_2O$$

Observations:

* The white powdery solid disappears.
* Heat is evolved.

What would be observed if copper oxide was used instead of the zinc oxide in this reaction?

Reaction with metal hydroxides

sulfuric acid + sodium hydroxide → sodium sulfate + water

$$H_2SO_4 + 2NaOH \rightarrow Na_2SO_4 + 2H_2O$$

Observations:

* This reaction is generally carried out in aqueous solution and as all the solutions are colourless and there is no gas evolved, thus there are limited observations to report. There is heat evolved but this can be hard to detect in a small reaction volume.

Reaction with metal carbonates

sulfuric acid + calcium carbonate → calcium sulfate + water + carbon dioxide

$$H_2SO_4 + CaCO_3 \rightarrow CaSO_4 + H_2O + CO_2$$

Observations:

* The white solid disappears.
* Bubbles of a colourless gas are evolved.
* Heat is evolved.

What would be observed if copper carbonate was used instead of the calcium carbonate in this reaction?

Reaction with metal hydrogen carbonates

sulfuric acid + sodium hydrogen carbonate → sodium sulfate + water + carbon dioxide

$$H_2SO_4 + 2NaHCO_3 \rightarrow Na_2SO_4 + 2H_2O + 2CO_2$$

Observations:

* The white solid disappears.
* Bubbles of a colourless gas are evolved.
* Heat is evolved.

Reaction with ammonia

sulfuric acid + ammonia → ammonium sulfate

$$H_2SO_4 + 2NH_3 \rightarrow (NH_4)_2SO_4$$

Observations:

* The distinctive odour of ammonia disappears.
* Heat is evolved.

Remember, when ammonia reacts with an acid it forms a salt only.

Remember:

*m*etal	+ *a*cid →	*s*alt +	*h*ydrogen			
metal oxide	+ acid →	salt +	water			
metal hydroxide	+ acid →	salt +	water			
metal carbonate	+ acid →	salt +	water	+	carbon dioxide	
metal hydrogen carbonate	+ acid →	salt +	water	+	carbon dioxide	

Knowing these general reactions can be a great help. They are studied in Chapter 6. Some of the reactions are important because the product is a gas. See the laboratory preparation of hydrogen and carbon dioxide in this chapter, pages 181 and 192.

As well as a salt, the product in the first reaction is hydrogen, and water is formed in all of the other reactions. In addition to this if the acid reacts with a carbonate or a hydrogen carbonate, carbon dioxide gas is produced.

These reactions are often used in questions where the examiner wishes to test your ability to write balanced chemical equations or your knowledge of observations.

▶ Exam questions

1 Ammonia is manufactured in the Haber process by reacting hydrogen and nitrogen.

a) Give a temperature and a pressure which are suitable for the Haber process and name the catalyst used. *(3 marks)*

b) Write a balanced symbol equation for the formation of ammonia from nitrogen and hydrogen. *(3 marks)*

c) Ammonia is used in the manufacture of nitric acid. Give **two** other uses of ammonia. *(2 marks)*

2 This question is about some non-metals and their compounds.

a) Both coal and oil contain sulfur as impurities and when these substances are burnt they produce a gas which causes acid rain.

i) Name the gas formed from burning sulfur that causes acid rain. *(1 mark)*

ii) Give **two** harmful effects of acid rain. *(2 marks)*

iii) Under the Clean Air Act, power stations must control emissions of gases which cause acid rain. Give **one** method of controlling these emissions. *(1 mark)*

iv) Give **one** important use of sulfur. *(1 mark)*

v) What does pure sulfur look like? *(2 marks)*

b) Fuels which contain carbon can burn to give carbon monoxide or carbon dioxide.

i) Write a balanced formula equation for the formation of carbon monoxide by the **incomplete** combustion of carbon. *(3 marks)*

ii) When burning fuels at home why is it important to ensure that there is plenty of oxygen present? *(2 marks)*

c) Some uses of non-metals are given below. For each use give **one** important reason why the non-metal is used.

i) Why is hydrogen used in weather balloons? *(1 mark)*

ii) Why is carbon dioxide used in fire extinguishers? *(1 mark)*

iii) Why is chlorine used in swimming pools? *(1 mark)*

3 This question is about non-metals and their compounds.

a) Copy and complete the table below by writing YES or NO to identify the correct properties for each gas. The first is done for you. *(4 marks)*

Gas	Compound	Colourless	Poisonous
hydrogen	NO	YES	NO
carbon dioxide			
chlorine			
helium			
carbon monoxide			

b) Hydrogen can be used to reduce copper(II) oxide using the apparatus below.

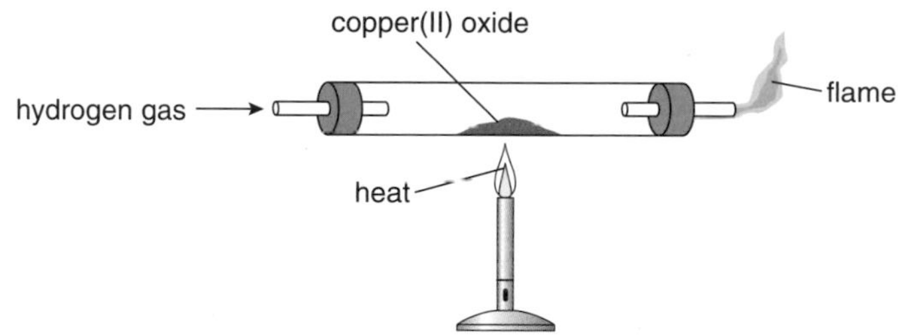

i) Give the colour change which takes place during this reaction. *(2 marks)*

ii) Name the **compound** formed when hydrogen reduces copper(II) oxide. *(1 mark)*

iii) Why is hydrogen termed a 'clean fuel'? *(1 mark)*

4 Burning coal and other fossil fuels has led to increased levels of carbon dioxide in the atmosphere.

a) Give **two** reasons why scientists are concerned about the increased levels of carbon dioxide in the atmosphere. *(2 marks)*

b) Name the acid which is formed when carbon dioxide is dissolved in water. *(1 mark)*

5 Burning fossil fuels containing sulfur produces a gas Z, which causes acid rain.

a) Name the gas, Z, that causes acid rain to be formed. *(1 mark)*

b) Give **two** reasons why acid rain is a serious environmental problem. *(2 marks)*

c) Give **one** way that fossil fuel power stations can reduce the amount of gas, Z. *(1 mark)*

6 When sulfur and iron are heated they react to form a compound, iron(II) sulfide.

a) Describe the appearance of sulfur. *(2 marks)*

b) Give **two** things you would observe when iron reacts with sulfur. *(2 marks)*

7 Concentrated sulfuric acid is a dehydrating agent.

a) Explain the meaning of a dehydrating agent. *(1 mark)*

b) Describe what you would observe when concentrated sulfuric acid is added to sugar. *(3 marks)*

8 a) Hydrogen is a powerful rocket fuel. The diagram shows the reaction which occurs in the combustion chamber of a rocket.

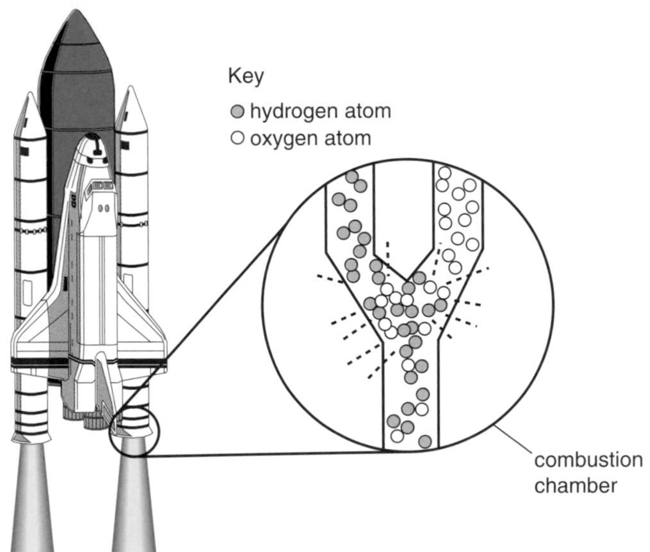

i) Explain what you understand by the term combustion. *(3 marks)*

ii) Explain why hydrogen is considered to be a 'clean fuel'. *(1 mark)*

b) Hydrogen is also a powerful reducing agent. The diagram shows the apparatus which could be used in the laboratory to reduce copper(II) oxide using hydrogen.

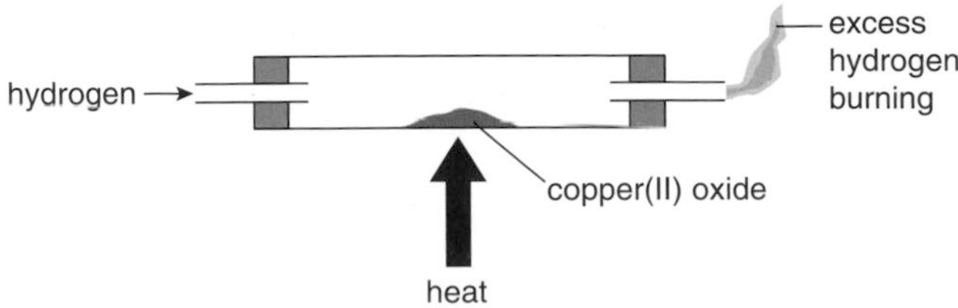

i) State **two** observations made during this reaction. *(2 marks)*

ii) Write a balanced symbol equation for the reduction of copper(II) oxide using hydrogen. *(2 marks)*

iii) Explain why this reaction is described as a reduction. *(2 marks)*

9 a) Carbon is a non-metallic element which exists as allotropes. Two allotropes of carbon are shown in the diagrams below.

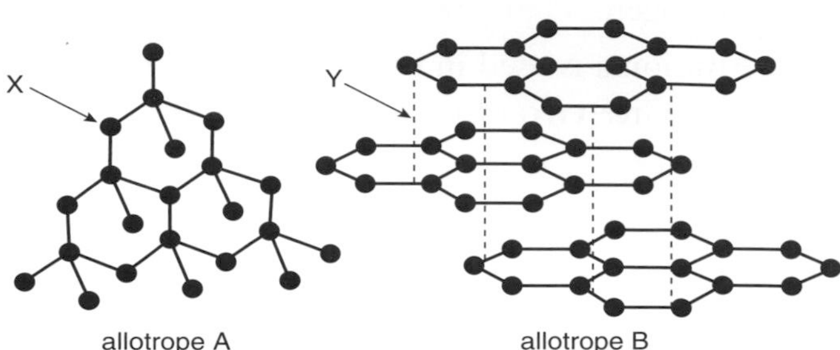

i) What is meant by the term **allotrope**? *(2 marks)*

ii) State the name of each allotrope. *(3 marks)*

iii) What is represented in the diagram of allotrope A by the black dot labelled X? *(1 mark)*

iv) What is represented in the diagram of allotrope B by the dashed line labelled Y? *(1 mark)*

b) Sulfur is another non-metallic element which exists as allotropes.

i) State **two** physical properties of sulfur. *(2 marks)*

ii) Name the three allotropes of sulfur. *(3 marks)*

c) Both sulfur and carbon burn in oxygen forming dioxides which dissolve in water forming acidic solutions.

i) Name **one other** element which forms a dioxide. *(1 mark)*

ii) Write a balanced symbol equation for the combustion of sulfur in oxygen. *(2 marks)*

iii) Write a balanced symbol equation for the reaction between sulfur dioxide and water. *(2 marks)*

iv) What environmental problem is caused by the presence of sulfur dioxide in the atmosphere? *(1 mark)*

15 Organic Chemistry I

Fossil fuels

Most of the energy we use in our homes, industry, schools, offices and transport comes from fossil fuels. When fossil fuels burn, the chemical energy of the fuel is converted into heat energy. In the home, the energy from fossil fuels is used mainly for heating, lighting and cooking while in industry much is used in the manufacture of materials, such as fertilisers, plastics, paints, metals, glass and other useful substances.

Methane gas, CH_4, which is the main component of **natural gas**, is an example of a fossil fuel and it burns producing heat energy as shown in the equations below:

methane + oxygen → carbon dioxide + water

$$CH_{4(g)} + 2O_{2(g)} \rightarrow CO_{2(g)} + 2H_2O_{(g)}$$

The general word equation for the complete burning of any fossil fuel is:

fossil fuel + oxygen → carbon dioxide + water

Figure 1 Products from fossil fuels

Coal, oil, peat, lignite and natural gas are all examples of fossil fuels and were formed over millions of years from dead animals and plants. Oil and natural gas were formed from tiny animals and plants that lived in tropical seas while coal was formed from forests and vegetation growing in swamplands.

Fossil fuels are **non-renewable energy** resources and this means that they are finite and once they are used up they cannot be replaced. It is estimated that the present supplies of **crude oil** will only last for around another fifty years. It is clear that in the future there is a need for consumers to ensure that our supplies of crude oil are used more economically and realise the urgent need to develop alternative energy resources. The development of **renewable energy** resources to replace fossil fuels is of particular interest. Renewable energy resources are continuously supplied by nature as they are used by the consumers. The main renewable energy resources are hydroelectric energy, wind, waves, tides and solar energy.

Crude oil

Crude oil is a viscous, dark brown **liquid mixture** and contains many hundreds of different substances including dissolved gases and solids. Both crude oil and natural gas are made from substances known as **hydrocarbons**. Some of the hydrocarbons in crude oil have only a few carbon atoms in each molecule but there are some with over seventy carbon atoms in each molecule.

> A hydrocarbon is a molecule that consists of carbon and hydrogen **only**.

The hydrocarbons in crude oil have different boiling points and because of this they can be separated into different fractions using **fractional distillation**. The different boiling points are related to the number of carbon atoms in the hydrocarbon. The greater the number of carbons in the molecule then the higher the boiling point.

Fractional distillation takes place in a steel tower as shown in Figure 2. The tower is very hot at the base and cooler at the top. Crude oil is fed in and heated in the furnace. The vapours are then fed into the fractionating tower. As the vapour mixture rises up the tower, different vapours condense at different levels and are separated. The small hydrocarbon molecules with the smallest number of carbon atoms and with the lowest boiling point will rise to the top of the tower while the larger hydrocarbon molecules with the highest boiling points will condense further down the tower. This process allows the different fractions to cool and condense at different levels. The fractions condensing at different levels are collected on trays.

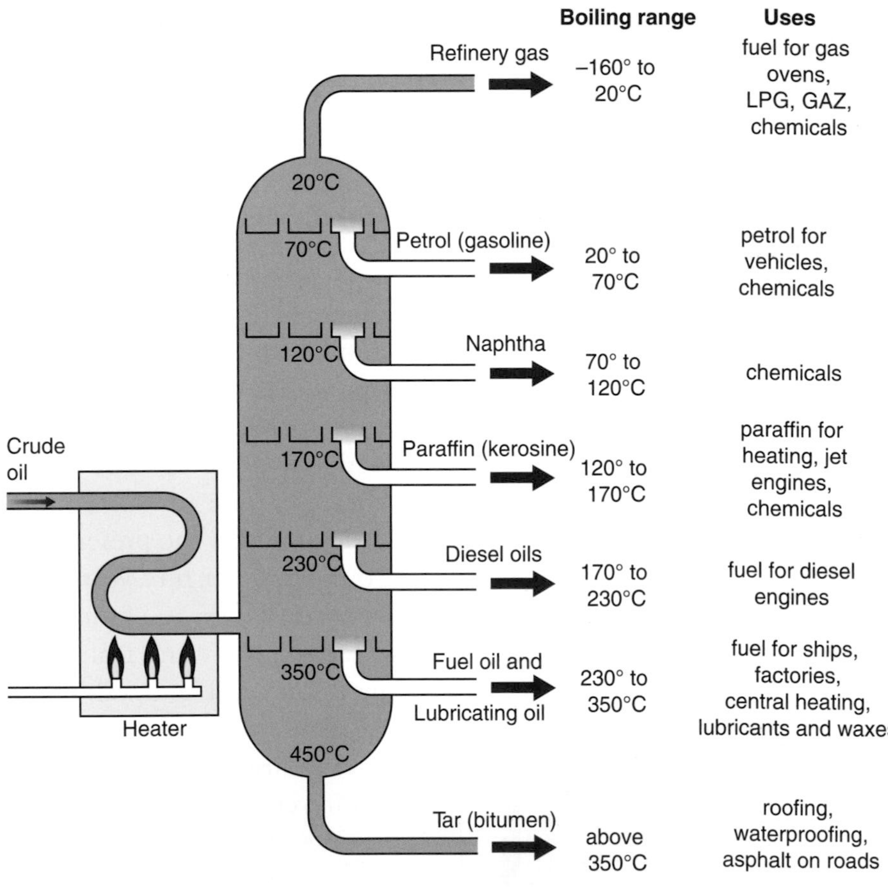

Figure 2 Fractional distillation of crude oil

Figure 2 shows the uses of the oil fractions in the chemical industry. Most of the fractions are used as fuels; the naphtha fraction, however, is widely used in the production of chemicals and polymers. It is used in the production of polymers such as polythene, polypropene and polyvinyl chloride and in the production of ethanol, ethanoic acid and other chemicals used in the production of paints, explosives, detergents and solvents.

The petro-chemical industry and oil spillages

Natural gas and crude oil are very important to our economy because they provide us with a range of fuels and a vast range of organic compounds for the chemical industry. These organic compounds are used to make dyes, plastics, fertilisers, medicines, paints, lubricants and many other important classes of materials.

Although it is difficult to think how we would survive without oil, pollution of seas by oil can be a major problem. The transportation of crude oil in large tankers and the extraction of oil from the seabed have resulted in a number of serious oil spills and leakages. Figure 3 shows how drilling for oil takes place in the seabed. Generally, **oil spillages** are cleaned up by spraying them with detergent. This breaks the oil up and allows bacteria to digest it.

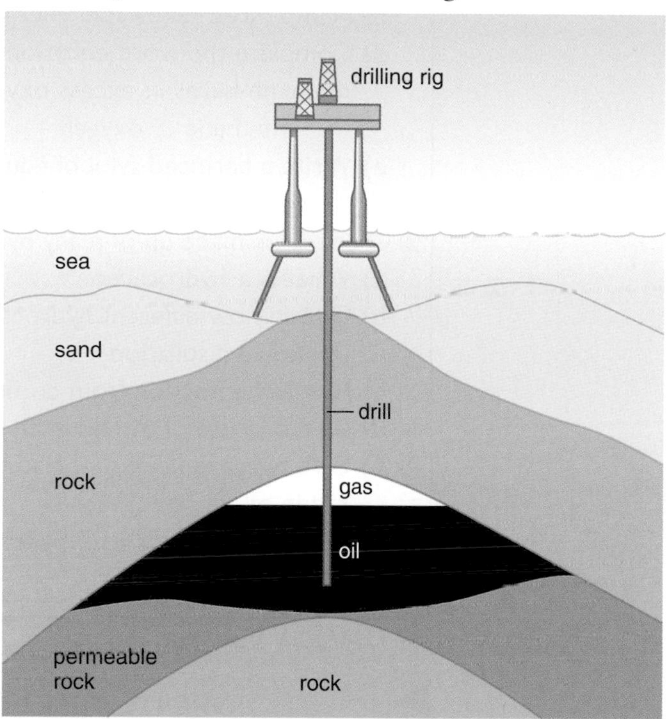

Figure 3 Drilling for oil and natural gas

Figure 4 Workers clean up the oil on the Pembrokeshire coast after the oil tanker Sea Empress ran aground in 1996

One of the worst spills in recent years involved the Liberian-owned supertanker, Sea Empress, that ran aground at St Anne's Head, Wales in 1996. In that incident 70,000 tonnes of crude oil spilled out into the sea, in an area that was renowned for its bird sanctuaries and its National Marine Park. There was serious water pollution and birds, fish and mammals were seriously affected (Figure 4).

The oil on the birds stopped them from flying and caused a breakdown in their thermal insulation. A number of birds were poisoned while others suffered severe irritation to the skin. Emergency teams were drafted in from Europe and Britain to help clean up the oil spill. Within weeks natural dispersal and the massive clean-up operation cleared most of the oil from the coastline.

Fossil fuels, combustion and air pollution

Air pollution is mainly caused by burning fossil fuels. During their combustion, harmful gases such as carbon monoxide, carbon dioxide, sulfur dioxide and oxides of nitrogen are released into the atmosphere along with soot and smoke. Power stations and motor vehicles cause the greatest part of this pollution. The greenhouse effect is discussed in detail in Chapter 14, page 185. Acid rain is discussed in detail in Chapter 14, page 203.

Questions

1 Natural gas, which is mainly methane, is a fossil fuel and is non-renewable.
   a) Name two other fossil fuels.
   b) What do you understand by the terms 'non-renewable' and 'fossil fuel'?
   c) Name three renewable energy sources.
   d) Complete the word equation to show what happens when methane burns in excess oxygen:
   methane + oxygen →
   e) Write a balanced symbol equation for methane burning in excess oxygen.

2 Crude oil is made up of many hydrocarbons.
   a) What is a 'hydrocarbon'?
   b) Explain how different hydrocarbons in crude oil are separated by fractional distillation.
   c) Name the fraction from crude oil that has the lowest boiling point.
   d) Give one use of the bitumen fraction obtained from crude oil.
   e) Give two problems associated with extraction and transport of crude oil.
   f) Why is it important to make the extraction of crude oil more efficient?

▶ Homologous series

In this section and the next chapter, the chemistry of four homologous series will be studied: alkanes (C_nH_{2n+2}), alkenes (C_nH_{2n}), alcohols ($C_nH_{2n+1}OH$) and carboxylic acids ($C_nH_{2n+1}COOH$).

A **homologous series** is a family of organic molecules that have the same general formula, show similar chemical properties, show a gradation in their physical properties and differ by a 'CH_2' unit.

▶ Alkanes

Alkanes have a general formula $\mathbf{C_nH_{2n+2}}$ and are obtained from crude oil, which is made up of many different hydrocarbons. Most of these hydrocarbons are alkanes. The simplest alkane is methane with a molecular formula CH_4. In methane there are four strong, single covalent bonds that join the hydrogen atoms to the carbon atoms. Table 1 gives the names, molecular and structural formulae, and physical state of the first four members of the alkanes.

Name	Molecular formula	Structural formula	State at room temperature
Methane	CH_4	H—C(H)(H)—H	gas
Ethane	C_2H_6	H—C(H)(H)—C(H)(H)—H	gas
Propane	C_3H_8	H—C(H)(H)—C(H)(H)—C(H)(H)—H	gas
Butane	C_4H_{10}	H—C(H)(H)—C(H)(H)—C(H)(H)—C(H)(H)—H	gas

Table 1 The first four members of the alkanes

Properties of alkanes

* They have low boiling points and melting points as shown in Table 2. It can also be seen that there is a gradual increase in these properties when moving from methane to butane.

n	C_nH_{2n+2}	Boiling point/°C	Melting point/°C
1	CH_4	−162	−183
2	C_2H_6	−89	−173
3	C_3H_8	−42	−187
4	C_4H_{10}	−1	−135

Table 2 Boiling and melting points of the alkanes

* Alkanes are **saturated** as they only contain C—C single bonds and do not contain any C=C double bonds.
* Alkanes are unreactive as they are saturated and only contain C—C and C—H single covalent bonds. These bonds are very strong and difficult to break.

Chemical reactions of alkanes

Combustion is the most important reaction of the alkanes. In a plentiful supply of oxygen they burn with a blue flame to produce carbon dioxide, water and heat energy. Due to the large amount of heat given out when they burn, alkanes are good **fuels**. Some important alkane fuels are:

* Natural gas, which is mainly methane, is used as a fuel for heating homes and providing electricity.
* Propane and butane are the main constituents of LPG (liquefied petroleum gas) which is used as 'Calor gas' and 'Gaz' and these gases are commonly used in caravans, boats and by campers.

The following symbol equations show what happens when propane and butane burn in excess oxygen:

$$C_3H_{8(g)} + 5O_{2(g)} \rightarrow 3CO_{2(g)} + 4H_2O_{(l)}$$
$$2C_4H_{10(g)} + 13O_{2(g)} \rightarrow 8CO_{2(g)} + 10H_2O_{(l)}$$

In a limited supply of oxygen there is incomplete combustion of the alkane, and carbon monoxide and water form, for example, methane burning in a limited supply of oxygen:

$$2CH_{4(g)} + 3O_{2(g)} \rightarrow 2CO_{(g)} + 4H_2O_{(l)}$$

As carbon monoxide has no smell and is extremely toxic it is dangerous to burn alkanes where there is insufficient oxygen present.

What energy changes take place when methane burns?

Consider what happens to methane when it burns in excess oxygen. The symbol equation for the reaction is:

$$CH_4 + 2O_2 \rightarrow CO_2 + 2H_2O$$

To determine the energy change which takes place in this reaction, we must consider the bonds formed and broken during the reaction. In addition, it is necessary to realise that **bond breaking is an endothermic process** and energy is required to break bonds while **bond formation is an exothermic process** and energy is given out when new bonds are formed.

The equation can be written to show the bonds that are broken and the new bonds that are formed:

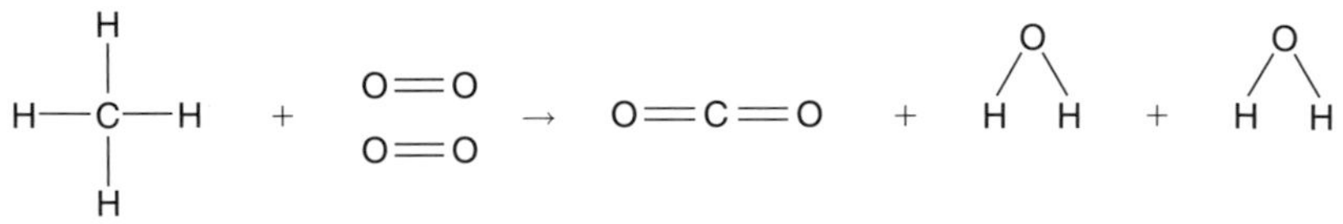

```
    H
    |                O=O                                 O          O
H—C—H     +                  →   O=C=O     +     / \     +    / \
    |                O=O                              H   H       H   H
    H
```

For the reactants CH_4 and O_2, four **single C—H** bonds and **two double O=O bonds** must be broken and this is an endothermic process requiring energy. For the new products there are **two C=O double bonds** and **four single O—H bonds** formed and this is an exothermic process. Overall there is more energy given out in the formation of the new bonds than is required to break the reactant bonds and hence the reaction overall is exothermic.

Alkenes

Alkenes are hydrocarbon molecules that contain a carbon-carbon double bond. The first two members of the alkenes are ethene, C_2H_4, and propene, C_3H_6. From the molecular formulae of ethene and propene it is seen that the general formula for alkenes can be written as C_nH_{2n}. Ethene and propene are important starting materials in the chemical industry because they are used to make useful polymeric materials such as polythene and polypropene.

Manufacture of alkenes

In the petrochemical industry ethene and propene are both manufactured by cracking of alkanes obtained from crude oil. Ethene is obtained from the catalytic cracking of decane:

$$\text{decane} \rightarrow \text{octane} + \text{ethene}$$

$$C_{10}H_{22} \rightarrow C_8H_{18} + C_2H_4$$

Physical properties of ethene and propene

Like ethane and propane, ethene and propene are colourless gases with low melting points and boiling points.

Alkene	Molecular formula	Structural formula	Melting point/°C	Boiling point/°C
Ethene	C_2H_4	H H C=C H H ethene	−168.9	−103.6
Propene	C_3H_6	H CH_3 C=C H H propene	−185.2	−46.3

Table 3 Physical properties of ethene and propene

Distinguishing between alkanes and alkenes

Alkanes are saturated hydrocarbons while alkenes are unsaturated molecules. This means that alkanes have only carbon–carbon single bonds while alkenes have a carbon–carbon double bond. Having a carbon–carbon double bond makes alkenes more reactive and this is seen in their reactions with bromine water.

If ethane and ethene are separately bubbled into test tubes of bromine water, the bromine water quickly goes from orange-brown to colourless for the ethene reaction; however, ethane does not react with the bromine water and the orange-brown colour remains.

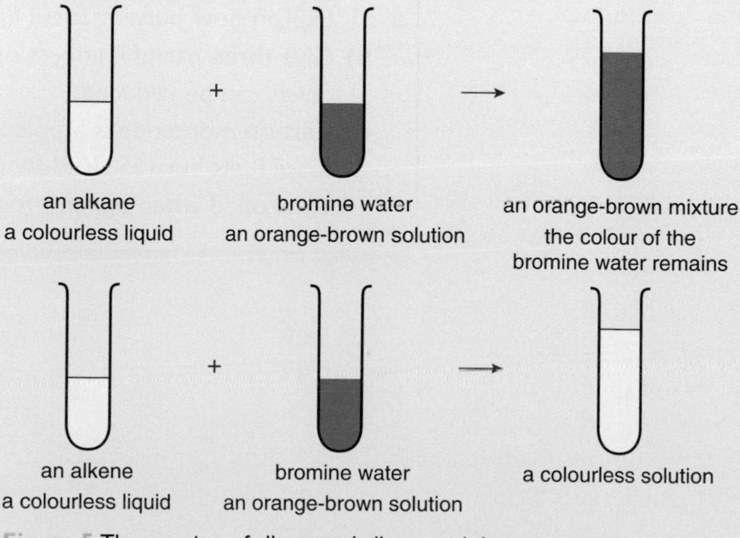

Figure 5 The reaction of alkane and alkene with bromine water

Combustion of ethene and propene

Alkenes undergo combustion in the same way as the alkanes; however, they burn with a smoky yellow flame.

ethene	+ oxygen	→	carbon dioxide	+	water	+ heat energy
$C_2H_{4(g)}$	+ $3O_{2(g)}$	→	$2CO_{2(g)}$		+ $2H_2O_{(l)}$	+ heat energy
propene	+ oxygen	→	carbon dioxide	+	water	+ heat energy
$C_3H_{6(g)}$	+ $4\frac{1}{2}O_{2(g)}$	→	$3CO_{2(g)}$		+ $3H_2O_{(l)}$	+ heat energy

Alkenes unlike alkanes are not used as fuels because it is more economical to use them in the production of important organic chemicals such as ethanol, ethanoic acid, plastics, solvents, detergents and many other useful products of the petrochemicals industry.

Questions

3 a) Describe fully what a homologous series is.
b) Give the general formula for the:
i) alkanes; **ii)** alkenes;
iii) alcohols; **iv)** carboxylic acids.
c) Give the molecular formula and the structural formula for:
i) ethane; **ii)** propene;
iii) methanol; **iv)** ethanoic acid.

4 a) Explain the difference between a saturated hydrocarbon and an unsaturated hydrocarbon.
b) Describe a chemical test that can be used to distinguish between ethane and propene. You should give the test reagent and describe any colour changes that take place.

5 a) Write balanced symbol equations to show the complete combustion of:
i) propane in air and **ii)** ethene in air.
b) Give the symbol equation to show what happens to methane when it is burned in a limited supply of air or oxygen.

6 a) Explain how burning fossil fuels causes global warming.
b) Give three harmful effects of acid rain and suggest how acid rain levels can be reduced.
c) Carbon monoxide is a poisonous gas which can be produced when fossil fuels burn in air. How can levels of carbon monoxide be controlled when burning fossil fuels?

16 Organic Chemistry 2

▶ Making polymers from alkenes

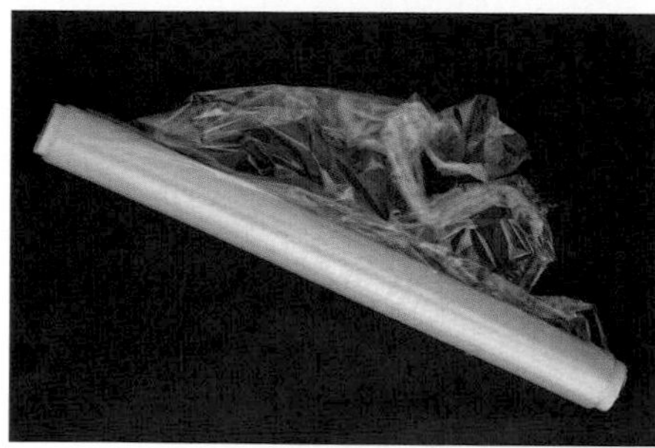

Figure 1 Common everyday polymers

Many important polymers are made from alkenes, for example, polythene and polyvinyl chloride (PVC). These polymers have many important properties which make them suitable for a wide range of uses. Polythene is used to make plastic bags and bottles while polyvinyl chloride is used to make window frames and guttering.

Figure 2 Some of the uses of polythene and polyvinyl chloride

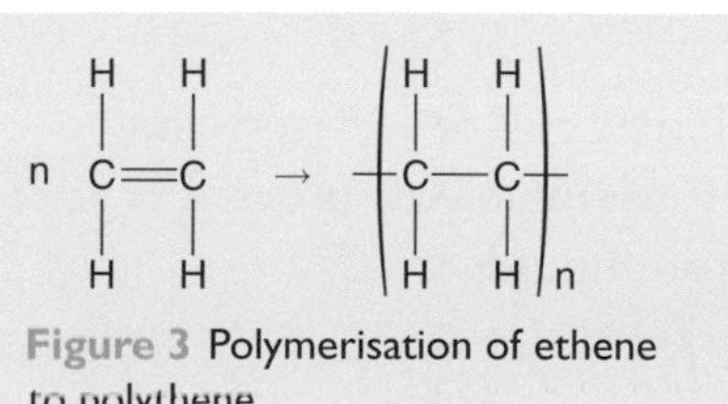

Figure 3 Polymerisation of ethene to polythene

The word '**polymer**' comes from Greek and means many parts. A polymer is described as a large organic **macromolecule** that has many small molecules chemically joined or added together to give a long chain molecule. The small molecules that add together to make the polymer are called **monomers**. The process of adding the monomers together is called **addition polymerisation**. The addition polymerisation of ethene is shown in Figure 3.

In the equation, the ethene molecule on the left hand side is the monomer which is being polymerised and n represents a large number of reacting monomers or ethene molecules. The double bond in ethene is broken and this allows the molecules to link up and chemically join together. This means that the final polymer has no double bonds. The n on the right hand side tells us that the n molecules of ethene have all joined together and that the structure in the brackets is repeated n times.

Figure 4 shows how three molecules of ethene join to form a chain. In the actual polythene chain there are many hundreds of molecules joined together.

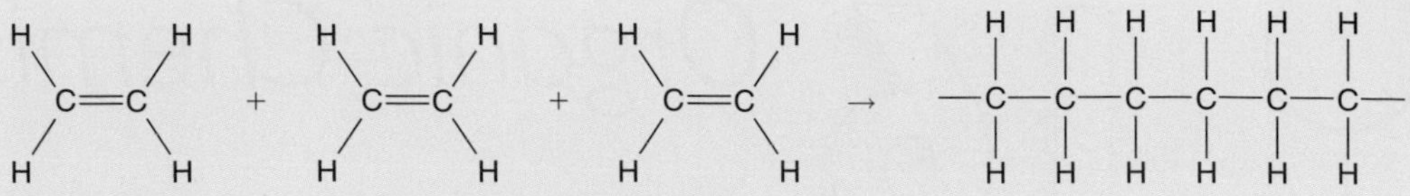

$$H_2C{=}CH_2 + H_2C{=}CH_2 + H_2C{=}CH_2 \rightarrow -CH_2-CH_2-CH_2-CH_2-CH_2-CH_2-$$

Figure 4 How ethene molecules join to form a chain

Vinyl chloride reacts in a similar way to ethene when it forms polyvinyl chloride. The equation for the reaction is as follows:

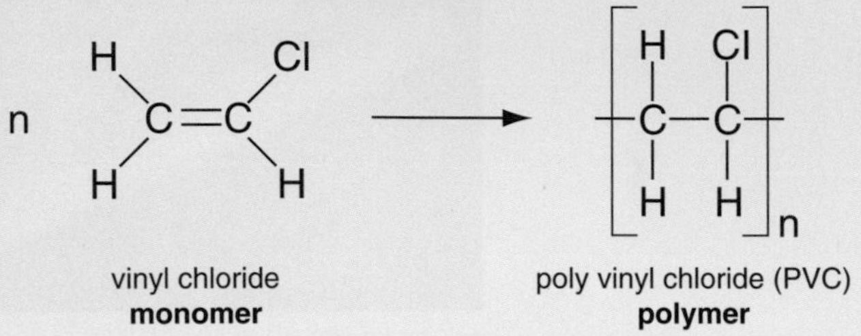

$$n\,CH_2{=}CHCl \longrightarrow \left[-CH_2-CHCl-\right]_n$$

vinyl chloride **monomer** → poly vinyl chloride (PVC) **polymer**

Table 1 relates the uses of polythene and PVC to their properties:

Monomer	Addition polymer	Properties	Uses
Polythene	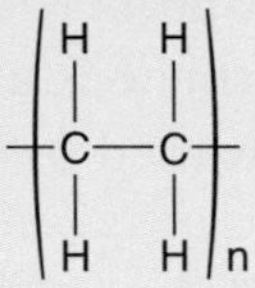 $\left[-CH_2-CH_2-\right]_n$	Light, flexible and resistant to attack by acids and alkalis	Cling film, plastic bags, bottles, buckets and basins
PVC	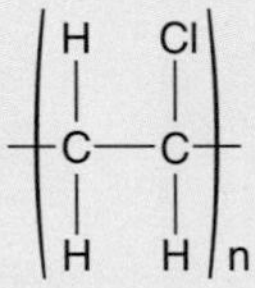 $\left[-CH_2-CHCl-\right]_n$	Tough, durable, water-proof and good insulator	Electric cables, guttering, drain pipes and umbrellas

Table 1 Properties and uses of the addition polymers, polythene and PVC

From the table, we can see that PVC is a good insulator, as well as being tough and durable. Such properties make it suitable to be used as an insulating material for electrical cables. Also, as it is waterproof and tough it can be used to make waterproof clothing and has many uses as a building material, for example, making windows, doors, drain pipes and guttering.

Polythene is a very light, flexible polymer and is very resistant to attack by acids and alkalis. It is therefore suitable to use as a packaging material and for bottles to store liquids.

Comparing the properties and uses of polymeric materials and traditional materials

Many modern materials have replaced the traditionally used materials because of their superior properties and, in many instances, their lower cost. The main benefits of plastics are:

* less dense than other materials
* are resistant to chemicals and water
* have excellent insulation properties
* are extremely long lasting
* are inexpensive to produce.

Figure 5 Traditional and modern materials

Two common examples where modern materials have replaced traditional materials are paper bags that have largely been replaced with plastic bags, and wooden window frames that have mostly been replaced by plastic window frames.

Plastic bags are much more durable and stronger than paper bags and are also waterproof and very cheap to produce. In a similar way, PVC window frames are tough, durable, waterproof and are good insulators. They do not have to be painted, require little maintenance and have a relatively low cost. So it is not surprising that in supermarkets, plastic bags have replaced paper bags and that many people now select plastic window frames rather than the traditional wooden ones.

As many new materials show superior properties to traditional ones, people generally now select modern materials rather than the more traditional materials.

Consider the data about the properties of steel and three polymeric materials in Table 2.

Material	Density/kg/m^3	Relative strength	Relative stiffness	Cost
Steel	7800	1.0	210	low
Polythene	960	0.02	0.6	low
Kevlar	1450	5.0	190	high
Nylon	1100	0.08	3	medium

Table 2 Properties of some materials

To decide on a material for a particular purpose it is important to carefully check the properties of the different materials to determine which one is most suitable. For example, choosing a material for a bulletproof vest from those materials in Table 2. A bulletproof vest should have a low density, have very high strength and be stiff. Of the four materials Kevlar is the best as it has a very high relative strength, has a low density and is stiff. One disadvantage of Kevlar is its high cost. Both polythene and nylon are unsuitable as they have low strength compared to Kevlar while steel is too dense and not nearly as strong as Kevlar.

Disposal problems of plastics

While many new materials have superior properties to traditional materials there are problems of disposal. Consider polythene and PVC. Both of these polymers are **non-biodegradable** and are not broken down by microbes like other organic matter. There are no bacteria that live on these plastics and so they may remain in landfill sites for over 500 years. With more and more plastic products being thrown away, the space to dispose of the waste is a concern. Approximately 85% of plastic waste ends up in **landfill sites**, with 7% **incinerated** and 8% being **recycled**.

Figure 6 a) Plastic waste has traditionally been dumped in landfill, it can now also be burned to produce electricity or b) recycled, such as these pellets of polythene

In recent years most of the old quarry sites available for landfill dumping have been used up. Dealing with plastics by this dumping method is now relatively expensive, especially with the introduction of government landfill tax on waste.

Incineration schemes burn waste plastics. The heat generated can be made to serve a useful purpose, either directly or to generate power. The main problems associated with **incineration** are pollution from the products of burning and the destruction of many resources that could have been recycled. During the incineration process, poisonous gases such as hydrogen chloride, carbon monoxide and hydrogen cyanide are given off. It is very important that these compounds are controlled and removed before any waste gases are released into the atmosphere.

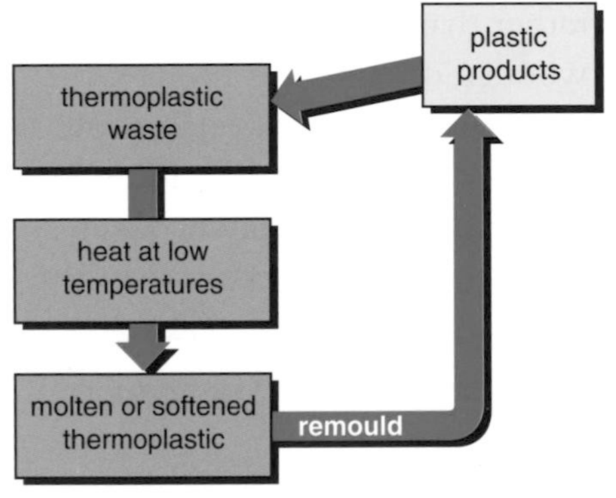

Figure 7 Recycling thermoplastics

Recycling of plastic waste is now becoming more and more popular. Figure 7 shows how thermoplastics are recycled. Recycling thermoplastics is carried out by melting the waste plastic and then remoulding it. Large quantities of the recycled plastic are used to make sheeting and plastic bags.

More recently chemists have developed new biodegradable plastics for film, packaging and containers. Figure 8 shows a biodegradable plastic bag made from maize starch. For the last 6 years in Sweden, McDonald's restaurants have used biodegradable plastics for all the meal containers that they provide as well as for the plastic cutlery. Thus all their catering waste can be converted into compost. In future years the use of biodegradable plastics will be an important method to help overcome the present environmental difficulty of the disposal of plastics.

Figure 8 A biodegradable plastic bag made from maize starch

Questions

1 Polythene is an important material for making food packaging.
  a) Give three reasons why polythene is a suitable material for food packaging.
  b) Name the monomer that is used to make polythene.
  c) What type of reaction is used to make polythene?

2 a) Polypropene is made from propene and has many uses.
  i) Give the molecular formula and the structural formula of propene.
  ii) Write a symbol equation to show how polypropene is made from propene.
  b) Polypropene is widely used in the manufacture of carpet. Explain why polypropene has replaced a more traditional material like wool.

3 Addition polymers such as polythene and PVC are non-biodegradable plastics.
  a) Explain fully the meaning of the term non-biodegradable.
  b) Give two different methods of disposing of addition polymers.
  c) What are the main advantages of recycling addition polymers?
  d) Give three ways that councils are promoting the recycling of plastics.

4 Vinyl chloride is used to make PVC which is an important building material.
  a) Give one use of PVC.
  b) Explain why vinyl chloride is not a hydrocarbon.
  c) Draw the structural formula of vinyl chloride.
  d) How many different elements are there in a vinyl chloride molecule?
  e) Write a symbol equation to show how PVC is made from vinyl chloride.

Alcohols

Methanol and ethanol are the first two members of the homologous series known as the alcohols, general formula $C_nH_{2n+1}OH$. The structural formulae and the physical properties of these two alcohols are shown in Table 3.

Alcohol	Molecular formula $C_nH_{2n+1}OH$	Structural formula	State	Boiling point/°C
Methanol	CH_3OH	H–C(H)(H)–O–H	colourless liquid	65
Ethanol	C_2H_5OH	H–C(H)(H)–C(H)(H)–O–H	colourless liquid	79

Table 3 Structural formulae and some physical properties of methanol and ethanol

From Table 3 it is seen from the structural formula that alcohols contain the **functional group** —OH. A functional group is a group of atoms in a structure that determines the characteristic reactions of a compound.

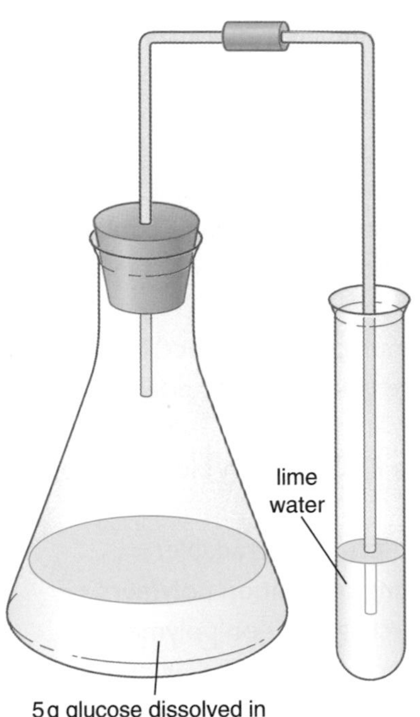

Figure 9 Using fermentation to make ethanol

Preparation of ethanol by fermentation and hydration

Fermentation

For thousands of years ethanol has been made from the two carbohydrates, sugar and starch. If yeast is added to sugar and left in a warm place at around 35 °C for a few days, the yeast converts the sugar (Figure 9) to ethanol and carbon dioxide.

Fermentation takes place when the enzymes in yeast convert the sugar to ethanol and carbon dioxide. The word equation is:

$$\text{sugar} \rightarrow \text{ethanol} + \text{carbon dioxide}$$

When the concentration reaches 15% the yeast is killed and the fermentation is stopped. Ethanol is obtained from the mixture using fractional distillation.

Hydration of ethene to ethanol

Ethanol can be made by adding water to the double bond in an ethene molecule. This type of reaction is called **hydration** because it involves adding water.

$$\text{ethene} + \text{water} \rightarrow \text{ethanol}$$

$$C_2H_{4(g)} + H_2O_{(g)} \rightarrow C_2H_5OH_{(g)}$$

The reaction is carried out under special conditions where steam and ethene are mixed under pressure and heated at 300 °C. As the reaction is slow it is necessary to use a catalyst of silicon dioxide coated with phosphoric acid.

Uses of ethanol

Ethanol has many important uses. It is an important **fuel**, is used to make **alcoholic drinks** and is an important **solvent**.

Ethanol as a fuel

Figure 10 A car fuelled by ethanol

Ethanol burns with an almost colourless flame forming carbon dioxide, water and heat energy.

$$C_2H_5OH_{(l)} + 3O_{2(g)} \rightarrow 2CO_{2(g)} + 3H_2O_{(g)} + \text{heat energy}$$

Like alkanes, ethanol is an important fuel. It has many advantages as a fuel such as:

* it is clean and smokeless
* it is a liquid and so is easily transferred and stored
* it does not produce sulfur dioxide/acid rain when it burns
* it is carbon neutral as it is produced from plants.

Countries such as Brazil that depend on imported oil have started to produce ethanol as a fuel. They produce ethanol by the fermentation of cane sugar and then use it to power motor vehicle engines.

Alcoholic drinks

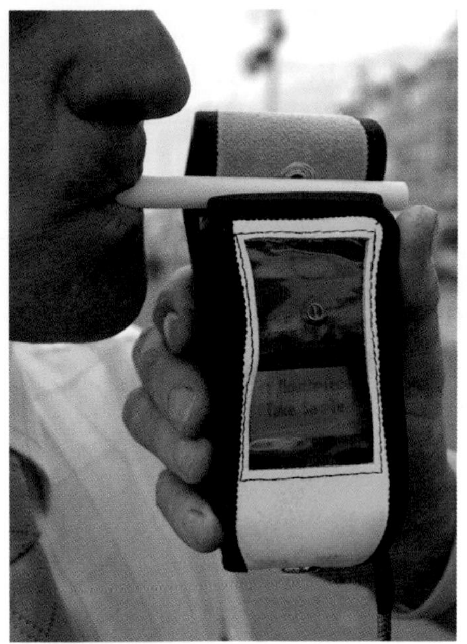

Figure 11 A driver undergoing a breathalyser test to check for alcohol consumption

Alcoholic drinks are made by fermentation. The fermentation of barley produces a weak solution of ethanol and this is how beer is made (about 3% ethanol). Wine is made by the fermentation of grapes and produces a solution of about 13% ethanol. Spirits such as rum, whiskey, brandy and gin are obtained by fractional distillation.

Many people socialise by going out with their friends for a drink. They find it enjoyable and relaxing. Nevertheless, it has to be realised that drinking in excess is harmful to our health causing serious illnesses such as heart disease, cirrhosis of the liver, damage to the nervous system, brain damage and alcoholism. Alcohol, like many other drugs, is addictive and those suffering from alcoholism find it difficult to live normal lives. Very often it leads to family and work problems. Experts agree that to reduce diseases and other problems caused by alcohol, people should stick to a safe drinking limit. This safe limit has been set at three units of alcohol per day for men and two units for women.

Small amounts of alcohol can affect people's judgement and their ability to drive, so it is important that people do not drive after consuming alcohol. Around 30% of road accidents are caused by drivers who have had alcohol, and many of these are young drivers. The legal limit for driving a car is 80 milligrams of alcohol per 100 cubic centimetres of blood (80 mg/100 cm^3 blood).

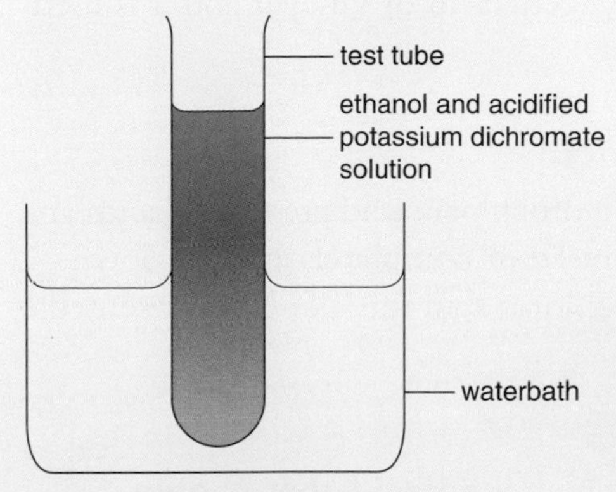

Figure 12 Reaction between ethanol and acidified potassium dichromate solution

The original breathalyser test to detect alcohol in the blood used a technique that involved a chemical reaction between an orange crystalline solid called potassium dichromate and exhaled air from the suspected offender. If the person had been drinking alcohol, the crystals turned from **orange** to **green**. The greater the amount of alcohol consumed, the more crystals turned green. This reaction is easily demonstrated in the laboratory by gently heating some ethanol with an acidified solution of potassium dichromate. More accurate methods involving **infra-red spectroscopy** are now used to determine the amount of alcohol in the blood. This method is based on absorption of infra-red radiation by alcohol molecules. The level of infra-red absorption indicates the amount of alcohol in the blood.

If alcohol or ethanol is exposed to air for a period of time the ethanol is oxidised to ethanoic acid. This is what happens to wine when it becomes 'vinegary' if it is left open to air. The ethanol in the wine is oxidised to ethanoic acid which is commonly known as vinegar.

Ethanol as a solvent

Ethanol is an important solvent and is used in cosmetics, toiletries, lacquers, glues, paints and inks.

Figure 13 Ethanol is used as a solvent in these beauty products

Carboxylic acids

Methanoic acid and **ethanoic acid** are the first two members of the homologous series known as the **carboxylic acids**. The general formula of carboxylic acids is $C_nH_{2n+1}COOH$. The structural formula and some of the physical properties of methanoic acid and ethanoic acid are given in Table 4.

Carboxylic acid	Molecular formula $C_nH_{2n+1}COOH$	Structural formula	State	Boiling point/ °C
Methanoic acid	HCOOH	H—C(=O)—O—H	Liquid	101
Ethanoic acid	CH_3COOH	H—C(H)(H)—C(=O)—O—H	Liquid	118

Table 4 Molecular formulae and structural formulae of methanoic acid and ethanoic acid

From the structural formulae in Table 4 it is seen that the functional group in carboxylic acids is **—COOH**. This acid functional group gives a number of chemical reactions which are characteristic of carboxylic acids. Some of these are shown below for ethanoic acid. This acid is commonly known as acetic acid or vinegar and it is used as a flavouring for food.

Figure 14 All these sauces contain the weak acid, ethanoic acid

Ethanoic acid as a weak acid

Acids such as sulfuric acid and hydrochloric acid are strong acids and this means that they are fully ionised or completely broken down into ions in solution. For hydrochloric acid this can be represented by the equation:

$$HCl_{(aq)} \rightarrow H^+_{(aq)} + Cl^-_{(aq)}$$

Ethanoic acid is a **weak acid**, which is **an acid that is only partially broken down into ions**. This is represented for ethanoic acid as follows:

$$CH_3COOH_{(aq)} \rightleftharpoons CH_3COO^-_{(aq)} + H^+_{(aq)}$$

Although ethanoic acid is a weak acid it does show the typical reactions of an acid. The following reactions of ethanoic acid are typical of carboxylic acids.

With **sodium carbonate**:

This reaction is used as a **test for carboxylic acids** as it produces carbon dioxide gas which will turn limewater milky.

Word equation:

ethanoic acid + sodium carbonate → sodium ethanoate + water + carbon dioxide

Balanced symbol equation:

$$2CH_3COOH + Na_2CO_3 \rightarrow 2CH_3COONa + H_2O + CO_2$$

As well as carbon dioxide gas bubbling off, heat is produced, the solid sodium carbonate disappears and a colourless solution remains.

With **sodium hydroxide**:

Sodium hydroxide solution neutralises ethanoic acid when solutions of the two are reacted. As it is a neutralisation reaction, heat is produced.

Word equation:

ethanoic acid + sodium hydroxide → sodium ethanoate + water

Symbol equation:

$$CH_3COOH + NaOH \rightarrow CH_3COONa + H_2O$$

With **magnesium**:

In this reaction heat is given out and bubbles of hydrogen gas are given off. As the reaction progresses the magnesium ribbon gets smaller and eventually disappears leaving a colourless solution.

Word equation:

ethanoic acid + magnesium → magnesium ethanoate + hydrogen

Symbol equation:

$$2CH_3COOH + Mg \rightarrow (CH_3COO)_2Mg + H_2$$

How can we use chemicals to distinguish between the four different homologous series?

Hexane, hexene, ethanoic acid and ethanol are all colourless liquids. If we had unlabelled bottles of these four liquids we could carry out chemical tests to identify each one. All the following tests must be carried out in a fume cupboard and gloves and safety glasses must be worn.

Test 1

Place a small sample of each liquid into separate test tubes. To each of the four liquids add bromine water. The liquid that causes the orange/brown bromine water to turn colourless is hexene. The bromine water colour will persist in the other three test tubes.

Test 2

Place a small sample of each of the remaining three liquids into separate test tubes and add a small amount of solid sodium carbonate to each. The liquid that produces bubbles of carbon dioxide is ethanoic acid. The carbon dioxide gas can be identified by allowing it to pass through limewater. The limewater will go milky or cloudy.

Test 3

Place a small sample of each of the remaining two liquids into separate test tubes. Add 2 cm^3 of orange potassium dichromate solution to each test tube followed by 1 cm^3 dilute sulfuric acid. Both test tubes are now heated in a water bath at 60 °C. The liquid that turns the acidified potassium dichromate from orange to green is ethanol while the liquid that remains orange contains hexane.

Questions

5 Ethanol can be made by the hydration of ethene or from sugar by fermentation.

a) Give the word and symbol equations for the hydration of ethene.
b) Draw the full structural formula for ethanol.

c) Describe the preparation of ethanol from sugar by fermentation.
d) What process is used to obtain a concentrated solution of ethanol from the fermentation solution?

6 a) Ethanol can undergo oxidation to ethanoic acid when exposed to the air.

i) Name a reagent in the laboratory which can be used to oxidise ethanol to ethanoic acid.
ii) Draw the structural formula of ethanoic acid showing all the chemical bonds.

b) Ethanoic acid is a weak acid and has many uses.

i) Explain why ethanoic acid is a weak acid.
ii) Give one use of ethanoic acid.

7 Ethanoic acid can be used to treat wasp stings, which are alkaline.

a) Give three observations you could make when ethanoic acid is added to sodium carbonate.
b) Name a metal which will react with ethanoic acid to produce hydrogen gas.
c) Copy and complete the following equations:

sodium carbonate + ethanoic acid → _______ + _______ + _______

$NaOH + CH_3COOH \rightarrow$ _______ + _______

Exam questions

1 This question is about fossil fuels.
Three possible answers to each part are given, but only **one** is correct.
Circle the correct answer. The first one has been done for you.
One fossil fuel is liquid petroleum gas. This is usually written as:

LPG (circled) **PG** **LG**

a) The element which all fossil fuels contain is:
carbon **hydrogen** **oxygen** *(1 mark)*

b) The gas given out when fossil fuels burn is:
hydrogen **oxygen** **carbon dioxide** *(1 mark)*

c) A substance which is not a fossil fuel is:
coal **wood** **peat** *(1 mark)*

d) When fossil fuels burn they always give out:
heat **dust** **loud sounds** *(1 mark)*

e) In order to burn fossil fuel you need:
hydrogen **nitrogen** **oxygen** *(1 mark)*

2 Before large amounts of natural gas were discovered under the North Sea, the main gas used in the UK was coal gas. The diagrams below show the composition of natural gas and coal gas.

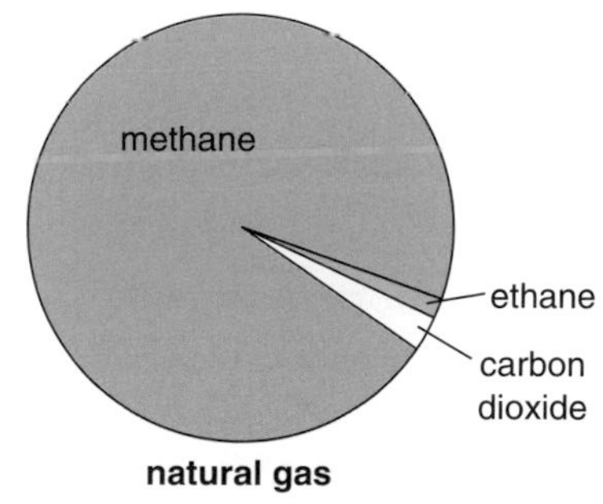

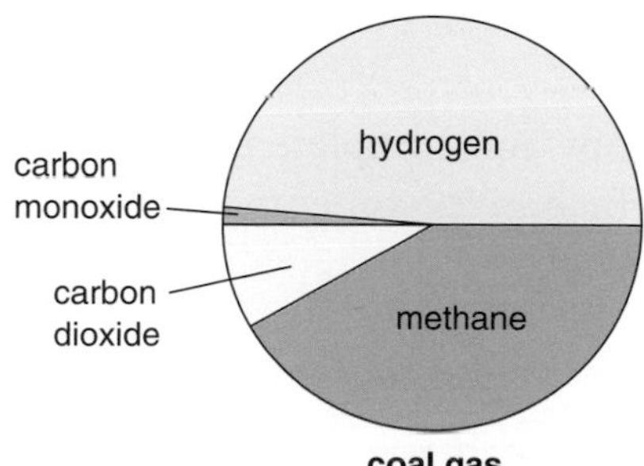

a) i) Describe a chemical test that you could use to show that both gases contained carbon dioxide. State the result for a positive test. *(3 marks)*

ii) Name the substance in coal gas which is toxic. *(1 mark)*

iii) Name the substances formed when natural gas burns in a plentiful supply of air. *(2 marks)*

iv) When both natural gas and coal gas burn, heat energy is given out. State the name used to describe a reaction which gives out heat. *(1 mark)*

v) Natural gas contains two **hydrocarbons**, ethane and methane. What is meant by the term hydrocarbon? *(2 marks)*

vi) Coal gas contains hydrogen. Write a balanced symbol equation for hydrogen burning in oxygen. *(3 marks)*

b) The table shows the percentage of different energy sources used in the UK in 2004.

Energy source	Percentage (%)
coal	26
crude oil	46
natural gas	18
nuclear power	3
hydroelectric power	6
others (wood, alcohol etc.)	0.5
solar power	0.5

i) Name **two** energy sources from the table which are renewable. *(2 marks)*

ii) Explain the difference between renewable and non-renewable sources of energy. *(2 marks)*

iii) One of the energy sources is also used to make many organic chemicals, for example, plastics. Name this energy source. *(1 mark)*

3 a) Two unknown organic **hydrocarbons**, A and B, belong to different **homologous series**.
Both A and B undergo **combustion** in an excess of air. The equation for the combustion of hydrocarbon A (C_xH_y) in an excess of air can be represented by:

$$C_xH_y + 3O_2 \rightarrow 2CO_2 + 2H_2O$$

Where x is the number of carbon atoms and y is the number of hydrogen atoms in hydrocarbon A.

i) What is meant by the term hydrocarbon? *(2 marks)*

ii) Explain what you understand by **combustion**. *(3 marks)*

iii) What is meant by the term **homologous series**? *(2 marks)*

iv) Determine the values x and y in hydrocarbon A using the equation given above. *(2 marks)*

v) Name hydrocarbon A. *(1 mark)*

When hydrocarbon B is bubbled through bromine water, the bromine water retains its colour yet when A is bubbled through bromine water, the colour of the bromine water disappears.

vi) What is the initial colour of bromine water? *(1 mark)*

vii) To which homologous series does hydrocarbon B belong? *(1 mark)*

b) A monomer has the following structural formula:

```
H   Cl
|   |
C===C
|   |
H   H
```

and forms a commonly used polymer.

i) What is the common name for the monomer shown above? *(1 mark)*

ii) Draw the structural formula of the polymer. *(2 marks)*

c) Polymers can be recycled or disposed of in landfill sites. Recycling is more expensive than disposal but is considered to be more ethically responsible. Recycling has a high profile in the media such as in news, films and newspaper reports.

i) Give **one** problem associated with disposal by landfill. *(1 mark)*

ii) State **one other** method of disposal of polymers. *(1 mark)*

iii) Suggest why recycling would be considered to be more ethically responsible than disposal. *(1 mark)*

4 Silicon in industry is made by the reaction of silicon dioxide with charcoal in an electric arc furnace.

$$SiO_2 + C \rightarrow Si + CO_2$$

The carbon reduces the silicon dioxide. The reaction is exothermic.

a) Explain in terms of **bond breaking and bond making** why this reaction is exothermic. *(5 marks)*

b) Explain why SiO_2 is described as being reduced in this reaction. *(2 marks)*

5 When methane burns in oxygen, heat is given out. The equation below describes the reaction.

$$CH_4 + 2O_2 \rightarrow CO_2 + 2H_2O$$

Explain, in terms of the bonds involved, why the reaction between methane and oxygen is **exothermic**. *(4 marks)*

6 a) Crude oil is a mixture of many organic substances; most of these substances are known as hydrocarbons. What is a hydrocarbon? *(2 marks)*

b) Ethane and ethene are both hydrocarbons with two carbon atoms. They belong to two different homologous series.

i) Copy and complete the table below with the names of the homologous series and the molecular formulae.

	Name of homologous series	Molecular formula
ethane		
ethene		

(4 marks)

ii) Give **two** features of a homologous series. *(2 marks)*

c) Ethene is an important organic chemical. It reacts with steam to form ethanol.

i) Write a balanced **symbol** equation for the reaction between ethene and steam. *(2 marks)*

ii) Copy and complete the following table which gives some information about ethanol:

	Molecular formula	Structural formula	Physical state at room temperature
ethanol	C_2H_5OH		

(1 mark) *(1 mark)*

iii) Why can ethanol not be described as a hydrocarbon? *(1 mark)*

iv) Ethanol is used in alcoholic drinks. How is ethanol manufactured for this purpose? *(1 mark)*

d) When ethanol is exposed to air, it is converted to ethanoic acid, CH_3COOH. Vinegar is a dilute solution of ethanoic acid.

i) Draw the structural formula of ethanoic acid. *(1 mark)*

ii) When sodium carbonate is added to a solution of ethanoic acid and stirred, a reaction occurs. Describe **two** things that you would expect to observe happening in this reaction. *(2 marks)*

iii) How would the reaction of sodium carbonate with hydrochloric acid differ from its reaction with ethanoic acid? *(1 mark)*

7 a) Most of our fuels come from animals and plants that lived millions of years ago. Fuels formed in this way are called fossil fuels and they are non-renewable fuels. Propane is a **non-renewable** fuel.

i) Name the homologous series of organic compounds to which propane belongs. *(1 mark)*

ii) Write a balanced symbol equation to show the complete combustion of propane. *(3 marks)*

iii) Explain what you understand by the term **non-renewable**. *(2 marks)*

b) Ethanoic acid is a weak acid and is the main constituent of vinegar.

i) Write the molecular formula of ethanoic acid. *(1 mark)*

ii) Draw the full structural formula of ethanoic acid, showing **all** bonds. *(2 marks)*

c) Ethanoic acid behaves as a typical weak acid. A student decided to investigate some of the reactions of ethanoic acid.

i) Some copper carbonate was added to a solution of ethanoic acid with stirring. Describe the observations the student would make during this reaction. *(3 marks)*

ii) A strip of magnesium metal was added to a solution of ethanoic acid. State the name of the gas given off during this reaction and describe a test which could be carried out to confirm the presence of this gas. *(3 marks)*

iii) Finally some sodium hydroxide solution was mixed with a solution of ethanoic acid. State the name and write the formula of the salt produced. *(2 marks)*

8 Organic compounds are used in medicine and first aid.

a) One of the first anaesthetics to be used in surgery was ethene. However, ethene is flammable and so halothane, $CF_3CHBrCl$, is now used instead.

i) Draw the structural formula of ethene. *(2 marks)*

ii) Describe a chemical test which could be used to show that ethene is unsaturated. Give the observations which would occur. *(3 marks)*

iii) Explain why halothane is not a hydrocarbon. *(1 mark)*

iv) Write a balanced symbol equation for the burning of ethene in excess air. *(3 marks)*

v) At room temperature and pressure, what is the physical state of ethene? *(1 mark)*

b) Hip and shoulder joints which have been damaged by arthritis can be replaced during surgery by a metal 'bone' which fits into a polythene cup. Polythene is a polymer made from ethene.

i) State **one** property of polythene which makes it suitable for this use. *(1 mark)*

ii) What is meant by the term polymer? *(2 marks)*

iii) Draw the structure of polythene. *(2 marks)*

c) Surgical spirit is used to sterilise surfaces and to cleanse cuts in the skin. It contains ethanol and a small amount of methanol.

i) Draw the structural formula of ethanol. *(2 marks)*

ii) The ethanol in surgical spirit is produced in industry from ethene. Write a balanced symbol equation for the production of ethanol from ethene. *(2 marks)*

iii) Alcoholic drinks also contain ethanol, which is produced by fermentation. Explain the process of fermentation. *(3 marks)*

d) In first aid, ethanoic acid is used to treat wasp stings, which are alkaline.

i) Draw the structural formula of ethanoic acid. *(2 marks)*

ii) State another use of ethanoic acid. *(1 mark)*

iii) Ethyl ethanoate is formed when ethanoic acid reacts with ethanol. Draw the structural formula of ethyl ethanoate. *(2 marks)*

9 a) Propane and propene are two important organic chemicals. They are both hydrocarbons, but they belong to two different homologous series.

i) What does the term **hydrocarbon** mean? *(2 marks)*

ii) Name the homologous series to which propane and propene belong. *(2 marks)*

iii) Name **two** features of a homologous series. *(2 marks)*

iv) Copy and complete the table below to show the molecular and structural formulae of both propane and propene.

Hydrocarbon	Molecular formula	Structural formula
Propane		
Propene		

(4 marks)

v) Describe a chemical test which you could carry out in the laboratory to distinguish between propane and propene. Copy the table below. State what you would observe.

Test	
Observations with propane	
Observations with propene	

(4 marks)

b) Polypropene is a useful plastic made from propene molecules.

i) Name the type of reaction that is used to produce polypropene from propene. *(2 marks)*

ii) What is the physical state of polypropene at room temperature? *(1 mark)*

c) Butane (C_4H_{10}) is used as a fuel. Give a balanced symbol equation for the complete combustion of butane. *(3 marks)*

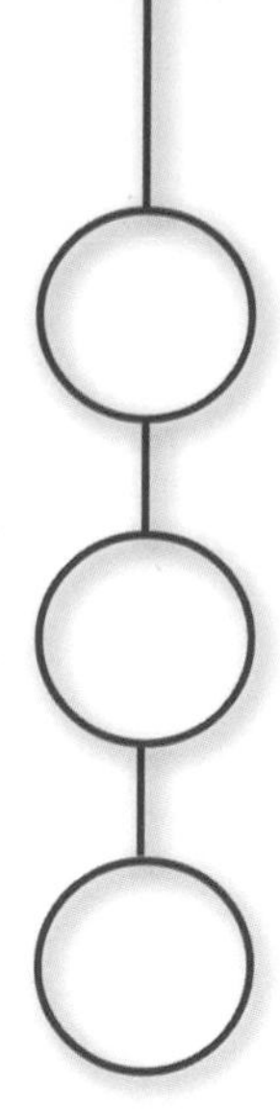

Quantitative Chemistry 2

The first chapter on quantitative chemistry (Chapter 8) focused on calculating reacting masses of solids. Here the focus will be on the calculation of concentration of a solution from data gathered from a titration. Again, being able to work out the number of moles contained in a substance is key to success.

▶ The percentage of an element in a compound

$$\% \text{ of an element in a compound} = \frac{\text{mass of element in one mole of the compound}}{\text{mass of one mole of the compound}} \times 100$$

Calculate the percentage by mass of nitrogen in ammonia (NH_3).

$$\% \text{ of N in } NH_3 = \frac{14}{17} \times 100 = 82.4\%$$

Questions

Try these examples.

1 Calculate the percentage of calcium in calcium carbonate $CaCO_3$.

2 Iron forms two common oxides, FeO and Fe_2O_3. Which oxide contains the greater percentage of iron?

3 Ammonium nitrate, NH_4NO_3, is used as a fertiliser due to the high usable nitrogen content. Calculate the percentage of nitrogen in ammonium nitrate. (Hint: Remember the element N appears in both the ions in this salt. **N**H_4**N**O_3.)

▶ Concentration

Remember: one litre (1 L) is equal to 1 dm^3.

The majority of reactions carried out in the laboratory are between reactants which are in aqueous solution, that is, dissolved in water. In order to calculate 'How Much?' in these reactions, the **concentration** of the chemical is useful.

The concentration of a solution is a measure of how much of a substance is dissolved in a known amount of water. Chemists quote concentration in moles per litre (mol/L) or moles per dm^3 (mol/dm^3) of solution. A solution which contains 1 mole of a solute dissolved in 1 dm^3 of water has a concentration of 1 mol/L or 1 mol/dm^3. A solution which has a concentration of 1 mol/dm^3 is a 1 molar solution.

You may have used acids or alkalis in the laboratory which have a concentration of 0.25 mol/dm^3 or 0.10 mol/dm^3.

Quantity	Units
mass	g
concentration	mol/dm^3 mol/L
volume	cm^3

Table 1

Questions

4 Calculate the concentration of a solution which contains 0.5 moles of solute dissolved in 1 dm^3 of water.

5 Calculate the concentration of a solution which contains 0.5 moles of solute dissolved in 100 cm^3 of water.

6 Calculate the concentration of a solution which contains 1.93 moles of solute dissolved in 164 cm^3 of water.

When asked the state of sodium hydroxide at room temperature students tend to say that sodium hydroxide is a liquid at room temperature. Sodium hydroxide is in fact a solid. It is sold in the form of small translucent pellets. Chemists use sodium hydroxide mainly in the form of a solution and thus students rarely see the pure solid form of the chemical.

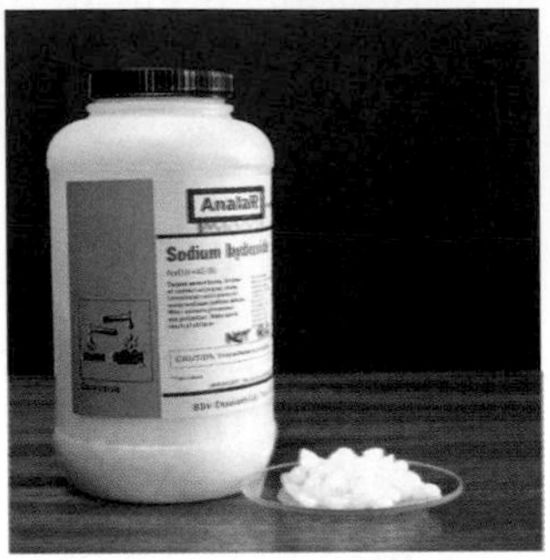

Figure 1 Sodium hydroxide pellets

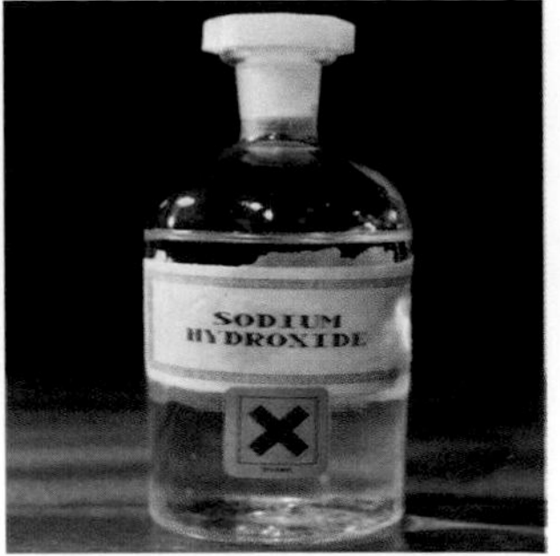

Figure 2 Sodium hydroxide solution

Number of moles $= \dfrac{V(\text{cm}^3) \times C(\text{mol/dm}^3)}{1000}$

Question 6 above may have proved a little more tricky than Questions 4 and 5. The following mathematical formulae show the simple relationship between the number of moles of a substance, the volume of water and the concentration of the solution.

Use the mathematical formula to answer Question 6.

$$\text{number of moles} = \frac{V \times C}{1000}$$

where V = volume

and C = concentration

$$1.93 = \frac{164 \times C}{1000}$$

$$\frac{1.93 \times 1000}{164} = C$$

concentration = 11.77 mol/dm^3

or concentration $= \dfrac{\text{moles}}{\text{volume (dm}^3)}$

$$= \frac{1.93}{0.164}$$

= 11.77 mol/dm^3

The answers are shown in two different ways. Some students prefer to change the subject of the formula or to learn three different mathematical formulae or indeed to use the triangle method. Some students prefer to learn one mathematical formula and to immediately substitute the values given in the question and then cross multiply. Choose the way which suits you best, and practise lots of questions. Either way you will arrive at the answer.

A solution of sodium hydroxide with a concentration of 0.1 mol/dm^3 is needed for a titration reaction. What mass of solid sodium hydroxide should be dissolved in 1 dm^3 of water?

Calculate the mass of sodium hydroxide which when dissolved in 1 dm^3 (1 litre) of water will produce a solution with a concentration of 0.1 mol/dm^3.

1 mole of NaOH dissolved in 1 dm^3 of water will produce a solution of 1 mol/dm^3.

0.1 mole of NaOH dissolved in 1 dm^3 of water will produce a solution of 0.1 mol/dm^3.

Mass = number of moles × RFM

Mass = 0.1 × 40 = 4 g of NaOH dissolved in 1 dm^3 of water will produce a solution of 0.1 mol/dm^3.

Number of moles $= \dfrac{\text{mass (g)}}{\text{RFM}}$

Question

7 Calculate the mass of sodium hydroxide (NaOH) which when dissolved in 500 cm^3 of water will produce a solution with a concentration of 0.18 mol/dm^3.

8 What mass of potassium carbonate (K_2CO_3) should be dissolved in 400 cm^3 of water to produce a solution with a concentration of 2.5 mol/dm^3?

This answer can also be calculated by using the two mathematical formulae for moles which we have learned to date.

$$\text{number of moles} = \frac{\text{volume (cm}^3) \times \text{concentration (mol/dm}^3)}{1000}$$

$$= \frac{1000\ \text{cm}^3 \times 0.1}{1000}$$

$$= 0.1 \text{ moles of sodium hydroxide}$$

$$\text{Mass of sodium hydroxide} = \text{moles} \times \text{RFM}$$

$$= 0.1 \times 40$$

$$= 4\,\text{g}$$

▶ The quantitative interpretation of equations

'How Much?' part two

In Chapter 8 the masses of products and reactants were calculated using balanced chemical equations. The volume and concentration of reacting substances or products can be calculated in the same way.

Sodium hydroxide and hydrochloric acid react together according to the balanced equation below.

$$NaOH + HCl \rightarrow NaCl + H_2O$$

A 25 cm^3 sample of sodium hydroxide (0.125 mol/dm^3) required 21.6 cm^3 of hydrochloric acid for complete neutralisation. Calculate the concentration of the hydrochloric acid.

Copy out the balanced chemical equation	NaOH +	HCl →	NaCl +	H_2O
Write in the ratio	1	1	1	1
Write in the information given in the question	25 cm^3 of 0.125 mol/dm^3	21.6 cm^3		
Calculate the number of moles $\left(\frac{\text{vol} \times \text{conc}}{1000}\right)$	$\frac{25 \times 0.125}{1000}$ = 0.003125 moles			
Use the molar ratio to work out the number of moles for all the substances in the equation	0.003125 moles	0.003125 moles	0.003125 moles	0.003125 moles
Answer the question $\left(\text{moles} = \frac{\text{vol} \times \text{conc}}{1000}\right)$		$\frac{0.003125 \times 1000}{21.6}$ = 0.145 mol/dm^3		

Examination questions may be written in a number of ways. The examiner may ask the question as a whole unit as in the previous example. Calculations like these can be awarded up to 7 marks. A correct answer automatically achieves the full marks. An incorrect answer is awarded marks for the correct stages of working out shown.

Examiners may choose to ask the question in a structured format as in Questions 9 and 10 on the next page.

Remember these questions can be completed in exactly the same way as the worked examples. Do not expect to be familiar with all of the chemical names in the examination questions. After all, the examiner has a lot of different chemicals to choose from! Do not let unfamiliar elements and compounds confuse you. Once you can do one question you can do them all!

Questions

9 Sodium hydroxide and hydrochloric acid react together according to the balanced equation below.

$$NaOH + HCl \rightarrow NaCl + H_2O$$

A 25 cm³ sample of sodium hydroxide (0.125 mol/dm³) required 21.6 cm³ of hydrochloric acid for complete neutralisation.

a) Calculate the number of moles of sodium hydroxide neutralised by the hydrochloric acid.

b) Use the balanced equation to deduce the number of moles of hydrochloric acid in 21.6 cm³.

c) Calculate the concentration of the acid.

Can you find the answers to the above questions in the working out on the previous page?

10 Potassium hydroxide and sulfuric acid react together according to the balanced chemical equation below.

$$2KOH + H_2SO_4 \rightarrow K_2SO_4 + 2H_2O$$

28.9 cm³ of sulfuric acid is required to neutralise 25 cm³ of potassium hydroxide of concentration 0.25 mol/dm³.

a) Calculate the number of moles of potassium hydroxide neutralised by the sulfuric acid.

b) Use the balanced equation to deduce the number of moles of sulfuric acid in 28.9 cm³.

c) Calculate the concentration of the acid in mol/dm³.

11 Borax ($Na_2B_4O_7$) is a salt which is used in cleaning agents. Borax dissolves in water to give a solution which acts as a weak alkali. 25.0 cm³ portions of a solution of borax were titrated against nitric acid of concentration 0.094 mol/dm³ (moles per litre). 26.6 cm³ of the nitric acid was required to neutralise the borax.

$$Na_2B_4O_7 + 2HNO_3 + 5H_2O \rightarrow 2NaNO_3 + 4H_3BO_3$$

Calculate the concentration of the borax solution.

▶ Titrations

Chemists use a technique known as a titration to find out the volume of one liquid which will react with a known volume of another. The same technique can be used to prepare salts as you have seen in Chapter 6, page 90.

Apparatus

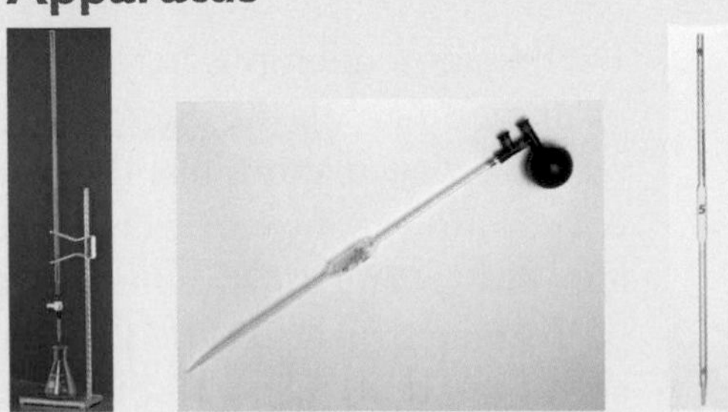

Figure 3 Apparatus: burette, pipette filler, pipette

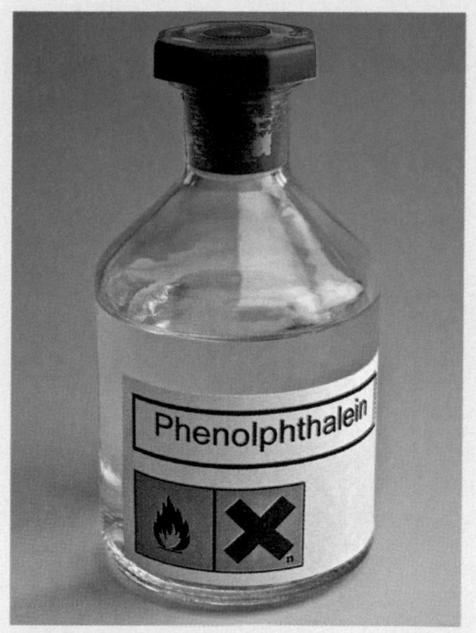

Figure 4 A reagent bottle of phenolphthalein

Preparation of the burette:

* rinse with deionised water
* rinse with the solution
* fill with solution
* allow the solution to run out until the bottom of the meniscus is on the zero line
* ensure the tip is full and there are no air bubbles.

Preparation and use of the pipette:

* rinse with deionised water
* using a pipette filler:
  – rinse with solution
  – fill with solution
* holding the pipette vertically with the volume line at eye level, run out the solution until the bottom of the meniscus is on the line.

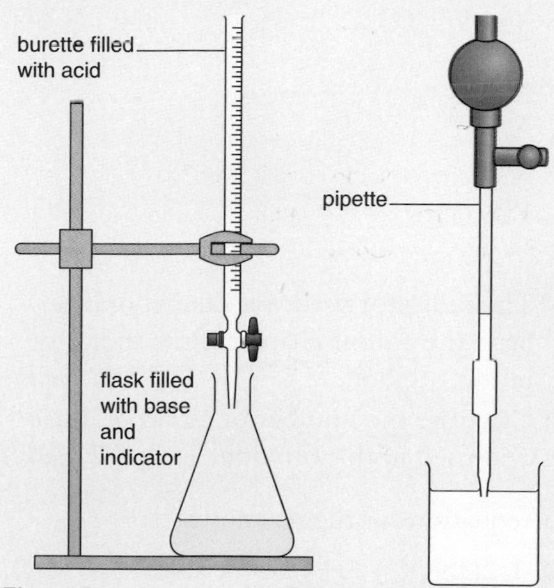

Figure 5

Method

Solution one: hydrochloric acid, concentration unknown

Solution two: sodium hydroxide, concentration 0.25 mol/dm^3

* Prepare the burette and fill with hydrochloric acid.
* Pipette 25 cm^3 of sodium hydroxide into a conical flask using a pipette filler.
* Add three drops of phenolphthalein indicator. Swirl the flask gently.
* Add the hydrochloric acid from the burette, swirling gently to mix the solutions.
* Stop adding the acid at the end point. (At the end point of this titration the indicator will change from pink to colourless.)
* Record the volume of hydrochloric acid added.

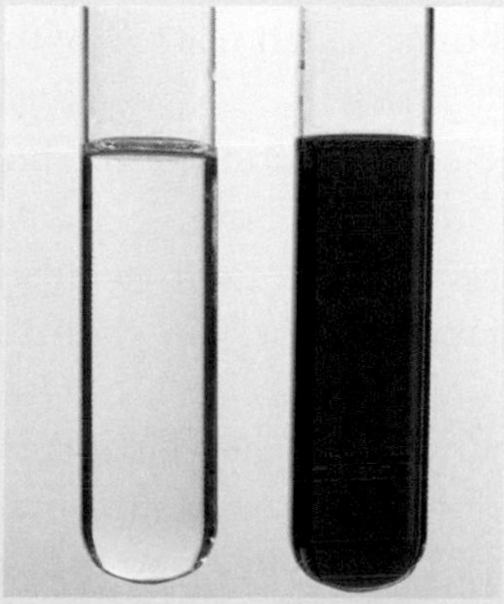

Figure 6 Phenolphthalein indicator in alkaline and neutral solution

Repeat the titration with fresh samples of sodium hydroxide until two concordant results are obtained. (Concordant results are ones which differ by less than 0.1 cm^3.)

The results may be recorded in a table similar to the one below.

Indicator		phenolphthalein	
Alkali	sodium hydroxide	25 cm^3	0.25 mol/dm^3
	Final burette reading/cm^3	Initial burette reading/cm^3	Volume of acid used/cm^3
Rough titration	21.3	0.0	21.3
1st accurate titration	41.0	21.3	19.7
2nd accurate titration	19.6	0.0	19.6
		average titre	19.65

The concentration of the hydrochloric acid may be calculated from the results. Hydrochloric acid and sodium hydroxide react together according to the following equation.

$$HCl + NaOH \rightarrow NaCl + H_2O$$

Using the information in the table calculate the concentration of the hydrochloric acid.

Copy out the balanced chemical equation	HCl +	NaOH →	NaCl +	H_2O
Write in the ratio	1	1	1	1
Write in the information given in the question	19.65 cm³	25 cm³ 0.25 mol/dm³		
Calculate the number of moles $\left(\frac{\text{vol} \times \text{conc}}{1000}\right)$		$\frac{25 \times 0.25}{1000}$ = 0.00625 moles		
Use the molar ratio to work out the number of moles for all the substances in the equation	0.00625 moles	0.00625 moles	0.00625 moles	0.00625 moles
Answer the question $\left(\text{moles} = \frac{\text{vol} \times \text{conc}}{1000}\right)$	$\frac{0.00625 \times 1000}{19.65}$ = 0.318 mol/dm³			

► Exam questions

1 Borax is a salt which is hydrated and is used in cleaning agents. The formula may be represented by $Na_2B_4O_7.xH_2O$. Borax dissolves in water to give a solution which acts as a weak alkali.

a) 4.775 g of Borax were weighed out and made up to a volume of 250 cm³ with deionised water. 25.0 cm³ portions of this solution were titrated against nitric acid of concentration 0.094 mol/dm³ (moles per litre). The results were recorded in the table below.

	Initial burette reading/cm³	Final burette reading/cm³	Volume of nitric acid used (titre)/cm³
Rough titration	0.0	26.9	26.9
1st accurate titration	0.0	26.7	26.7
2nd accurate titration	0.0	26.5	26.5

i) Calculate the average titre. *(2 marks)*

ii) The indicator used was methyl orange. State the colour change of the indicator in this titration. *(2 marks)*

iii) Calculate the number of moles of nitric acid used in this titration. *(2 marks)*

b) The equation for the reaction is

$$Na_2B_4O_7 + 2HNO_3 + 5H_2O \rightarrow 2NaNO_3 + 4H_3BO_3$$

i) Use the equation to deduce the number of moles of borax which reacted with the nitric acid. *(2 marks)*

ii) Calculate the concentration of the borax in mol/dm³ (moles per litre). *(2 marks)*

iii) From the mass of borax used, calculate the concentration of borax in g/dm³. *(1 mark)*

iv) Using your answers to parts **ii)** and **iii)** find the formula mass of the borax $Na_2B_4O_7.xH_2O$, and hence find the value of x. (Relative atomic masses: H = 1, B = 11, O = 16, Na = 23) *(3 marks)*

2 Sulfur dioxide is an oxide of the non-metal sulfur. It can be produced in the reaction of sodium thiosulfate, $Na_2S_2O_3$, with hydrochloric acid, HCl.

$Na_2S_2O_3 + 2HCl \rightarrow 2NaCl + S + SO_2 + H_2O$

A solution of sodium thiosulfate is prepared by dissolving 5.53 g of $Na_2S_2O_3$ in deionised water. The hydrochloric acid has a concentration of 2 mol/dm^3 (moles per litre).

a) Calculate the number of moles of sodium thiosulfate used. (Relative atomic masses: Na = 23, S = 32, O = 16) *(2 marks)*

b) Calculate the number of moles of hydrochloric acid required to react with this number of moles of sodium thiosulfate in **a)**. *(2 marks)*

c) Calculate the volume of hydrochloric acid required to react completely with the sodium thiosulfate solution. *(2 marks)*

3 The formula for an **insoluble unknown** metal hydroxide can be written $M(OH)_2$. 3.0 g of solid $M(OH)_2$ is added to 50.0 cm^3 of 1 mol/dm^3 (moles per litre) hydrochloric acid with stirring. Some solid $M(OH)_2$ is observed lying at the bottom.

The solution is filtered and the residue washed with some water and dried. The mass of unreacted $M(OH)_2$ is 0.55 g.

a) What mass of $M(OH)_2$ reacted with the hydrochloric acid? *(1 mark)*

b) Calculate the number of moles of hydrochloric acid used. *(2 marks)*

c) Using the balanced symbol equation:

$$M(OH)_2 + 2HCl \rightarrow MCl_2 + 2H_2O$$

calculate the number of moles of $M(OH)_2$ required to react with the hydrochloric acid. *(2 marks)*

d) Using the answers to **b)** and **c)** above, calculate the relative formula mass (RFM) of $M(OH)_2$. *(2 marks)*

e) Determine the relative atomic mass (RAM) of M and identify it using your Periodic Table. *(2 marks)*

4 a) Lead is extracted from the ore galena, PbS. The ore is roasted in air to produce lead(II) oxide, PbO. (Relative atomic masses: Pb = 207, S = 32, O = 16)

$$2PbS_{(s)} + 3O_{2(g)} \rightarrow 2PbO_{(s)} + 2SO_{2(g)}$$

i) Calculate the mass of lead(II) oxide, PbO, produced from 2.39 kg of galena, PbS. *(5 marks)*

The lead(II) oxide is reduced to lead by heating it with carbon in a blast furnace.

$$PbO_{(s)} + C_{(s)} \rightarrow Pb_{(l)} + CO_{(g)}$$

The molten lead is tapped off from the bottom of the furnace.

ii) Using your answer to part **a) i)**, calculate the mass of lead that would eventually be produced. *(3 marks)*

b) Titration is a technique used by chemists to find the concentration of a substance. The apparatus used in a titration is shown below.

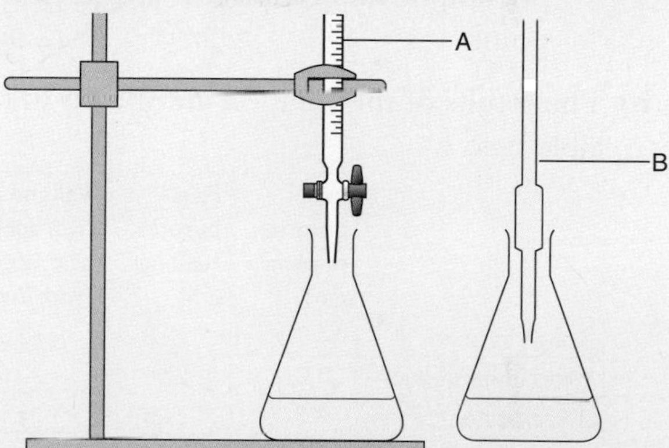

i) Identify the pieces of apparatus A and B. *(2 marks)*

ii) Describe in detail, stating precautions to ensure safety and accuracy, how you would transfer 25.0 cm^3 of an alkali into a conical flask using the piece of apparatus A. *(4 marks)*

c) Limewater is calcium hydroxide solution. In a titration to find the concentration of calcium hydroxide in limewater, 25.0 cm^3 of limewater required 16.4 cm^3 of hydrochloric acid of concentration 0.040 mol/dm^3 for neutralisation. (Relative atomic masses: Ca = 40; O = 16; H =16)

$$Ca(OH)_2 + 2HCl \rightarrow CaCl_2 + 2H_2O$$

Calculate the concentration of the calcium hydroxide in mol/dm^3 (moles per litre). *(4 marks)*

5 Barium hydroxide is a Group II metal hydroxide which is often found in drain cleaners. To determine the concentration of a solution of barium hydroxide $Ba(OH)_2$, 25.0 cm^3 of the solution was placed in a conical flask with a few drops of phenolphthalein indicator and titrated with a solution of hydrochloric acid of concentration 0.2 mol/dm^3 (moles per litre). The balanced symbol equation for the reaction is:

$$Ba(OH)_2 + 2HCl \rightarrow BaCl_2 + 2H_2O$$

a) i) Describe in detail, stating precautions to ensure safety and accuracy, how you would place 25.0 cm^3 of barium hydroxide solution into the conical flask. *(4 marks)*

ii) State the colour change of the phenolphthalein indicator at the end point. *(2 marks)*

b) The results of the titration are shown in the table below.

	Initial burette reading/ cm^3	Final burette reading/ cm^3	Volume of hydrochloric acid used (titre)/cm^3
Rough titration	0.0	22.8	22.8
1st accurate titration	0.0	22.4	22.4
2nd accurate titration	0.0	22.5	22.5

i) Calculate the average titre. *(2 marks)*

ii) Calculate the number of moles of hydrochloric acid used in this titration. *(2 marks)*

iii) Use the balanced symbol equation to deduce the number of moles of barium hydroxide which reacted with the hydrochloric acid. *(2 marks)*

iv) Calculate the concentration of the barium hydroxide solution in mol/dm^3 (moles per litre). *(2 marks)*

c) Calcium is a Group II metal which reacts with nitric acid according to the balanced symbol equation (relative atomic masses: H = 1, N = 14, O = 16, Ca = 40)

$$Ca + 2HNO_3 \rightarrow Ca(NO_3)_2 + H_2$$

i) 0.2 g of calcium metal was reacted with excess nitric acid. Calculate the volume of hydrogen gas which was produced in this reaction (1 mole of any gas occupies 24 dm^3). *(5 marks)*

ii) If the concentration of the nitric acid was 2.0 mol/dm^3 (moles per litre) calculate the volume of nitric acid needed to completely react with the 0.2 g of calcium. *(4 marks)*

iii) The calcium nitrate produced in this reaction is often used in fertilisers. Calculate the percentage of nitrogen, by mass, present in calcium nitrate. *(3 marks)*

6 An insoluble unknown metal hydroxide can be written $M(OH)_2$ where M represents the metal M.
3.0 g of solid $M(OH)_2$ is added to 50.0 cm^3 of 1 mol/dm^3 (moles per litre) hydrochloric acid with stirring. Some solid $M(OH)_2$ is observed lying at the bottom.
The solution is filtered and the residue washed with some water and dried. The mass of unreacted $M(OH)_2$ is 0.55 g.

i) What mass of $M(OH)_2$ reacted with the hydrochloric acid? *(1 mark)*

ii) Calculate the number of moles of hydrochloric acid used? *(2 marks)*

iii) Using the balanced symbol equation

$$M(OH)_2 + 2HCl \rightarrow MCl_2 + 2H_2O$$

calculate the number of moles of $M(OH)_2$ required to react with the hydrochloric acid. *(2 marks)*

iv) Using the answers to **i)** and **iii)** above, calculate the relative formula mass (RFM) of $M(OH)_2$. *(2 marks)*

v) Determine the relative atomic mass (RAM) of M and identify it using your Periodic Table. *(2 marks)*

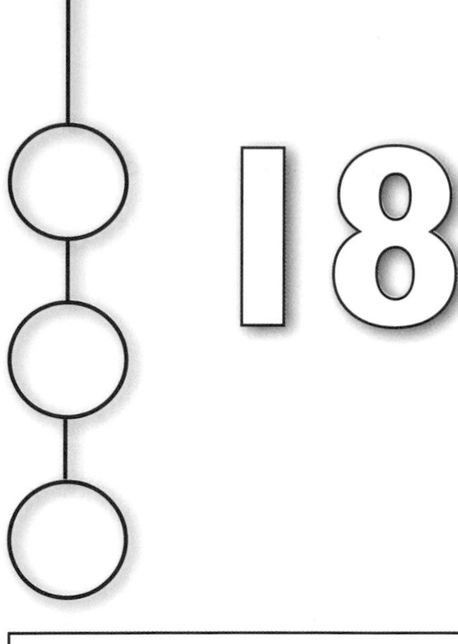

Energetics

► Exothermic reactions

Fuels, such as coal or natural gas, store chemical energy and when they burn they convert their chemical energy into heat energy.

$$CH_4 + 2O_2 \rightarrow CO_2 + 2H_2O + \textbf{Heat energy}$$

Power stations use this heat energy to turn water into steam, which is used to turn turbines. The turbines turn generators to produce electricity.

A chemical reaction that gives out heat is called an **exothermic reaction**.

In addition to combustion reactions the following reactions are also exothermic reactions.

Exothermic reactions are chemical reactions which give out heat energy.

Neutralisation

hydrochloric acid + sodium hydroxide → sodium chloride + water

$$HCl_{(aq)} + NaOH_{(aq)} \rightarrow NaCl_{(aq)} + H_2O_{(l)}$$

Displacement reactions

zinc + copper sulfate → copper + zinc sulfate

$$Zn_{(s)} + CuSO_{4(aq)} \rightarrow Cu_{(s)} + ZnSO_{4(aq)}$$

Hydration

Anhydrous (white) copper(II) sulfate reacts with water to form hydrated (blue) copper(II) sulfate. During this reaction heat is given out.

copper(II) sulfate + water → hydrated copper(II) sulfate

$$CuSO_{4(s)} + 5H_2O_{(l)} \rightarrow CuSO_4.5H_2O_{(s)}$$

Rusting

iron + oxygen + water → hydrated iron(III) oxide

$$2Fe_{(s)} + 3O_{2(g)} + xH_2O_{(l)} \rightarrow Fe_2O_3.xH_2O_{(s)}$$

combustion

neutralisation

hydration

rusting

Figure 1 **a** A modern limekiln and **b** the remains of an ancient limekiln

Endothermic reactions

While many chemical reactions are exothermic, there are also those which take in heat energy and these are called endothermic reactions.

Thermal decomposition

Thermal decomposition is the breaking down of a compound by heat. It is an example of an endothermic reaction.

Copper(II) carbonate is a green solid that is readily broken down by heat to form black copper(II) oxide and carbon dioxide.

copper(II) carbonate → copper(II) oxide + carbon dioxide

$$CuCO_{3(s)} \rightarrow CuO_{(s)} + CO_{2(g)}$$

When limestone is heated strongly it breaks down into calcium oxide and carbon dioxide. Calcium oxide, commonly known as quick lime, is a basic oxide.

calcium carbonate → calcium oxide + carbon dioxide

$$CaCO_{3(s)} \rightarrow CaO_{(s)} + CO_{2(g)}$$

Limestone, impure calcium carbonate, and the solid product from its thermal decomposition, calcium oxide, are extremely important raw materials for industry. They have a wide variety of uses.

Limestone is used in the blast furnace to remove the acidic impurities contained in the iron ore which would greatly decrease the quality of the iron produced.

It is an ingredient in paint manufacture, plastic manufacture, ceramic tile adhesives and even babies' nappies. Calcium oxide is used in the construction industry, in the manufacture of bricks, mortar and plaster, in the manufacture of glass and in poultry feed. The calcium oxide is produced by the thermal decomposition of the limestone in a limekiln. Figure 1 shows a modern limekiln and the remains of an ancient limekiln.

Figure 2 A working limestone quarry

The vast quantity of limestone required for all of these uses and for the production of calcium oxide is obtained by quarrying (Figure 2).

There are abundant sources of limestone in Northern Ireland and the quarrying of the raw material creates jobs in the locality, bringing prosperity to other local businesses. However, quarrying of limestone destroys natural habitats, creates noise pollution (blasting the stone, crushing the stone, the quarrying vehicles and the delivery vehicles) and dust pollution. It leaves unsightly gaps in the landscape.

▶ Explaining why a reaction is exothermic or endothermic

Consider the combustion reaction between methane and oxygen. Methane (CH_4) burns in oxygen (O_2) to produce carbon dioxide, water and heat energy. It is an exothermic reaction.

$$\text{methane} + \text{oxygen} \rightarrow \text{carbon dioxide} + \text{water}$$

$$CH_{4(g)} + 2O_{2(g)} \rightarrow CO_{2(g)} + 2H_2O_{(g)}$$

Figure 3 The reaction between methane and oxygen

Figure 3 illustrates the bonds in the molecules involved in this combustion reaction. The bonds in the reactants, in this case methane and oxygen, must be broken before the new bonds in the products, in this case carbon dioxide and water, can be made.

Energy is required to break the bonds in the reactants. Breaking bonds is an endothermic process.

Energy is released when the bonds in the products are made. Making bonds is an exothermic process.

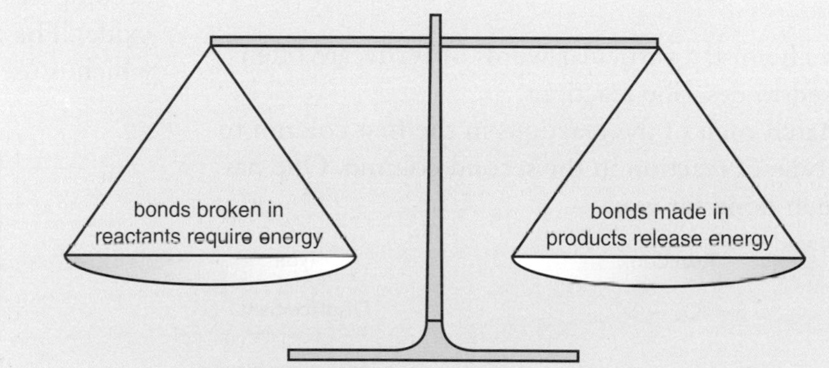

Figure 4 A balance between the energy required to break bonds and the energy released when bonds are formed

The overall energy change in the reaction is a balance between these two processes.

The combustion of methane is an exothermic process because more energy is released when the bonds in water and carbon dioxide are made than is required when the bonds in the methane and the oxygen are broken.

Consider the thermal decomposition of calcium carbonate.

$$\text{calcium carbonate} \rightarrow \text{calcium oxide} + \text{carbon dioxide}$$

$$CaCO_{3(s)} \rightarrow CaO_{(s)} + CO_{2(g)}$$

The thermal decomposition of calcium carbonate is an endothermic process because the energy required to break the bonds in the calcium carbonate is more than the energy released when the bonds in carbon dioxide and water are formed.

▶ Exam questions

1 The following reactions A and B can be classified in different ways.

A copper(II) carbonate → copper (II) oxide + carbon dioxide

B sodium hydroxide + hydrochloric acid → sodium chloride + water

Copy and complete the table by placing a tick (✓) in each column for reactions A and B indicating which terms apply to each reaction. *(3 marks)*

Term	Reaction	
	A	B
Exothermic		
Endothermic		
Thermal decomposition		
Thermal cracking		
Combustion		
Neutralisation		
Displacement		

2 In chemistry, particular words or terms are often used to describe reactions.
Match each of the reactions in the first column to a type of reaction in the second column. One has been done for you. *(5 marks)*

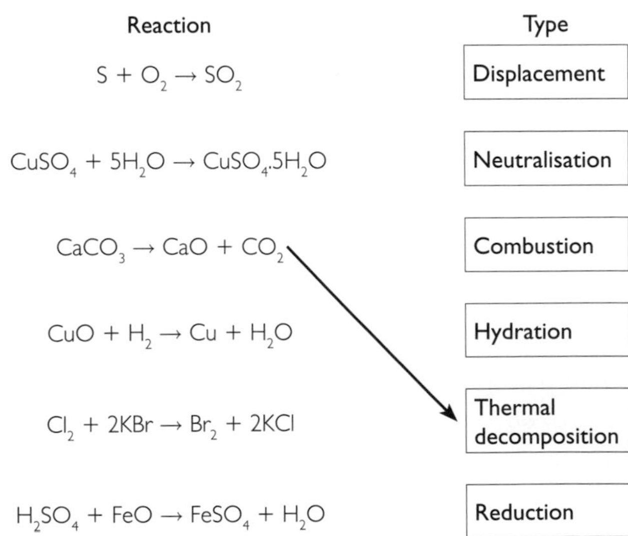

3 State the colours of:

a) copper *(1 mark)*

b) copper(II) oxide *(1 mark)*

c) copper(II) carbonate *(1 mark)*

4 Many metal compounds are coloured solids. Others are white. Give the correct colour for each of the following four compounds. Choose from the list of colours. *(2 marks)*

white green red brown blue black

a) copper(II) carbonate

b) magnesium oxide

c) hydrated copper(II) sulfate

d) anhydrous copper(II) sulfate

5 Identify this substance

- I am a black solid.
- I can be made by heating a green solid very strongly.
- I can also be made by burning one of the metal elements.
- I react with dilute sulfuric acid to give a blue solution.

What compound am I? *(2 marks)*

6 In industry, limestone undergoes thermal decomposition to make quicklime (calcium oxide). The diagram below represents a limekiln which is used for this process.

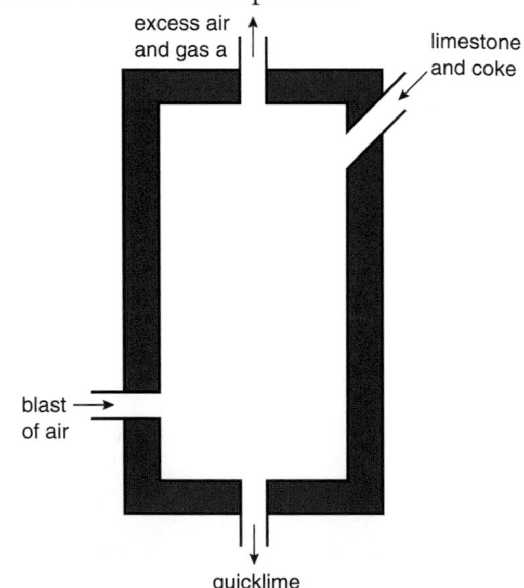

a) What is meant by the term thermal decomposition? *(2 marks)*

b) Write a balanced symbol equation for the thermal decomposition of limestone. *(2 marks)*

c) The decomposition of limestone is endothermic. What is the meaning of the term endothermic? *(2 marks)*

7 A method of producing silicon in industry is by the reaction of silicon dioxide with charcoal in an electric arc furnace.

$$SiO_2 + C \rightarrow Si + CO_2$$

The carbon reduces the silicon dioxide. The reaction is exothermic.
Explain in terms of **bond breaking and bond making** why this reaction is exothermic. *(5 marks)*

8 Heat plays an important role in many industrial processes, such as the production of iron in the blast furnace and the production of aluminium by electrolysis.
In the blast furnace, blasts of hot air are blown in at the bottom of the furnace. This causes one of the raw materials, limestone, to break down.
Carbon dioxide is a waste gas produced in the blast furnace.

a) Name an ore from which iron may be extracted. *(1 mark)*

b) What term is used to describe the breaking down of a compound using heat? *(2 marks)*

c) Write a balanced symbol equation for the breaking down of limestone using heat. *(2 marks)*

d) What is the main purpose of adding limestone to the blast furnace? *(1 mark)*

e) State **one** environmental problem caused by the release of carbon dioxide into the atmosphere. *(1 mark)*

9 Hydrogen is a powerful rocket fuel. The diagram shows the reaction which occurs in the combustion chamber of a rocket.

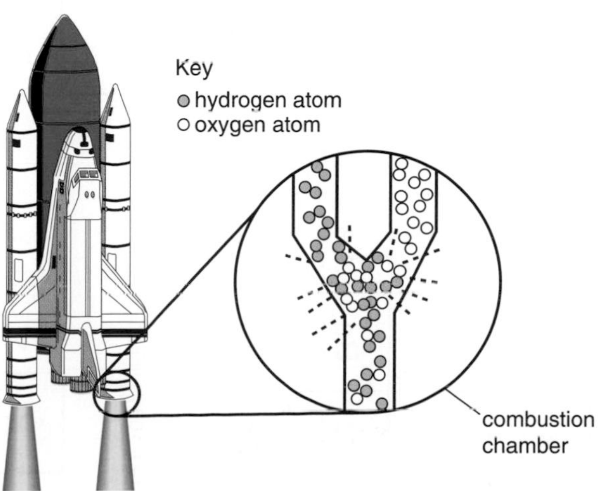

a) Explain what you understand by the term combustion. *(3 marks)*

b) Explain why hydrogen is considered to be a 'clean' fuel. *(1 mark)*

c) The equation for the reaction which occurs in the combustion chamber is:

$$2H_2 + O_2 \rightarrow 2H_2O$$

Explain in terms of bonds, why the reaction in the combustion chamber is exothermic. *(5 marks)*

10 Calcium carbonate thermally decomposes to form calcium oxide. Calcium oxide (lime) has a high melting point and can be heated to a high temperature without melting so that it emits white light, called limelight.

a) Explain what is meant by thermal decomposition. *(2 marks)*

b) Write a balanced symbol equation for the thermal decomposition of calcium carbonate. *(2 marks)*

c) Explain why calcium oxide has a high melting point. *(2 marks)*

11 The reaction between hydrogen gas and oxygen gas is exothermic, i.e., heat is given out. The equation below describes the reaction.

$$2H_2 + O_2 \rightarrow 2H_2O$$

Explain, in terms of the bonds involved, why the reaction between hydrogen and oxygen is exothermic. *(4 marks)*

12 When methane burns in oxygen, heat is given out. The equation below describes the reaction.

$$CH_{4(g)} + 2O_{2(g)} \rightarrow CO_{2(g)} + 2H_2O_{(g)}$$

Explain, **in terms of the bonds involved**, why the reaction between methane and oxygen is exothermic. *(6 marks)*

Appendix 1 The Periodic Table

I 1	II 2											III 3	IV 4	V 5	VI 6	VII 7	0
					1 H Hydrogen 1												4 He Helium 2
7 Li Lithium 3	9 Be Beryllium 4											11 B Boron 5	12 C Carbon 6	14 N Nitrogen 7	16 O Oxygen 8	19 F Fluorine 9	20 Ne Neon 10
23 Na Sodium 11	24 Mg Magnesium 12											27 Al Aluminium 13	28 Si Silicon 14	31 P Phosphorous 15	32 S Sulfur 16	35.5 Cl Chlorine 17	40 Ar Argon 18
39 K Potassium 19	40 Ca Calcium 20	45 Sc Scandium 21	48 Ti Titanium 22	51 V Vanadium 23	52 Cr Chromium 24	55 Mn Manganese 25	56 Fe Iron 26	59 Co Cobalt 27	59 Ni Nickel 28	64 Cu Copper 29	65 Zn Zinc 30	70 Ga Gallium 31	73 Ge Germanium 32	75 As Arsenic 33	79 Se Selenium 34	80 Br Bromine 35	84 Kr Krypton 36
85 Rb Rubidium 37	88 Sr Strontium 38	89 Y Yttrium 39	91 Zr Zirconium 40	93 Nb Niobium 41	95 Mo Molybdenum 42	99 Tc Technetium 43	101 Ru Ruthenium 44	103 Rh Rhodium 45	106 Pd Palladium 46	108 Ag Silver 47	112 Cd Cadmium 48	115 In Indium 49	119 Sn Tin 50	122 Sb Antimony 51	128 Te Tellurium 52	127 I Iodine 53	131 Xe Xenon 54
133 Cs Caesium 55	137 Ba Barium 56	139 La lanthanum 57 *	178 Hf Hafnium 72	181 Ta Tantalum 73	184 W Tungsten 74	186 Re Rhenium 75	190 Os Osmium 76	192 Ir Iridium 77	195 Pt Platinum 78	197 Au Gold 79	201 Hg Mercuy 80	204 Tl Thallium 81	207 Pb Lead 82	209 Bi Bismuth 83	210 Po Polonium 84	210 At Astatine 85	222 Rn Radon 86
223 Fr Francium 87	226 Ra Radium 88	227 Ac Actinium 89 †															

*58–71 Lanthanum series
†90–103 Actinium series

*	140 Ce Cerium 58	141 Pr Praseodymium 59	144 Nd Neodymium 60	147 Pm Promethium 61	150 Sm Samarium 62	152 Eu Europium 63	157 Gd Gadolinium 64	159 Tb Terbium 65	162 Dy Dysprosium 66	165 Ho Holmium 67	167 Er Erbium 68	169 Tm Thulium 69	173 Yb Ytterbium 70	175 Lu Lutetium 71
†	232 Th Thorium 90	231 Pa Protactinium 91	238 U Uranium 92	237 Np Neptunium 93	242 Pu Plutonium 94	243 Am Americium 95	247 Cm Curium 96	245 Bk Berkelium 97	251 Cf Californium 98	254 Es Einsteinium 99	253 Fm Fermium 100	256 Md Mendelevium 101	254 No Nobelium 102	257 Lr Lawrencium 103

a X b	a = relative atomic mass X = atomic symbol b = atomic number

Index